Preparing to Use Algebra

SECOND EDITION

Preparing to Use Algebra

SECOND EDITION

ALBERT P. SHULTE
Assistant Director, Mathematics Education
Oakland Schools
Pontiac, Michigan

ROBERT E. PETERSON
Chairman, Mathematics Department
Fraser High School
Fraser, Michigan

LAIDLAW BROTHERS • PUBLISHERS
A Division of Doubleday & Company, Inc.
RIVER FOREST, ILLINOIS
Irvine, California   Atlanta, Georgia   Dallas, Texas   Toronto, Canada

About the cover: The cover design was made from a photograph of a highly magnified view of sugar crystals viewed under polarized light.

EDITORIAL STAFF

Project Director: Albert F. Kempf
Senior Editor: Thomas J. Richards
Staff Editors: Janice Ziebka Chandler, Donald W. Collins
Production Editors: Egidia M. Lauraitis, Katherine G. Rossow
Art Director: Gloria Muczynski

ILLUSTRATORS

Text: Joann Daley, John D. Firestone & Associates, Paul Hazelrigg

ISBN 0-8445-**1957**-x

Copyright © 1978, 1975 by Laidlaw Brothers, Publishers

A Division of Doubleday & Company, Inc.

Printed in the United States of America

4 5 6 7 8 9 10 11 12 13 14 15   6 5 4 3 2 1 0

Contents

Chapter 1
Simple
Sentences

1.1 Order of Operations...................... 2
1.2 Variables............................... 5
1.3 Open Sentences......................... 8
1.4 Sets and Sentences..................... 11
1.5 Equations and the Balance Beam.......... 15
1.6 Inequalities and the Balance Beam....... 19
1.7 Pictures of Solution Sets............... 23
Vocabulary and Chapter Review.......... 27
Chapter Test........................... 29
Activities for Chapter 1................. 30
Mathematics and Flying................. 31

Chapter 2
Solving Open
Sentences

Getting Ready for Chapter 2............. 32
2.1 Equations On the Beam.................. 34
2.2 Equations Off the Beam.................. 37
2.3 Inequalities On the Beam................ 40
2.4 Inequalities Off the Beam................ 43
2.5 Graphing Open Sentences............... 46
2.6 Equation Review....................... 49
2.7 Inequality Review...................... 51
2.8 Two-Step Equations.................... 53
2.9 Formulas.............................. 57
2.10 Two-Step Inequalities*.................. 61
Vocabulary and Chapter Review.......... 63
Chapter Test........................... 65
Activities for Chapter 2................. 66
Mathematics and Photography.......... 67

Chapter 3
Ordered Pairs
and Graphing

Getting Ready for Chapter 3............. 68
3.1 Ordered Pairs.......................... 70
3.2 Graphing Ordered Pairs................. 73
3.3 Functions............................. 76
3.4 Using Graphs.......................... 80
3.5 Using Functions....................... 84
3.6 Enlarging and Reducing*................. 88
3.7 Sliding by Graphing*.................... 92
Vocabulary and Chapter Review.......... 95
Chapter Test........................... 98
Activities for Chapter 3................. 99
Mathematics and Telephones...........100

*Optional

Chapter 4
Number Theory

Getting Ready for Chapter 4. 101
4.1 Factors and Divisibility. 103
4.2 Shortcuts to Divisibility. 106
4.3 Primes and Composites. 108
4.4 Exponents and Powers. 111
4.5 Summing It Up*. 114
4.6 Greatest Common Factor. 118
4.7 Least Common Multiple. 120
Vocabulary and Chapter Review. 123
Chapter Test. 125
Activities for Chapter 4. 126
Mathematics and Space Travel. 127

Chapter 5
Operations and
Their Properties

Getting Ready for Chapter 5. 128
5.1 Sets of Numbers and Closure. 130
5.2 Inverse Operations. 132
5.3 Commutative Properties. 136
5.4 Associative Properties. 140
5.5 Zero and One. 143
5.6 Distributive Property. 145
Vocabulary and Chapter Review. 148
Chapter Test. 150
Activities for Chapter 5. 151
Mathematics and Transplanting Trees. 152

Chapter 6
Operations
with Fractions

Getting Ready for Chapter 6. 153
6.1 Meaning of Fractions. 155
6.2 Multiplication. 159
6.3 Simplifying Fractions. 161
6.4 Fractions and Mixed Numerals. 163
6.5 More Multiplication. 166
6.6 Division. 169
6.7 Addition and Subtraction. 172
6.8 Least Common Denominator. 176
6.9 More Addition and Subtraction. 179
6.10 Problem Solving*. 181
Vocabulary and Chapter Review. 184
Chapter Test. 186
Activities for Chapter 6. 187
Mathematics and Welding. 188

Chapter 7
Operations
with Decimals

Getting Ready for Chapter 7. 189
7.1 Decimals. 191
7.2 Addition and Subtraction. 194
7.3 Multiplication. 197

Optional

7.4	Division	199
7.5	More Division	201
7.6	Solving Problems	204
7.7	Scientific Notation*	208
	Vocabulary and Chapter Review	212
	Chapter Test	214
	Activities for Chapter 7	215
	Mathematics and Typesetting	216

Chapter 8
Integers

	Getting Ready for Chapter 8	217
8.1	Whole Numbers and Their Opposites	219
8.2	Addition on a Number Line	221
8.3	Adding Integers	223
8.4	Subtracting Integers	226
8.5	Multiplying Integers	228
8.6	More About Multiplying Integers	230
8.7	Dividing Integers	232
8.8	Integers and the Coordinate System*	234
	Vocabulary and Chapter Review	237
	Chapter Test	239
	Activities for Chapter 8	240
	Mathematics and Air Conditioning	241

Chapter 9
Sentences
with Integers

	Getting Ready for Chapter 9	242
9.1	Solving Equations by Addition	244
9.2	Solving Equations by Subtraction	246
9.3	Solving Equations by Division	249
9.4	Solving Equations by Multiplication	252
9.5	Inequalities with Integers	255
9.6	Graphing Open Sentences	257
9.7	Solving Inequalities by Multiplication*	260
9.8	Solving Inequalities by Division*	263
9.9	Graphing Inequalities*	266
9.10	Two-Step Equations	268
	Vocabulary and Chapter Review	270
	Chapter Test	272
	Activities for Chapter 9	273
	Mathematics and Power Lines	274

Chapter 10
Problem
Solving

	Getting Ready for Chapter 10	275
10.1	Taking Notes	277
10.2	Number Tricks	279
10.3	Translating Sentences	281
10.4	How Great It Is	284
10.5	Two-Step Problems	287

10.6	Spaced Out	291
10.7	Table the Problem	293
	Vocabulary and Chapter Review	297
	Chapter Test	299
	Activities for Chapter 10	300
	Mathematics and Typing	301

Chapter 11
Ratio and
Proportion

	Getting Ready for Chapter 11	302
11.1	Ratios	304
11.2	Equivalent Ratios	309
11.3	Proportions	312
11.4	Per Cent	315
11.5	More Per Cent	318
11.6	Fractions, Decimals, Per Cents	320
11.7	Solving Per Cent Problems	323
11.8	Using Fractions or Decimals*	326
	Vocabulary and Chapter Review	329
	Chapter Test	331
	Activities for Chapter 11	332
	Mathematics and Music	333

Chapter 12
Indirect
Measurement

	Getting Ready for Chapter 12	334
12.1	Similar Figures	336
12.2	Corresponding Angles and Sides	341
12.3	Similar Triangles	345
12.4	Measuring with Similar Triangles	348
12.5	Sporting Problems	352
12.6	Maps*	356
	Vocabulary and Chapter Review	361
	Chapter Test	364
	Activities for Chapter 12	365
	Mathematics and Pipelines	366

Chapter 13
Rational
Numbers

	Getting Ready for Chapter 13	367
13.1	Rational Numbers	369
13.2	Addition and Subtraction with Decimals	372
13.3	Addition and Subtraction with Fractions	375
13.4	Solving Equations	378
13.5	Multiplication and Division with Decimals	381
13.6	Multiplication and Division with Fractions	384
13.7	Solving Equations	387
13.8	Equation Review	390
13.9	Two-Step Equations	392
	Vocabulary and Chapter Review	395
	Chapter Test	397

Optional

Activities for Chapter 13. 398
Mathematics and Plumbing. 399

**Chapter 14
Using
Algebra**

Getting Ready for Chapter 14. 400
14.1 Proportions. 402
14.2 Powerful Formulas. 405
14.3 Per Cent. 410
14.4 Dots, Dives, and Chirps. 413
14.5 Interest. 417
14.6 It's a Puzzle*. 419
Vocabulary and Chapter Review. 422
Chapter Test. 424
Activities for Chapter 14. 425
Mathematics and Electricity. 426

**Chapter 15
Approximation
and
Measurement**

Getting Ready for Chapter 15. 427
15.1 Rounding Numbers. 429
15.2 Estimating. 432
15.3 Estimating in the Real World. 435
15.4 English Units of Measure. 438
15.5 Comparing Measurements. 440
15.6 Metric Units of Measure. 443
15.7 Computing with Measures. 447
Vocabulary and Chapter Review. 450
Chapter Test. 452
Activities for Chapter 15. 453
Mathematics and Conservation. 454

**Chapter 16
Square Root**

Getting Ready for Chapter 16. 455
16.1 Square Roots*. 457
16.2 Estimating Square Roots*. 459
16.3 Using a Table*. 461
16.4 Finding Square Roots*. 463
16.5 Square Roots of Rational Numbers*. 466
16.6 Square Root and Equations*. 468
16.7 The Pythagorean Property*. 472
16.8 Using the Pythagorean Property*. 476
16.9 Square Root and Formulas*. 480
Vocabulary and Chapter Review. 482
Chapter Test. 484
Activities for Chapter 16. 485
Mathematics and Police Work. 486
• Table of Squares and Square Roots. 487
• Index. 489

Special Topics

Working on the Railroad 10

Which Way? 45

How Many Guests? 79

Operation: Decode 105

Playing the Same Game 122

Soda Splitting 135

How Is the Weather? 158

Carpenter's Puzzle 165

The Weight of a Brick 171

Making Money 196

One Inch of Rain 203

Who Hears the Music First? 211

Who Won? 225

A Number Trick 227

Links of Chain 248

Who Missed the Bus? 251

Crossing the River 265

Gear Ratio 308

Which Job Would You Take? 322

Matchless Problems 383

A Weighty Problem 394

Balance the Cup 442

Which Card Is It? 446

On Target 462

Pigs for Poke! 465

Pennies 471

Early Bird 475

Stuck in the Trunk 479

Simple Sentences _____ 1

Before making repairs, a good mechanic learns when to use each tool, how to use it, and what it is used for.

Before solving problems, a good problem-solver needs a set of mathematical tools. In this chapter you will learn when to use some of those tools (operations, variables, equations, inequalities), how to use them, and what they are used for.

1.1 ◆ ORDER OF OPERATIONS

You probably remember playing number games like the following.

Start with 4. Add 5. Multiply by 3.
What is the result?

You followed the directions by thinking

4 + 5 is 9, and 9 × 3 is 27.

The operations were done in the order they were given. You knew that you were to multiply the sum of 4 and 5 by 3.

This number game could be given by the following phrase.

$$4 + 5 \times 3$$

Given this phrase, you have to decide which operation to do first.

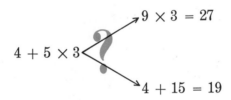

To make sure that a phrase names only one number, let's agree to use the following rule for the order of operations.

▌ First multiply and divide from left to right. ▌
▌ Then add and subtract from left to right. ▌

Example 1: What number does each phrase name?

a. $4+5\times3$

$4+15$ Multiply first.

19 Then add.

b. $18\div3-2$

$6-2$ Divide first.

4 Then subtract.

c. $7+5-4$

$12-4$ Add and subtract

8 from left to right.

d. $5\times4\div2$

$20\div2$ Multiply and divide

10 from left to right.

The distance around, or *perimeter* of, this rectangle is $7 + 3 + 7 + 3$ or 20 centimeters.

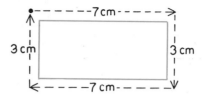

You can use a different order of operations to find the perimeter. The perimeter is 2 times the sum of the length and the width. You usually use ( ) to show which operation to do first.

$$2 \times (7 + 3) = 2 \times 10$$

$$= 20 \qquad \text{The perimeter is 20 centimeters.}$$

Do the operations within the ( ) first. Then use the rule for the order of operations.

Example 2: What number does each phrase name?

a. $(4 + 5) \times 3$

$9 \quad \times 3$

27

b. $18 \div (3 - 2)$

$18 \div \quad 1$

18

c. $15 \div (3 + 2) - 1$

$15 \div \quad 5 \quad - 1$

$3 \quad - 1$

2

d. $(9 + 7) \div 4 + (2 \times 3)$

$16 \quad \div 4 + \quad 6$

$4 \quad + \quad 6$

10

The exercises in this book are of three kinds.

Exercises marked	Will help you to
A	Understand the basic ideas in the lesson.
B	Practice using the basic ideas.
C	Discover new uses of the basic ideas or consider interesting sidelights.

Exercises

A Which operation should you do first?

1. $7 + 5 - 2$ 2. $7 + (5 - 2)$ 3. $10 - 3 + 6$

4. $10 - (3 + 6)$ 5. $4 \times 6 \div 3$ 6. $4 \times (6 \div 3)$

7. $5 \times 2 + 3$ 8. $(5 \times 2) + 3$ 9. $12 \div 2 + 4$

10. $12 \div (2 + 4)$ 11. $14 \div (2 + 5) - 1$ 12. $(14 \div 2) + 5 - 1$

B Find the number named by each phrase.

13. $18 - 7 + 5$ 14. $23 + 4 - 2$

15. $5 \times 4 + 7$ 16. $3 + 6 \times 4$

17. $6 \times 3 \div 2$ 18. $12 \div 2 \times 3$

19. $28 \div 4 + 3$ 20. $20 + 16 \div 2$

21. $7 \times (6 + 5)$ 22. $12 - (2 + 9)$

23. $(10 + 8) \div 6$ 24. $42 \div (3 + 4)$

25. $(32 - 12) \div 5$ 26. $(5 + 7) \times 3$

27. $(9 \times 4) \div (11 - 5)$ 28. $(17 - 9) \times (2 + 7)$

29. $32 \div (6 + 2) \times 5$ 30. $14 \times (8 - 5) - 26$

C Find the number named by each phrase.

Example: $[(11 + 7) \div 3] - 5$

$\qquad$ [18 $\div 3] - 5$ Do the operations in ( ) first.

$\qquad\qquad\qquad\qquad 6 \quad - 5$ Then do the operations in [ ].

$\qquad\qquad\qquad\qquad\qquad 1$ Subtract.

31. $6 + [4 \times (5 - 2)]$ 32. $[(14 + 6) \div 4] - 2$

33. $[(21 - 5) + 4] \div 5$ 34. $47 - [3 \times (21 \div 7)]$

35. $9 \times [6 + (5 - 4)]$ 36. $[(9 + 6) \times 3] + 13$

Suppose your car is in need of a tune-up. You take it to Jim's Auto Service. You do not know how long the tune-up will take.

Let h represent the number of hours it takes to tune up your car. Then you can write the following phrase for the cost of the tune-up.

> **Complete Tune-Up**
>
> **$12 per hour**
>
> **plus**
>
> **$15 for parts**
>
> JIM'S AUTO SERVICE

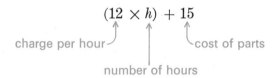

$$(12 \times h) + 15$$

charge per hour   number of hours   cost of parts

There are several ways to indicate multiplication. "Twelve times h" can be written in the following ways.

$$12 \times h \qquad 12(h) \qquad 12h$$

By using the shortest of these, the phrase for the cost of the tune-up can be changed to

$$12h + 15.$$

When used in this way, the letter h may be replaced by different numbers. It is an example of a *variable*.

> A **variable** is any symbol, like h, x, or $\square$, that may be replaced by numbers.

Example 1: Suppose it takes 2 hours for the tune-up of your car. To find the cost, replace h with 2 and find the value of the phrase.

$$12h + 15 = 12(2) + 15 \qquad \text{Replace } h \text{ with 2.}$$
$$= 24 + 15 \qquad \text{Multiply.}$$
$$= 39 \qquad \text{Add.}$$

The cost of the tune-up is $39.

Example 2: Find the value of $7 + (x \div 3)$ if $x = 36$.

$$7 + (x \div 3) = 7 + (36 \div 3) \qquad \text{Replace } x \text{ with 36.}$$
$$= 7 + 12 \qquad \text{Divide.}$$
$$= 19 \qquad \text{Add.}$$

Example 3: Find the value of $16 + n - 5$ if $n = 9$.

$$16 + n - 5 = 16 + 9 - 5 \qquad \text{Replace } n \text{ with 9.}$$
$$= 25 - 5 \qquad \text{Add.}$$
$$= 20 \qquad \text{Subtract.}$$

Exercises

A What is the variable in each phrase?

1. $17 - x$ **2.** $\square + 31$ **3.** $5n + 2$

4. $29 - 3r$ **5.** $3(t + 4)$ **6.** $13b \div 4$

7. $43c$ **8.** $3d + 7$ **9.** $6y - 1$

B Replace the variable with 4. Find the value of each phrase.

10. $12x$ **11.** $9n + 17$ **12.** $21(\triangle - 1)$

13. $8a - 15$ **14.** $35 \div (3 + y)$ **15.** $16 + 5x$

16. $11x - 20$ **17.** $n \times n$ **18.** $3a + 2a$

Replace the variable with 7. Find the value of each phrase.

19. $31 - x + 5$ **20.** $6y \div 3$ **21.** $4(n + 13)$

22. $82 - 5y$ **23.** $9 \div (x - 4)$ **24.** $17 - 2x + 6$

25. $8x - 3x$ **26.** $y \times y$ **27.** $5a + 4a$

Find the value of each phrase.

28. $7 + 3x$ Replace x with 3.

29. $9x - 13$ Replace x with 6.

30. $(x + 6) \div 3$ Replace x with 9.

31. $75 \div (x - 2)$ Replace x with 7.

32. $51 + 4x$ Replace x with 8.

33. a. Write a phrase for the cost of having x plugs installed.

   b. Find the cost of having 6 plugs installed.

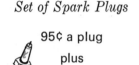

Set of Spark Plugs

95¢ a plug
plus
$8 for labor

34.

DINO'S PIZZAS

 $4 each

$3 for any delivery

   a. Write a phrase for the cost of n pizzas with delivery.

   b. Find the cost of 5 pizzas with delivery.

C Replace x with 2 and y with 5. Find the value of the phrase.

Example: $3x + y = 3(2) + 5$ Replace x with 2 and y with 5.

$$= 6 + 5 \quad \text{Multiply}$$

$$= 11 \quad \text{Add.}$$

35. $x + 7y$ **36.** $4x + y$ **37.** $6x + 3y$

38. $x(y + 8)$ **39.** $7(y - x)$ **40.** $8y - 6x$

1.3 ◆ OPEN SENTENCES

Classify each sentence below as *True, False,* or *Can't decide.*

a. Florida is one of the 50 states in the U.S.A.

b. Australia is the largest continent.

c. Dick Tracy is a comic-strip character.

d. He won an Olympic gold medal.

e. She was a famous scientist.

f. It is my worst subject.

Why couldn't you decide on sentences **d, e,** and **f?**

If you replace *She* in sentence **e** with *Madame Curie,* most people would mark the sentence *True.* If you replace *She* with *The Witch from Puf'n'Stuf,* most people would mark the sentence *False.* If you replace *She* with *Memphis,* the sentence is not only *False,* the replacement doesn't even fit—Memphis is a city, not a woman.

Classify each sentence below as *True, False,* or *Can't decide.*

g. $3 + 5 = 8$　　　　　　**h.** $\square + 6 = 10$

i. $4 + 7 = 9$　　　　　　**j.** $1111 \times 9 = 9999$

k. $8 - n > 15$　　　　　　**m.** $3a < 9$

　　　　is greater than　　　　　　is less than

Why couldn't you decide on sentences **h, k,** and **m?**

Sentences **h, k,** and **m** are neither true nor false. They are called *open sentences.* If you replace $\square$ with 4 in $\square + 6 = 10$, the sentence is *True.* If you replace $\square$ with 7, the sentence is *False.*

> An **open sentence** contains one or more variables and is neither true nor false.

Exercises

A Tell whether each sentence is *True, False,* or *Open.*

1. Lake Erie is one of the Great Lakes.

2. Football is called the national anthem.

3. It is the smallest state in the U.S.A.

4. Martha Washington invented the light bulb.

5. John F. Kennedy was a President of the U.S.A.

6. He is bigger than you.

7. Chess is a card game.

8. She is a United States Senator.

9. One meter is shorter than one yard.

10. Chicago is the largest city in Illinois.

11. $2 \times 2 \times 2 \times 2 \times 2 = 32$ 12. $8 + \square = 14$

13. $7 - n > 3$ 14. $7 - 5 > 3$

15. $7 - 5 < 3$ 16. $8x = 16$

17. $2x + x = 11 + 7$ 18. $39 = 13 + 13 + 13$

19. $81 > 3 \times 20$ 20. $26 > 2 \times 7$

B For each open sentence, find a replacement that makes it true. Then find a replacement that makes it false.

21. It is the capital of the U.S.A.

22. It is the third letter of the English alphabet.

23. He invented the telephone.

24. She discovered radium.

OPEN SENTENCES   9

25. $7 + \square = 19$

26. $4 \times \square + 3 = 11$

27. $13 > 2n$

28. $n \div 5 = 7$

29. $3 \times 2 < a$

30. $x - 6 = 13$

C Find a number that will make each sentence true.

Example: $3a + a = 32$ ⟶ Replace both a's with the same number.

$$3(8) + 8 = 32$$

$$24 \ \ + 8 = 32 \quad \text{Multiply.}$$

$$32 = 32 \quad \text{Add.}$$

Since $32 = 32$ is true, 8 makes the sentence true.

31. $a + a = 18$

32. $3x + x < 7$

33. $x + 2x = 12$

34. $3a - a > 5$

35. $n + 2 = 2 + n$

36. $4x + 2 = 3x + 4$

Working on the Railroad

The westbound train is to pick up cars 1 and 2, place them behind the engine in that order, and continue on its way.

The engine has a coupling on the front for use in switching. When the switching is completed, car 3 should be in its original position.

How would you do the switching?

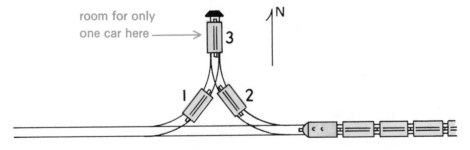

room for only one car here ⟶

3

↑N

Brian's lawn mower has broken down. He needs a bolt to repair it. On his father's workbench is a jar of bolts of different sizes. Since Brian doesn't know what size bolt he needs, he takes the jar to the mower. He tries each bolt until he finds one that fits.

You can try to solve a sentence like $n + 7 = 10$ the same way Brian solved his bolt problem. You need a set of numbers like {1, 2, 3, 4, 5, 6} to try in place of n. You can try each number to see whether it makes the sentence true or false.

$$n + 7 = 10 \qquad \{1, 2, 3, 4, 5, 6\}$$

$1 + 7 = 10$	False	$4 + 7 = 10$	False
$2 + 7 = 10$	False	$5 + 7 = 10$	False
$3 + 7 = 10$	True	$6 + 7 = 10$	False

The number three made the sentence true. It was the *only* number that did.

The set of numbers that can replace a variable is called the **replacement set**.

The set of numbers that makes a sentence true is called the **solution set**.

$$n + 7 = 10 \qquad \{1, 2, 3, 4, 5, 6\} \qquad \{3\}$$

variable   replacement set   solution set

Example 1:   *Sentence*   *Replacement set*

$$3x + 4 = 13$$ $\{1, 2, 3, 4\}$

$3(1) + 4 = 13$ $3(3) + 4 = 13$

   $7 = 13$ False $13 = 13$ True

$3(2) + 4 = 13$ $3(4) + 4 = 13$

   $10 = 13$ False $16 = 13$ False

The solution set $= \{3\}$.

Example 2: $2n > 7$ $\{0, 1, 2, 3, 4, 5\}$

$2(0) > 7$ $2(3) > 7$

   $0 > 7$ False $6 > 7$ False

$2(1) > 7$ $2(4) > 7$

   $2 > 7$ False $8 > 7$ True

$2(2) > 7$ $2(5) > 7$

   $4 > 7$ False $10 > 7$ True

The solution set is $\{4, 5\}$.

Example 3: $n + 5 = 12$ $\{4, 5, 6\}$

$4 + 5 = 12$ False $6 + 5 = 12$ False

$5 + 5 = 12$ False

The solution set $= \{\ \ \}$.

   $\{\ \ \}$ and $\varnothing$ are symbols for the **empty set**. The empty set has *no* numbers. If a solution set is empty, there are no numbers in the replacement set that make the sentence true.

Example 4: $3(x + 2) = 3x + 6$ $\{2, 4, 6, 8, 10\}$

$3(2 + 2) = 3(2) + 6$ $3(8 + 2) = 3(8) + 6$

$3(4) = 6 + 6$ $3(10) = 24 + 6$

$12 = 12$ True $30 = 30$ True

$3(4 + 2) = 3(4) + 6$ $3(10 + 2) = 3(10) + 6$

$3(6) = 12 + 6$ $3(12) = 30 + 6$

$18 = 18$ True $36 = 36$ True

$3(6 + 2) = 3(6) + 6$

$3(8) = 18 + 6$

$24 = 24$ True

The solution set $= \{2, 4, 6, 8, 10\}$.

Exercises

A For which example did the solution set contain the following?

1. only one number

2. only two numbers

3. all the numbers in the replacement set

4. no numbers

B Use $\{0, 1, 2, 3, 4, 5\}$ as the replacement set. Find the solution set for each sentence.

5. $n + 8 = 12$ **6.** $3n = 15$

7. $4x \div 2 = 2x$ **8.** $8x + 4 = 5$

9. $n > n + 1$ **10.** $n + 1 > n$

11. $2(x + 1) = 2x + 1$ **12.** $2(x + 1) = 2x + 2$

13. $4x + 3 = 11$ **14.** $6n - 4 = 20$

Find the solution set for each sentence.

Sentence	Replacement set
15. $2n - 2 = 12$	$\{5, 7, 9, 13\}$
16. $2n - 3 < 4$	$\{2, 3, 5, 8, 12\}$
17. $2x + 5 = 17$	$\{4, 6, 8, 10\}$
18. $24 - 3y = 15$	$\{2, 3, 4, 5, 6\}$
19. $31 = 7n + 3$	$\{2, 3, 4, 5\}$
20. $4x - 8 = 0$	$\{1, 2, 3, 4\}$
21. $5(x - 4) = 5x - 20$	$\{5, 6, 7, 8\}$
22. $3n + 15 = 3(n + 5)$	$\{0, 1, 2, 3\}$
23. $3n > 2n$	$\{2, 3, 4, 5\}$
24. $4x = 10$	$\{3, 4, 5, 6\}$

C The replacement set is $\{50, 51, 52, 53\}$. Find the solution set for each sentence.

25. $2x + 7 = 3x - 44$ **26.** $4x + 4 = 2(2x + 2)$

27. $3n < 156$ **28.** $5x - 10 = 5(x - 1)$

29. $2x - 1 > 103$ **30.** $n + 19 = 19 + n$

You have already found solution sets by trying *all* the numbers in the replacement set. This can take a long time if there are lots of numbers in the replacement set. In fact, it is impossible if the replacement set has too many numbers.

Let's look for an easier way to *solve* open sentences.

> *Solve* means "find the numbers that make the sentence true."

Suppose you want to solve the equation $n + 3 = 5$. The $=$ means the two sides of the equation name the same number, so the equation is in balance. You can show the equation on a balance beam.

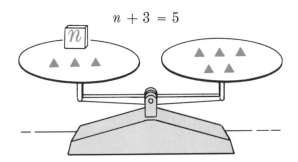

$$n + 3 = 5$$

The left side has a block marked n and 3 weights. The right side has 5 weights like those on the left. The problem is to find what n weighs.

Whatever you do, you must keep the equation in balance. To find what n weighs, get n by itself on one side. To do that, take the 3 weights off the left side. To keep the balance, you must also take 3 weights off the right side.

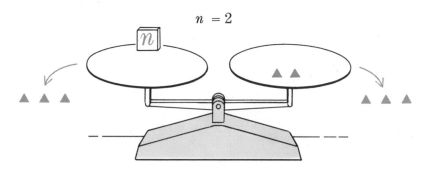

$$n = 2$$

The new equation is $n = 2$. You can give that as the answer, or you can give the solution set as $\{2\}$. You have *solved* the equation! To be sure your answer is correct, replace n with 2 in the original equation to see if it makes the sentence true.

Check: $n + 3 = 5$

$2 + 3 = 5$

$5 = 5$ It checks!

Example 1: Solve $n + 7 = 12$.

Step 1: Show the equation on a balance beam.

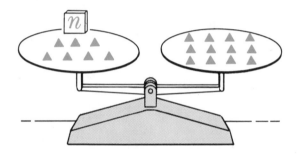

Step 2: Remove 7 weights from each side.

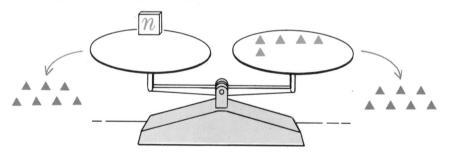

Step 3: Write the new equation.

$$n = 5$$

Step 4: Check the answer in the original equation.

$$n + 7 = 12$$

$$5 + 7 = 12$$

$$12 = 12$$ It checks!

Example 2: Solve $n + 8 = 24$.

Let's try it without the balance beam.

Step 1: Subtract 8 from each side.

$$n + 8 = 24$$

$$n + 8 - 8 = 24 - 8$$

$$n + 0 = 16$$

$$n = 16$$

Step 2: Check the answer in the original equation.

$$n + 8 = 24$$

$$16 + 8 = 24$$

$$24 = 24 \quad \text{It checks!}$$

Exercises

A Solve the equations shown on the balance beams.
In all exercises, the replacement set is the whole numbers.

1.

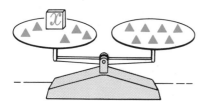

2.

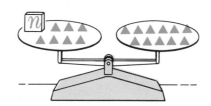

3.

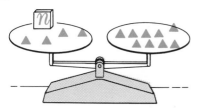

4.

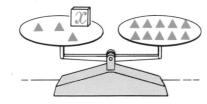

B Solve and check each equation. Use the balance beam if it helps.

5. $n + 5 = 13$ **6.** $x + 4 = 11$

7. $y + 23 = 39$ **8.** $a + 9 = 21$

9. $x + 4 = 14$ **10.** $n + 15 = 26$

11. $c + 2 = 7$ **12.** $x + 18 = 36$

Solve and check each equation.

13. $y + 6 = 19$ **14.** $n + 10 = 43$

15. $x + 11 = 33$ **16.** $a + 2 = 9$

17. $n + 21 = 56$ **18.** $t + 30 = 72$

19. $x + 105 = 308$ **20.** $n + 7 = 10$

21. $y + 46 = 81$ **22.** $a + 55 = 90$

23. $x + 87 = 90$ **24.** $n + 240 = 354$

25. $y + 100 = 579$ **26.** $x + 750 = 1275$

C Solve and check each equation.

27. $17 = x + 8$ **28.** $64 = n + 29$

29. $y + (5 + 3) = 39$ **30.** $x + (26 - 12) = 57$

31. $n + 13 = 4(9 + 2)$ **32.** $y + 10 = 16 + (18 \div 3)$

INEQUALITIES AND THE BALANCE BEAM 1.6

The inequality $n + 5 > 11$ is shown on the balance beam below. The $>$ means that $n + 5$ *is greater than* 11. The left side is lower because its load is greater than the load on the right.

$$n + 5 > 11$$

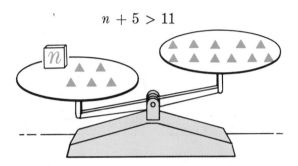

The beam is unbalanced. When solving the inequality, you must keep the beam unbalanced in the same way.

To solve the inequality, remove 5 weights from each side. That leaves the position of the balance unchanged, and it leaves n by itself on one side.

$$n > 6$$

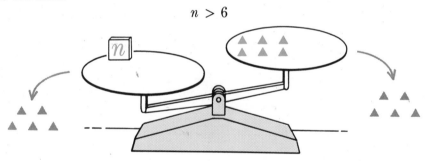

The new inequality is $n > 6$. You can give that as the answer. It means that n can be any number greater than 6. You have solved the inequality!

To check the answer, replace n in the original inequality by any number greater than 6. Since $7 > 6$, let's try 7.

$$n + 5 > 11$$

$$7 + 5 > 11$$

$$12 > 11 \quad \text{It checks!}$$

Example 1:   Solve $n + 3 < 8$.

Step 1:   Show the inequality on a balance beam.

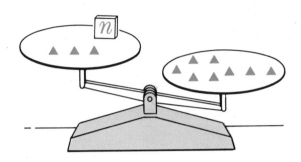

The left side is higher because its load
is less than the load on the right.

Step 2:   Remove 3 weights from each side.

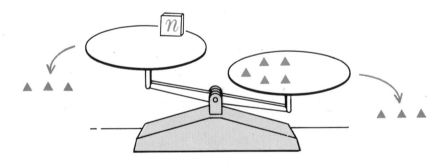

Step 3:   Write the new inequality.

$$n < 5$$

Step 4:   Check the answer in the original inequality. Try any
number less than 5.

$$n + 3 < 8$$

$$4 + 3 < 8$$

$$7 < 8 \quad \text{It checks!}$$

Example 2: Solve $n + 6 > 13$.

Let's try it without the balance beam.

Step 1: Subtract 6 from each side.

$$n + 6 > 13$$

$$n + 6 - 6 > 13 - 6$$

$$n + 0 > 7$$

$$n > 7$$

Step 2: Check the answer in the original inequality. Try any number greater than 7.

$$n + 6 > 13$$

$$8 + 6 > 13$$

$$14 > 13 \quad \text{It checks!}$$

Exercises

Ⓐ Solve the inequalities shown on the balance beams. In all exercises, the replacement set is the whole numbers.

1.

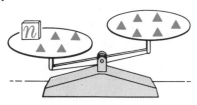

2.

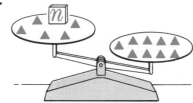

3.

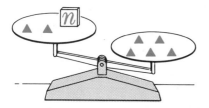

4.

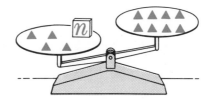

B Solve and check each inequality. Use the balance beam if it helps.

5. $n + 6 < 7$ **6.** $x + 8 < 12$

7. $y + 2 > 11$ **8.** $n + 7 > 20$

9. $x + 18 < 18$ **10.** $a + 10 < 45$

11. $n + 12 > 23$ **12.** $y + 17 > 32$

Solve and check each inequality.

13. $n + 4 < 10$ **14.** $x + 1 < 17$

15. $y + 23 < 39$ **16.** $a + 9 < 21$

17. $x + 4 < 14$ **18.** $n + 15 < 26$

19. $y + 23 > 39$ **20.** $a + 9 > 21$

21. $n + 47 > 80$ **22.** $y + 50 > 63$

23. $x + 92 > 101$ **24.** $n + 100 > 326$

25. $n + 260 < 452$ **26.** $x + 137 < 532$

C Solve and check each inequality.

27. $13 > x + 4$ **28.** $64 < n + 29$

29. $a + (12 + 7) > 32$ **30.** $y + (31 - 18) < 42$

31. $n + 9 > 5(11 - 7)$ **32.** $x + 12 < 47 - 3(9)$

The balance beam helped you "see" how to solve open sentences. It is also helpful to "see" solution sets. The usual way to do that is to graph the solution sets.

In this lesson, the replacement set is the whole numbers.

Example 1: Solve $n + 7 = 12$ and graph the solution set.

    Step 1: Solve the equation.

$$n + 7 = 12$$

$$n + 7 - 7 = 12 - 7 \qquad \text{Subtract 7 from each side.}$$

$$n + 0 = 5$$

$$n = 5$$

    Step 2: Check the answer.

$$n + 7 = 12$$

$$5 + 7 = 12 \qquad \text{Replace } n \text{ with 5.}$$

$$12 = 12 \qquad \text{It checks!}$$

The solution set is $\{5\}$.

    Step 3: Make a number line.

    Step 4: Graph the solution set.

Draw a dot at 5.

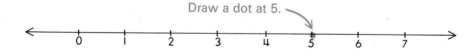

> The **graph** of an equation like $n + 7 = 12$ is a single point.

Example 2:   Solve $n + 3 < 7$ and graph the solution set.

Step 1:   Solve the inequality.

$$n + 3 < 7$$

$$n + 3 - 3 < 7 - 3 \qquad \text{Subtract 3 from each side.}$$

$$n + 0 < 4$$

$$n < 4$$

Step 2:   Check. Try numbers less than 4.

$$n + 3 < 7 \qquad\qquad\qquad n + 3 < 7$$

$$1 + 3 < 7 \qquad\qquad\qquad 3 + 3 < 7$$

$$4 < 7 \quad \text{They check!} \qquad\quad 6 < 7$$

The solution set is $\{0, 1, 2, 3\}$.

Step 3:   Graph the solution set.

Draw dots for 0, 1, 2, and 3.

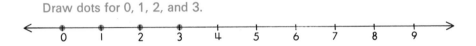

Example 3:   Solve $n + 9 < 10$ and graph the solution set.

Step 1:   Solve and check.

$$n + 9 < 10 \qquad\qquad\qquad n + 9 < 10$$

$$n + 9 - 9 < 10 - 9 \qquad\qquad 0 + 9 < 10$$

$$n + 0 < 1 \qquad\qquad\qquad 9 < 10 \quad \text{It checks!}$$

$$n < 1$$

The solution set is $\{0\}$.

Step 2:   Graph the solution set.

Draw a dot for 0.

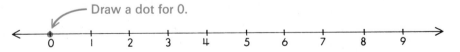

Exercises

A How would you graph each set on a number line ?

1. $\{4, 5, 6\}$

2. whole numbers greater than 8

3. $\{3\}$

4. whole numbers less than 6

5. $\{\ \ \}$

6. whole numbers greater than 4

7. $\{0, 1, 2, 3, 4, 5\}$

8. all whole numbers

B Solve each open sentence and graph the solution set.

9. $n + 4 = 9$

10. $n + 6 = 12$

11. $n + 9 = 11$

12. $n + 8 = 8$

13. $n + 6 < 8$

14. $n + 4 < 10$

15. $n + 2 < 4$

16. $n + 4 < 4$

17. $n + 1 > 3$

18. $n + 3 > 6$

19. $n + 2 > 2$

20. $n + 4 > 7$

C Solve each open sentence for the given replacement set. Graph the solution set.

Open sentence	*Replacement set*
21. $n + 3 = 7$	$\{0, 2, 4, 6, 8\}$
22. $n + 3 = 7$	$\{1, 3, 5, 7, 9\}$
23. $n + 1 > 4$	$\{4, 5, 6, 7, 8\}$
24. $n + 1 > 4$	$\{0, 1, 2, 3\}$
25. $n + 1 > 4$	$\{2, 3, 4\}$

26. Can the solution set of an equation be $\{\ \ \}$? (See Ex. 22.)

27. If you use different replacements sets, can an open sentence have different solution sets? (See Ex. 21–22 or Ex. 23–25.)

VOCABULARY

Match each term with the best example or description.

1. variable

    a. to find the solution set

2. open sentence

    b. the set of numbers that make a sentence true

3. replacement set

    c. $19 - 8 > 7$

4. solution set

    d. $3x + 2 = 17$

5. empty set

    e. the symbol n in $5n + 4$

6. solve

    f. the set that contains no numbers

7. equation

    g. the set of numbers that can replace a variable

8. inequality

    h. a sentence containing an equal sign ($=$)

CHAPTER REVIEW

Find the number named by each phrase.   1.1

1. $7 + 2 \times 4$
2. $(9 \times 11) - 46$
3. $18 - 9 \div 3$
4. $(5 \times 6) \div (17 - 7)$
5. $21 \div (5 + 2)$
6. $24 \div (2 + 6) - 3$

Replace the variable with 5. Find the value of each phrase.   1.2

7. $7y - 20$
8. $(n + 7) \times 4$
9. $18 + 2x$
10. $65 \div (a + 8)$

Tell whether each sentence is *True, False*, or *Open*.   1.3

11. Idaho is a state.
12. $9 + n = 17$
13. It is a vegetable.
14. $87 \div 3 = 26$
15. A snake is an insect.
16. $3 \times 13 < 40$

Find the number named by each phrase.

1. $21 - 6 \div 3$

2. $(17 - 8) \div (2 + 1)$

3. $(4 + 5) \times 9$

4. $32 - (6 \times 3) + 7$

Replace the variable with 3. Evaluate each phrase.

5. $14 - 4x$

6. $(a + 6) \times 11$

7. $7y + 8$

8. $72 \div (15 - n)$

Tell whether each sentence is *True, False,* or *Open.*

9. She is a poet.

10. $(x - 4) \times 8 < 22$

11. $(3 \times 4) + 5 = 17$

12. $64 \div 8 > 8$

Solve and check each open sentence.

13. $x + 7 = 13$

14. $y + 12 = 37$

15. $n + 2 < 17$

16. $a + 6 < 23$

17. $y + 5 > 9$

18. $x + 15 > 31$

Solve each open sentence. Graph the solution set.

19. $n + 8 = 12$

20. $n + 2 < 5$

21. $n + 5 > 11$

22. $n + 17 = 17$

Activities for Chapter 1

Activity 1

Make a balance beam. You might use two paper cups, a ruler, a round pencil or drinking straw, a paper clamp, and two paper clips as shown. Place the paper-clip hooks at the 1″ and 11″ marks.

Activity 2

Use the balance beam you made to do the following.

1. Place 10 paper clips on each side.

2. Remove half the paper clips from each side.

3. Place 2 more paper clips on each side.

4. Remove 1 paper clip from each side.

5. Did the beam stay balanced at all times?

Activity 3

Start with the balance beam empty.

1. Place 4 paper clips on the left side. Place 3 paper clips on the right side. Is the beam balanced? If not, which way did it tip?

2. Double the number of clips on the right side. Which way does the beam tip now?

3. Put on enough more clips to make it balance. How many paper clips were needed? On which side?

Mathematics and Flying

When you fly an airplane, its speed through the air is called *airspeed*.

The speed and direction of the wind usually cause your speed over the ground, called *ground speed*, to be different than your airspeed.

When flying with the wind, you have a tail wind. In that case, the ground speed is the sum of the airspeed and the tail-wind speed.

tail-wind speed

airspeed — ground speed

$$a + w = g$$

Example: Suppose the tail-wind speed is 15 mph and your ground speed is 210 mph. Find your airspeed.

$a + w = g$

$a + 15 = 210$ — Replace w with 15 and g with 210.

$a + 15 - 15 = 210 - 15$ — Subtract 15 from each side.

$a + 0 = 195$

$a = 195$ — Your airspeed is 195 mph.

Try this formula in the following problems.

1. At your flight altitude the wind is from due south at 18 mph. You are flying due north at a ground speed of 206 mph. Find your airspeed.

2. An air traffic controller reports that you have a tail wind of 27 mph. You want to make a ground speed of 185 mph. At what airspeed should you fly?

Getting Ready for Chapter 2

Match each item in the first column with the best description.

1.2 **1.** $3n$ **a.** $x + 2$ is greater than 9.

     2. $3 \div n$ **b.** $x + 2$ is less than 9.

1.3 **3.** $x + 2 = 9$ **c.** an open sentence that is an equation

     4. $x + 2 < 9$ **d.** a closed sentence

     5. $x + 2 > 9$ **e.** the graph of $\{3, 4\}$

     6. $7 + 2 = 9$ **f.** the graph of all whole numbers greater than 2

1.7 **7.**   **g.** three times n

     8.   **h.** three divided by n

1.2 Find the value of each phrase.

     9. $n - 8$ if $n = 19$

     10. $5a + 6$ if $a = 7$

     11. $13 + 3x - 6$ if $x = 2$

     12. $(4n \div 3) - 7$ if $n = 6$

     13. $(28 \div 4) \times (y + 2)$ if $y = 3$

Solve and check each open sentence.

1.5 **14.** $n + 7 = 15$ **15.** $x + 10 = 45$ **16.** $n + 56 = 83$

1.6 **17.** $y + 72 > 72$ **18.** $x + 3 < 8$ **19.** $n + 7 > 13$

     20. $y + 20 > 23$ **21.** $a + 8 < 14$

1.7 Graph each set of numbers on a number line.

     22. $\{3, 4, 5, 6\}$ **23.** whole numbers less than 5

     24. $\{7\}$ **25.** whole numbers greater than 6

2.1 ◆ EQUATIONS ON THE BEAM

You have solved open sentences like $n + 7 = 12$ and $n + 2 < 5$ both with and without the help of a balance beam. Suppose you want to solve the equation $2n = 8$. You can show the equation on a balance beam.

$$2n = 8$$

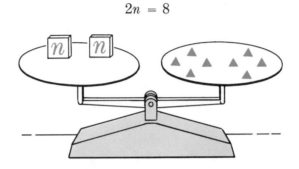

There are two blocks marked n on the left side. You want only *one* block marked n on that side. To get that, remove half the blocks. To keep the beam balanced, remove half the weights from the right side.

$$n = 4$$

The new equation is $n = 4$. You can give that as the answer, or you can give the solution set as {4}.

To check your answer, replace n with 4 in the original equation to see if it makes the sentence true.

$$\text{Check:} \quad 2n = 8$$
$$2(4) = 8$$
$$8 = 8 \quad \text{It checks!}$$

Example 1:   Solve $2n = 8$ without the balance beam.

Step 1:   Divide each side by 2.

$$2n = 8$$

$$\frac{2n}{2} = \frac{8}{2}$$

$$n = 4$$

Step 2:   Check your answer.

$2n = 8$ Original equation

$2(4) = 8$ Replace *n* with 4.

$8 = 8$ It checks!

Example 2:   Solve $3n = 15$ with and without the balance beam.

Step 1:   Show the equation.

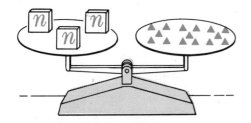

$$3n = 15$$

Step 2:   Divide each side by 3.

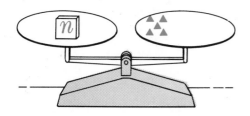

$$\frac{3n}{3} = \frac{15}{3}$$

$$n = 5$$

Step 3:   Check your answer.

$3n = 15$ Original equation

$3(5) = 15$ Replace *n* with 5.

$15 = 15$ It checks!

It is hard to show equations like $n - 3 = 6$ and $\frac{n}{4} = 8$ on a balance beam. But they are easy to solve.

Example 1: Solve and check $n - 3 = 6$.

> *Step 1:* $n - 3 = 6$ means 3 less than some number is equal to 6. To find the number, add 3 to each side.
>
> $$n - 3 = 6$$
>
> $$n - 3 + 3 = 6 + 3 \quad \text{Add 3 to each side.}$$
>
> $$n + 0 = 9$$
>
> $$n = 9$$

> *Step 2:* Check the answer.
>
> $$n - 3 = 6 \quad \text{Original equation}$$
>
> $$9 - 3 = 6 \quad \text{Replace } n \text{ with 9.}$$
>
> $$6 = 6 \quad \text{It checks!}$$

Example 2: Solve and check $n - 7 = 15$.

$$n - 7 = 15$$

$$n - 7 + 7 = 15 + 7 \quad \text{Add 7 to each side.}$$

$$n + 0 = 22$$

$$n = 22$$

Check the answer.

$$n - 7 = 15 \quad \text{Original equation}$$

$$22 - 7 = 15 \quad \text{Replace } n \text{ with 22.}$$

$$15 = 15 \quad \text{It checks!}$$

Example 3: Solve and check $\frac{n}{4} = 8$.

Step 1: $\frac{n}{4} = 8$ means some number divided by 4 is equal to 8. To find the number, multiply each side by 4.

$$\frac{n}{4} = 8$$

$$\frac{n}{4} \times 4 = 8 \times 4 \qquad \text{Multiply each side by 4.}$$

$$n = 32$$

Step 2: Check the answer.

$$\frac{n}{4} = 8 \qquad \text{Original equation}$$

$$\frac{32}{4} = 8 \qquad \text{Replace } n \text{ with 32.}$$

$$8 = 8 \qquad \text{It checks!}$$

Example 4: Solve and check $\frac{n}{7} = 50$.

$$\frac{n}{7} = 50$$

$$\frac{n}{7} \times 7 = 50 \times 7 \qquad \text{Multiply each side by 7.}$$

$$n = 350$$

Check the answer.

$$\frac{n}{7} = 50 \qquad \text{Original equation}$$

$$\frac{350}{7} = 50 \qquad \text{Replace } n \text{ with 350.}$$

$$50 = 50 \qquad \text{It checks!}$$

Exercises

A To solve each equation, what number would you add to each side ?

1. $n - 8 = 13$ **2.** $x - 10 = 34$ **3.** $a - 12 = 50$

4. $y - 1 = 11$ **5.** $n - 7 = 16$ **6.** $x - 23 = 8$

To solve each equation, by what number would you multiply each side ?

7. $\frac{n}{5} = 8$ **8.** $\frac{x}{2} = 13$ **9.** $\frac{y}{9} = 2$

10. $\frac{a}{7} = 12$ **11.** $\frac{n}{11} = 6$ **12.** $\frac{c}{20} = 5$

B Solve and check each equation. (See Examples 1 and 2.)

13. $n - 6 = 10$ **14.** $n - 7 = 17$ **15.** $x - 8 = 18$

16. $y - 6 = 6$ **17.** $c - 4 = 2$ **18.** $n - 12 = 0$

19. $x - 7 = 1$ **20.** $n - 21 = 11$ **21.** $a - 17 = 13$

22. $y - 8 = 5$ **23.** $z - 19 = 14$ **24.** $x - 9 = 28$

Solve and check each equation. (See Examples 3 and 4.)

25. $\frac{n}{1} = 10$ **26.** $\frac{n}{5} = 10$ **27.** $\frac{n}{10} = 11$

28. $\frac{n}{4} = 15$ **29.** $\frac{n}{15} = 0$ **30.** $\frac{n}{8} = 12$

31. $\frac{x}{7} = 30$ **32.** $\frac{y}{2} = 34$ **33.** $\frac{a}{20} = 4$

34. $\frac{x}{6} = 9$ **35.** $\frac{n}{3} = 17$ **36.** $\frac{z}{9} = 11$

C Solve and check each equation.

37. $n - (32 \div 8) = 16$ **38.** $n - 13 = 20 \div (17 - 12)$

39. $\frac{n}{72 \div 9} = 6$ **40.** $\frac{n}{5} = 15 - (3 \times 4)$

41. $17 = \frac{n}{14 - 9}$ **42.** $n - (7 \times 5) = 26 \div 2$

EQUATIONS OFF THE BEAM   39

2.3 ◆ INEQUALITIES ON THE BEAM

Which open sentence is shown on the balance beam?

a. $3n > 15$ **b.** $3n = 15$ **c.** $3n < 15$

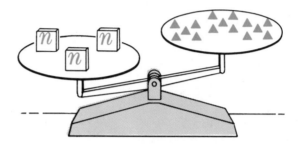

If you said **a,** you're right! The side with 3 blocks marked n is heavier than the side with 15 weights, so $3n$ *is greater than* 15.

You can solve $3n > 15$ by dividing each side by 3.

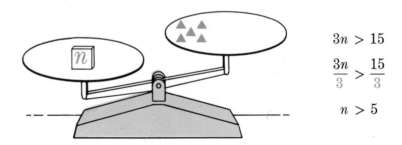

$$3n > 15$$

$$\frac{3n}{3} > \frac{15}{3}$$

$$n > 5$$

The new sentence is $n > 5$. You can give that as the answer.

To check the answer, try any numbers greater than 5 in the original sentence.

Replace n with 6.
$$3n > 15$$
$$3(6) > 15$$
$$18 > 15$$
They check!

$$3n > 15$$
$$3(10) > 15$$ Replace n with 10.
$$30 > 15$$

9. 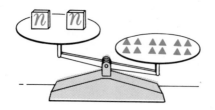 **10.**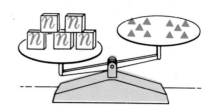

Solve and check each inequality.

11. $3n > 24$ **12.** $8n < 64$ **13.** $5n < 5$

14. $7n > 35$ **15.** $10n > 70$ **16.** $2n < 22$

17. $6n < 54$ **18.** $4n > 80$ **19.** $9n < 72$

20. $15n > 90$ **21.** $25n < 100$ **22.** $8n > 64$

23. $20n > 100$ **24.** $11n < 77$ **25.** $12n > 108$

26. $17n < 289$ **27.** $13n > 1001$ **28.** $153n < 306$

29. $50n < 300$ **30.** $75n > 300$ **31.** $13n < 260$

32. $16n > 160$ **33.** $14n < 154$ **34.** $45n > 900$

C Solve and check each inequality.

35. $5n < (72 \div 4) + 7$ **36.** $(36 \div 4)n > 81$

37. $6n > 4 + (47 - 39)$ **38.** $(8 \times 2)n > 100 - (4 \times 17)$

39. $(5 \times 3)n < 75$ **40.** $(21 \div 3)n < 32 + (48 \div 2)$

By now you are becoming an expert in solving some kinds of inequalities. You will work with two other kinds of inequalities in this lesson.

Example 1: Solve and check $n - 5 < 10$.

Step 1: Since 5 is subtracted from n, add 5 to each side.

$$n - 5 < 10$$

$$n - 5 + 5 < 10 + 5 \quad \text{Add 5 to each side.}$$

$$n < 15$$

Step 2: Check your answer. Try whole numbers less than 15 in the original inequality.

$n - 5 < 10$	$n - 5 < 10$
Replace n with 14. $\quad 14 - 5 < 10$	$6 - 5 < 10$ $\quad$ Replace n with 6.
$9 < 10$ $\quad$ They check!	$1 < 10$

Example 2: Solve and check $\frac{n}{7} > 43$.

Step 1: Since n is divided by 7, multiply each side by 7.

$$\frac{n}{7} > 43$$

$$\frac{n}{7} \times 7 > 43 \times 7 \quad \text{Multiply each side by 7.}$$

$$n > 301$$

Step 2: Check your answer. Try whole numbers greater than 301 in the original inequality.

$\frac{n}{7} > 43$	$\frac{n}{7} > 43$	$\frac{n}{7} > 43$
$\frac{302}{7} > 43$	$\frac{420}{7} > 43$	$\frac{700}{7} > 43$
$43\frac{1}{7} > 43$ $\quad$ They check!	$60 > 43$ $\quad$ They check!	$100 > 43$

List the solution sets.

$$\{12, 13, 14, 15, \cdots\} \qquad \{\cdots, 11, 12, 13, 14\}$$

Find the numbers that are in both solution sets.

$$\{12, 13, 14\}$$

31. $n - 6 < 4$ and $\frac{n}{3} > 2$ **32.** $\frac{n}{6} < 8$ and $n - 15 > 30$

33. $\frac{n}{7} > 0$ and $n - 2 < 3$ **34.** $n - 11 < 93$ and $\frac{n}{10} > 10$

35. $\frac{n}{6} < 7$ and $n - 8 > 30$ **36.** $\frac{n}{8} < 8$ and $n - 30 > 30$

Which Way?

Jon was working on an algebra assignment. He had to decide whether to add or to multiply the three numbers recorded on his paper. He decided to do it both ways. Much to his surprise, the answers were the same.

What were the numbers?

2.5 ◆ GRAPHING OPEN SENTENCES

In Section 1.7 you graphed solution sets of equations like $n + 5 = 8$ and of inequalities like $x + 6 < 9$ and $y + 2 > 5$. You drew a dot on a number line for each number in the solution set.

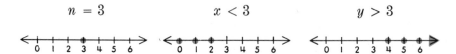

$$n = 3 \qquad\qquad x < 3 \qquad\qquad y > 3$$

You will graph the solution sets of other equations and inequalities in this lesson. The replacement set will be the whole numbers.

Example 1: Solve $\frac{x}{4} = 6$. Graph the solution set.

Step 1: Solve the equation. Check the answer.

$$\frac{x}{4} = 6 \qquad\qquad\qquad Check: \quad \frac{x}{4} = 6$$

$$\frac{x}{4} \times 4 = 6 \times 4 \qquad\qquad\qquad \frac{24}{4} = 6$$

$$x = 24 \qquad\qquad\qquad\qquad 6 = 6 \quad \text{It checks!}$$

The solution set is $\{24\}$.

Step 2: Graph the solution set.

Draw a dot at 24.

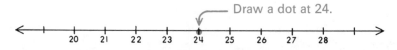

Example 2: Solve $3x < 12$. Graph the solution set.

Step 1: Solve the inequality. Check the answer.

$$3x < 12 \qquad\qquad Check: \quad 3x < 12$$

$$\frac{3x}{3} < \frac{12}{3} \qquad\qquad\qquad 3(2) < 12$$

$$x < 4 \qquad\qquad\qquad\qquad 6 < 12 \quad \text{It checks!}$$

The solution set is $\{0, 1, 2, 3\}$.

Step 2: Graph the solution set.

Draw dots at 0, 1, 2, and 3.

Example 3: Solve $x - 6 > 10$. Graph the solution set.

Step 1: Solve the inequality. Check the answer.

$x - 6 > 10$	*Check:* $x - 6 > 10$
$x - 6 + 6 > 10 + 6$	$18 - 6 > 10$
$x > 16$	$12 > 10$ It checks!

The solution set is all whole numbers greater than 16. You can show that by writing {17, 18, 19, $\cdots$}.

Step 2: Graph the solution set.

The dots and the $\longrightarrow$ show that all whole numbers greater than 16 are in the graph.

Exercises

Ⓐ What set of numbers is graphed on each number line?

1.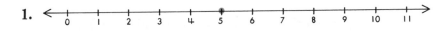

2.

3.

4.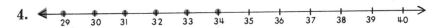

Solve each equation. Graph the solution set.

5. $x - 4 = 12$ 6. $\frac{x}{4} = 5$ 7. $\frac{x}{2} = 15$

8. $x - 8 = 17$ 9. $7x = 21$ 10. $9x = 63$

11. $\frac{x}{8} = 0$ 12. $x + 3 = 8$ 13. $12x = 48$

14. $x - 11 = 1$ 15. $15x = 15$ 16. $\frac{x}{10} = 7$

Solve each inequality. Graph the solution set.

17. $\frac{x}{4} < 10$ 18. $x - 5 > 10$ 19. $2x > 12$

20. $x + 8 < 12$ 21. $\frac{x}{3} > 5$ 22. $x + 7 < 8$

23. $\frac{x}{4} < 12$ 24. $7x < 14$ 25. $x + 7 > 8$

26. $x - 5 > 1$ 27. $9x < 9$ 28. $\frac{x}{1} > 10$

Find all the whole numbers that make both inequalities true. Graph that set of numbers.

Example: $\frac{x}{2} > 5$ and $x + 3 < 18$

$$\frac{x}{2} > 5 \qquad\qquad\qquad x + 3 < 18$$

$$\frac{x}{2} \times 2 > 5 \times 2 \qquad\qquad x + 3 - 3 < 18 - 3$$

$$x > 10 \qquad\qquad\qquad x < 15$$

The solution set is   The solution set is

$\{11, 12, 13, \cdots\}$. $\{\cdots, 12, 13, 14\}$.

The whole numbers that make both inequalities true are greater than 10 and less than 15. Or you can say, "the whole numbers between 10 and 15" or $\{11, 12, 13, 14\}$.

29. $\frac{x}{4} > 2$ and $\frac{x}{3} < 4$ 30. $3x > 9$ and $2x < 12$

31. $x - 4 > 6$ and $x + 8 < 24$ 32. $x - 6 > 10$ and $x + 6 < 7$

Exercises

A To solve each equation, what would you do on each side?

1. $n - 18 = 6$

2. $n + 9 = 10$

3. $10n = 130$

4. $\frac{n}{8} = 17$

B Solve and check each equation.

5. $n + 6 = 10$

6. $n - 4 = 10$

7. $7n = 49$

8. $\frac{n}{6} = 2$

9. $n - 2 = 0$

10. $n + 6 = 14$

11. $3n = 45$

12. $8n = 56$

13. $\frac{n}{16} = 2$

14. $\frac{n}{17} = 17$

15. $6n = 18$

16. $n + 6 = 19$

17. $3n = 15$

18. $n - 5 = 4$

19. $\frac{n}{4} = 0$

20. $\frac{n}{7} = 1$

21. $3n = 24$

22. $n - 27 = 43$

23. $n + 51 = 65$

24. $\frac{n}{16} = 5$

25. $12n = 60$

26. $n - 98 = 2$

27. $53n = 106$

28. $\frac{n}{25} = 20$

29. $15n = 150$

30. $\frac{n}{30} = 30$

31. $n + 56 = 57$

32. $n - 75 = 25$

33. $50n = 300$

34. $\frac{n}{11} = 23$

C Solve and check each equation.

35. $n + (18 \div 3) = 47 - 21$

36. $n - (15 \times 2) = 72 - (42 + 12)$

37. $(75 \div 15)n = 13 + 22$

38. $(3 \times 6)n = (17 + 19) \times 2$

39. $\frac{n}{7 \times 5} = (90 - 72) \div 6$

40. $\frac{n}{21 \div 7} = 5 \times (6 + 4)$

41. $n - (17 + 3) = (4 \times 7) \div 7$

42. $n + 34 = (100 \div 4) + 9$

Now that you have been "checked out" on equations, it's time to get checked out on inequalities. You will work with the kinds of inequalities you have solved so far.

Example 1: Solve and check $n - 4 > 6$.

$$n - 4 > 6$$
$$n - 4 + 4 > 6 + 4$$
$$n > 10$$

Check:
$$n - 4 > 6$$
$$11 - 4 > 6$$
$$7 > 6$$

$$n - 4 > 6$$
$$20 - 4 > 6$$
$$16 > 6$$

Example 2: Solve and check $n + 3 < 4$.

$$n + 3 < 4$$
$$n + 3 - 3 < 4 - 3$$
$$n < 1$$

Check:
$$n + 3 < 4$$
$$0 + 3 < 4$$
$$3 < 4$$

Example 3: Solve and check $3n > 9$.

$$3n > 9$$
$$\frac{3n}{3} > \frac{9}{3}$$
$$n > 3$$

Check:
$$3n > 9$$
$$3(4) > 9$$
$$12 > 9$$

$$3n > 9$$
$$3(8) > 9$$
$$24 > 9$$

Example 4: Solve and check $\frac{n}{4} < 11$.

$$\frac{n}{4} < 11$$
$$\frac{n}{4} \times 4 < 11 \times 4$$
$$n < 44$$

Check:
$$\frac{n}{4} < 11$$
$$\frac{40}{4} < 11$$
$$10 < 11$$

$$\frac{n}{4} < 11$$
$$\frac{16}{4} < 11$$
$$4 < 11$$

INEQUALITY REVIEW   51

In earlier lessons, you had to do one of the following to solve an equation.

> Add the same number to both sides.
>
> Subtract the same number from both sides.
>
> Multiply both sides by the same number.
>
> Divide both sides by the same number.

In this lesson, you will have to do more than one of these to solve the equations.

Example 1: Solve and check $2x - 3 = 17$.

Step 1: Get the term containing the variable on one side by itself. To do that, add 3 to each side.

$$2x - 3 = 17$$
$$2x - 3 + 3 = 17 + 3 \quad \text{Add 3 to each side.}$$
$$2x + 0 = 20$$
$$2x = 20$$

Step 2: You already know how to solve the new equation. Divide each side by 2.

$$2x = 20$$
$$\frac{2x}{2} = \frac{20}{2} \quad \text{Divide each side by 2.}$$
$$x = 10$$

Step 3: Check your answer.

$$2x - 3 = 17 \quad \text{Original equation}$$
$$2(10) - 3 = 17 \quad \text{Replace } x \text{ with 10.}$$
$$20 - 3 = 17$$
$$17 = 17 \quad \text{It checks!}$$

Example 2:   Solve and check $4x + 5 = 29$.

Step 1:   Since 5 is added to $4x$, subtract 5 from each side.

$$4x + 5 = 29$$
$$4x + 5 - 5 = 29 - 5 \quad \text{Subtract 5 from each side.}$$
$$4x = 24$$

Step 2:   To solve the new equation, divide each side by 4.

$$\frac{4x}{4} = \frac{24}{4} \quad \text{Divide each side by 4.}$$
$$x = 6$$

Step 3:   Check your answer.

$$4x + 5 = 29 \quad \text{Original equation}$$
$$4(6) + 5 = 29 \quad \text{Replace } x \text{ with 6.}$$
$$24 + 5 = 29$$
$$29 = 29 \quad \text{It checks!}$$

Example 3:   Solve and check $\frac{y}{6} + 4 = 12$.

$$\frac{y}{6} + 4 = 12$$

$$\frac{y}{6} + 4 - 4 = 12 - 4 \quad \text{Subtract 4 from each side.}$$

$$\frac{y}{6} = 8$$

$$\frac{y}{6} \times 6 = 8 \times 6 \quad \text{Multiply each side by 6.}$$

$$y = 48$$

Check your answer.

$$\frac{y}{6} + 4 = 12 \quad \text{Original equation}$$

$$\frac{48}{6} + 4 = 12 \quad \text{Replace } y \text{ with 48.}$$

$$8 + 4 = 12$$
$$8 = 8 \quad \text{It checks!}$$

Example 4: Solve and check $\frac{n+7}{3} = 12$.

$$\frac{n+7}{3} = 12$$

$$\frac{n+7}{3} \times 3 = 12 \times 3 \quad \text{Multiply each side by 3.}$$

$$n + 7 = 36$$

$$n + 7 - 7 = 36 - 7 \quad \text{Subtract 7 from each side.}$$

$$n = 29$$

Check your answer.

$$\frac{n+7}{3} = 12 \quad \text{Original equation}$$

$$\frac{29+7}{3} = 12 \quad \text{Replace } n \text{ with 29.}$$

$$\frac{36}{3} = 12$$

$$12 = 12 \quad \text{It checks!}$$

Exercises

[A] Tell the two steps you would use to solve each equation.

1. $3x - 7 = 8$

2. $4x + 9 = 29$

3. $\frac{n}{2} + 10 = 36$

4. $\frac{n-5}{7} = 4$

5. $\frac{a+10}{5} = 12$

6. $\frac{a}{8} - 11 = 21$

7. $\frac{x}{4} + 7 = 47$

8. $\frac{x-18}{6} = 5$

9. $9y - 17 = 19$

10. $10y + 3 = 83$

11. $\frac{n+7}{3} = 11$

12. $\frac{n}{5} - 14 = 6$

[B] Solve and check each equation.

13. $6x - 3 = 39$

14. $7x + 13 = 62$

15. $\frac{x}{3} + 9 = 45$

16. $\frac{x-8}{3} = 11$

17. $\frac{x+1}{9} = 9$

18. $\frac{x}{4} - 14 = 6$

19. $\frac{x}{10} + 17 = 21$

20. $\frac{x-2}{4} = 6$

21. $8x - 9 = 7$

22. $12x + 5 = 77$

23. $\frac{x+25}{4} = 7$

24. $\frac{x}{9} - 3 = 17$

25. $3x - 2 = 10$

26. $8x + 4 = 76$

27. $\frac{x}{6} + 5 = 10$

28. $\frac{x}{7} - 5 = 11$

29. $11x - 5 = 28$

30. $\frac{x-1}{4} = 5$

31. $\frac{x}{8} + 1 = 4$

32. $4x - 6 = 10$

33. $13x + 3 = 42$

34. $52x - 104 = 364$

C Solve and check each equation.

35. $5x - (2 \times 6) = 17 - (36 \div 9)$

36. $(14 \div 2)x + 8 = (72 \div 6) + 3$

37. $\frac{x + (4 \times 3)}{4} = (23 - 21) + 7$

38. $\frac{x}{2 \times 3} - (32 \div 8) = (4 + 5) \times 2$

(*Hint:* The following equations require more than two steps.)

39. $\frac{3x+4}{7} = 4$

40. $\frac{5x-3}{6} = 7$

41. $\frac{2x-4}{5} + 7 = 11$

42. $\frac{6x+3}{5} - 9 = 30$

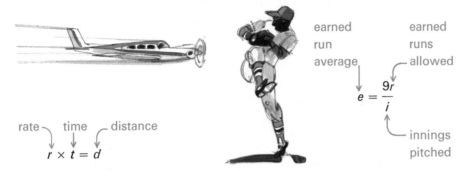

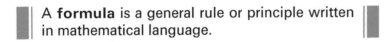

The equations shown above are called *formulas*. Formulas are useful in mechanics, sports, travel, business, electronics, and many other daily activities.

> A **formula** is a general rule or principle written in mathematical language.

When using a formula, follow these steps.

(1) Replace the variables whose values are known or given. This will usually leave only one variable.

(2) Solve the resulting equation.

(3) Answer the problem. Include the proper unit of measure ($, inches, seconds, meters, grams, and so on).

Example 1: The ground speed of an airplane is 140 mph. How long will it take the airplane to go 560 miles?

Step 1: Replace the variables whose values are given.

$$r \times t = d$$

$$140t = 560 \qquad \text{Replace } r \text{ with 140 and } d \text{ with 560.}$$

Step 2: Solve the new equation.

$$\frac{140t}{140} = \frac{560}{140} \qquad \text{Divide each side by 140.}$$

$$t = 4$$

Step 3: Answer the problem.

The time is *4 hours*.

Example 2: A pitcher has an earned run average of 2. He has pitched 63 innings. How many earned runs has he allowed?

Step 1: Replace the variables whose values are given.

$$e = \frac{9r}{i}$$

$$2 = \frac{9r}{63} \quad \text{Replace } e \text{ with 2 and } i \text{ with 63.}$$

Step 2: Solve the new equation.

Since 2 and $\frac{9r}{63}$ name the same number, you can interchange the two sides of the equation. This is not necessary, but do so if it helps you.

$2 = \dfrac{9r}{63}$	$\dfrac{9r}{63} = 2$
$2 \times 63 = \dfrac{9r}{63} \times 63 \quad$ Multiply each side by 63.	$\dfrac{9r}{63} \times 63 = 2 \times 63$
$126 = 9r$	$9r = 126$
$\dfrac{126}{9} = \dfrac{9r}{9} \quad$ Divide each side by 9.	$\dfrac{9r}{9} = \dfrac{126}{9}$
$14 = r$	$r = 14$

Step 3: Answer the problem.

r stands for the number of earned runs, so the answer is *14 earned runs*.

Exercises

A Use the formulas on page 57 to solve these problems.

1. A train is going 67 mph. How long will it take the train to go 268 miles?

2. The surface speed of a submarine is 28 knots (nautical miles per hour). How far can it travel in 8 hours?

3. A pitcher allowed 21 earned runs in 189 innings. What is his earned run average?

B Use the formulas for a rectangle to solve the following problems.

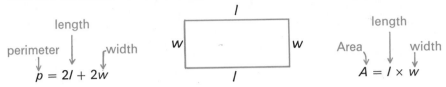

length → perimeter → width

$p = 2l + 2w$

Area, length → width

$A = l \times w$

4. Find the perimeter of a rectangle 8 cm by 13 cm.

5. You have 82 feet of fence to enclose a rectangular plot. The width is to be 14 feet. How long should it be?

6. What is the area of the picture on this piece of 35 mm movie film?

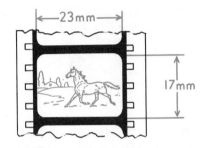

7. The area of a rectangular opening for an air duct is to be 126 square inches. To fit into the wall, it can be only 14 inches long. How wide must it be?

Solve the following.

8. Use $F = \frac{9C}{5} + 32$ to change a temperature reading from degrees Celsius (C) to degrees Fahrenheit (F), or vice versa.

   a. 25°C. = _____°F.   **b.** 70°C. = _____°F.

   c. 59°F. = _____°C.   **d.** 221°F. = _____°C.

9. The number of points (p) a football team scores in a game can be found from the following formula.

$$p = 6t + 1c + 3f + 2s$$

touchdowns   safeties

conversions   field goals

   a. Suppose $p = 43$, $t = 5$, $f = 3$, and $s = 0$. Find c.

   b. Suppose $p = 36$, $t = 4$, $c = 4$, and $s = 1$. Find f.

10. Nancy's handicap is 58. Her scratch score was 133. What was her final score?

11. Peg's final score was 147. Her handicap is 42. What was her scratch score?

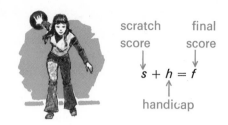

scratch score   final score

$$s + h = f$$

handicap

C Solve these problems.

If $w \times d = W \times D$, the lever is balanced.

If $w \times d < W \times D$, the rock is lifted.

12. How far from the pivot point must the 120-pound person sit in order to balance the lever?

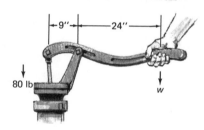

13. With how many pounds would you have to push to lift the pump rod?

14. The distance a free-falling object travels is given by the following formula.

$$S = 16 \times t \times t$$

distance (ft)   time (sec)

a. How far would a stone fall in 3 seconds?

b. How long would it take a ball to drop 400 feet?

You are now ready for more difficult inequalities—those that re-quire more than one step to solve. They are solved in the same way as the equations in Section 2.8, except that the solution set may con-tain many numbers.

Example 1: Solve and check $7x - 5 > 16$.

$$7x - 5 > 16$$

$$7x - 5 + 5 > 16 + 5 \quad \text{Add 5 to each side.}$$

$$7x > 21$$

$$\frac{7x}{7} > \frac{21}{7} \qquad \text{Divide each side by 7.}$$

$$x > 3$$

Check your answer.

$7x - 5 > 16$	Original inequality	$7x - 5 > 16$
Replace x with 4. $7(4) - 5 > 16$		$7(13) - 5 > 16$ Replace x with 13.
$28 - 5 > 16$		$91 - 5 > 16$
$23 > 16$	They check!	$86 > 16$

Example 2: Solve and check $\frac{x}{6} + 4 < 12$.

$$\frac{x}{6} + 4 < 12$$

$$\frac{x}{6} + 4 - 4 < 12 - 4 \quad \text{Subtract 4 from each side.}$$

$$\frac{x}{6} < 8$$

$$\frac{x}{6} \times 6 < 8 \times 6 \quad \text{Multiply each side by 6.}$$

$$x < 48$$

Check your answer.

$$\frac{x}{6} + 4 < 12 \qquad \text{Original inequality} \qquad \frac{x}{6} + 4 < 12$$

Replace x with 42.
$$\frac{42}{6} + 4 < 12 \qquad\qquad \frac{6}{6} + 4 < 12 \quad \text{Replace x with 6.}$$

$$7 + 4 < 12 \qquad\qquad\qquad 1 + 4 < 12$$

$$11 < 12 \quad \text{They check!} \qquad 5 < 12$$

Exercises

A Tell the two steps you would use to solve each inequality.

1. $8x - 3 < 21$ **2.** $4x + 8 > 8$ **3.** $\frac{x}{6} + 4 > 10$

4. $\frac{x}{5} - 4 < 5$ **5.** $\frac{x-3}{7} < 4$ **6.** $\frac{x+8}{10} > 1$

B Solve and check each inequality.

7. $8x - 4 < 12$ **8.** $4x + 3 < 15$

9. $5x + 4 < 29$ **10.** $15x - 75 > 0$

11. $11x + 11 < 121$ **12.** $10x - 90 > 160$

13. $\frac{x}{8} - 5 > 4$ **14.** $\frac{x}{6} + 3 < 12$

15. $\frac{x}{16} + 4 < 4$ **16.** $\frac{x}{16} - 4 > 4$

17. $\frac{x+5}{8} < 5$ **18.** $\frac{x-13}{3} < 2$

19. $\frac{x-9}{4} > 5$ **20.** $\frac{x+12}{7} > 2$

21. $18x - 7 > 11$ **22.** $17x + 34 < 51$

23. $\frac{x}{5} + 3 < 10$ **24.** $\frac{x}{8} - 5 > 6$

C Find all the whole numbers that make both inequalities true.

25. $8x - 3 < 21$ and $4x + 8 > 8$

26. $\frac{x}{6} + 4 > 10$ and $6x + 6 < 102$

27. $\frac{x}{7} + 8 < 16$ and $\frac{x}{5} - 4 > 5$

28. $72x - 18 > 54$ and $16x + 12 < 44$

Use the following words to complete the sentences.

formula   *inequality*   *equation*   *variable*   *graph*

1. $6x + 5 = 13$ is an ____.

2. $6x + 5 > 13$ is an ____.

3. A general rule or principle like $r \times t = d$ is a ____.

4. In $3y = 27$, y is a ____.

5.   is the ____ of $\{1, 2, 3\}$.

CHAPTER REVIEW

Solve and check each equation.   2.1

1. $7n = 14$ **2.** $5a = 65$

3. $12x = 84$ **4.** $9y = 0$

5. $x - 7 = 15$ **6.** $n - 5 = 2$ 2.2

7. $y - 32 = 17$ **8.** $x - 11 = 0$

9. $\frac{n}{5} = 12$ **10.** $\frac{x}{8} = 10$

11. $\frac{y}{20} = 6$ **12.** $\frac{n}{3} = 31$

Solve and check each inequality.   2.3

13. $2n < 18$ **14.** $5n > 15$

15. $8x > 24$ **16.** $10y < 120$

17. $n - 11 < 3$ **18.** $x - 5 > 1$ 2.4

19. $y - 3 > 7$ **20.** $n - 31 < 8$

21. $\frac{x}{7} > 1$ **22.** $\frac{n}{6} < 5$

23. $\frac{n}{10} < 2$ **24.** $\frac{y}{9} > 0$

Solve each open sentence. Graph the solution set.

25. $n - 7 = 2$ **26.** $\frac{y}{6} = 3$

27. $5x = 20$ **28.** $y + 3 = 3$

29. $\frac{n}{4} < 1$ **30.** $4y < 12$

31. $x - 2 > 3$ **32.** $n + 5 > 14$

2.6   Solve and check each open sentence.

33. $n + 11 = 16$ **34.** $x - 3 = 12$

35. $7y = 28$ **36.** $\frac{n}{4} = 9$

2.7   **37.** $n - 3 > 2$ **38.** $x + 7 < 10$

39. $5y > 30$ **40.** $\frac{n}{2} < 4$

2.8   Solve and check each equation.

41. $3x - 4 = 8$ **42.** $8x + 5 = 21$

43. $\frac{n}{7} + 3 = 5$ **44.** $\frac{n + 8}{2} = 7$

45. $\frac{x - 6}{9} = 9$ **46.** $\frac{a}{4} - 3 = 7$

2.9   Solve each problem.

47. A cabin cruiser made a 72-mile trip across Lake Michigan at an average speed of 24 mph. How many hours did the trip take? ($r \times t = d$)

48. In a science experiment you are to heat a mixture to 100°C. You have only a Fahrenheit scale. What Fahrenheit reading would you use? ($F = \frac{9C}{5} + 32$)

49. A rectangular window has a perimeter of 156 inches. The width is 30 inches. How long is the window? ($p = 2l + 2w$)

2.10   Solve and check each inequality.

50. $3x + 5 < 23$ **51.** $\frac{n}{4} - 3 > 6$

52. $\frac{a + 4}{2} > 5$ **53.** $8x - 3 < 29$

Solve and check each equation.

1. $x + 7 = 19$

2. $y - 12 = 8$

3. $9n = 72$

4. $\frac{x}{6} = 96$

5. $4n - 5 = 19$

6. $7y + 2 = 72$

7. $\frac{x}{8} + 7 = 10$

8. $\frac{n - 6}{3} = 10$

Solve and check each inequality.

9. $3x < 39$

10. $\frac{n}{7} > 2$

11. $n - 8 > 2$

12. $y + 5 < 6$

● **13.** $\frac{x}{4} - 9 > 0$

● **14.** $10n - 7 < 33$

● **15.** $\frac{n + 7}{5} < 5$

● **16.** $9x + 10 > 19$

Solve each open sentence. Graph the solution set.

17. $\frac{x}{2} = 6$

18. $n + 8 = 13$

19. $y + 3 < 7$

20. $6n > 12$

Solve each problem.

21. A rectangular label is to have an area of 1080 square millimeters. It can be only 40 millimeters long. How wide must it be? ($A = lw$)

22. An automobile was driven 300 miles and got 15 miles per gallon. How many gallons of gasoline were used? ($d = mg$, where $d =$ distance, $m =$ miles per gallon, and $g =$ number of gallons.)

Activities for Chapter 2

Activity 1

Mark an ink dot on a strip of rubber band. Straighten the rubber strip along a ruler as shown below—your thumbs at the 0 and 4 marks and the dot at the 2 mark.

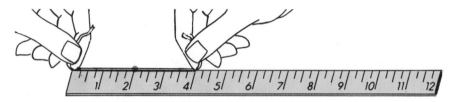

1. Stretch the rubber strip by moving your right thumb 2 inches to the right. How far did the dot move?

2. Repeat step 1 by moving your right thumb 4 inches, 6 inches, and 8 inches to the right. How far did the dot move each time?

3. Let T be the distance your thumb moves. Let d be the distance the dot moves. Write a formula to tell how to find d if you know T.

Activity 2

Draw figures having 3 sides, 4 sides, 5 sides, 6 sides, 7 sides, and 8 sides as shown below. Then draw line segments to separate each figure into as few triangles as possible.

Number of sides	3	4	5	6	7	8
Number of triangles	1	2				

Write a formula to tell how to find the number of triangles (t) if you know the number of sides (s).

Mathematics and Photography

The drawing below shows how the picture on a slide is projected onto a screen. If the picture is magnified M times, we say the *magnifying power* is M.

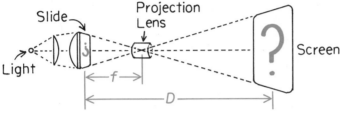

$$M = \frac{D - f}{f}$$

D = distance from screen to slide
f = focal length of lens

Example: Suppose the focal length of the lens in your projector is 3 inches. How far from the slide would you have to place the screen to have a magnifying power of 35?

$M = \frac{D - f}{f}$

$35 = \frac{D - 3}{3}$ Replace M with 35 and f with 3.

$35 \times 3 = \frac{D - 3}{3} \times 3$ Multiply each side by 3.

$105 = D - 3$

$105 + 3 = D - 3 + 3$ Add 3 to each side.

$108 = D$ Set the screen 108″ from the slide.

1. If the focal length is 8 cm and the screen is 312 cm from the slide, what is the magnifying power?

2. Suppose the focal length is 5 inches. You want a magnifying power of 40. How far from the slide would you set the screen?

Getting Ready for Chapter 3

1.1 Find the number named by each phrase.

1. $5 + 2(\frac{12}{3})$

2. $15 \div (21 - 18)$

3. $(38 - 15) \times 2$

4. $(5 + 4) \times (17 - 8)$

1.2 Find the value of each phrase.

5. $8y - 11$ if $y = 4$

6. $7(\frac{x}{8}) + 16$ if $x = 56$

7. $(5a \div 2) + 7$ if $a = 6$

8. $\frac{n+5}{3} - 1$ if $n = 7$

Solve each equation.

2.1 **9.** $4n = 36$

10. $7x = 91$

2.2 **11.** $y - 18 = 6$

12. $\frac{x}{5} = 12$

2.8 **13.** $3x + 5 = 17$

14. $\frac{n}{4} + 8 = 21$

15. $\frac{n+2}{6} = 19$

16. $12x - 41 = 31$

2.9 Solve these problems.

17. The Wildcats made 23 field goals and 14 free throws. What was their score?

18. The Cardinals scored 71 points in a game. They made 29 field goals. How many free throws did they make?

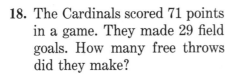

$$p = 2g + f$$

total points — field goals — free throws

19. The base of a triangle is 18 cm long. The altitude is 5 cm long. Find the area of the triangle.

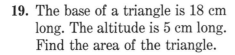

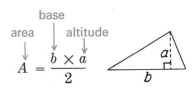

$$A = \frac{b \times a}{2}$$

area — base — altitude

Ordered Pairs and Graphing __ 3

City streets usually form a rectangular grid as shown in the photograph. Going from one intersection to another can be described by using a pair of numbers—a *number* of blocks east or west and a *number* of blocks north or south.

In this chapter you will use the same sort of grid to graph ordered pairs of numbers. Graphing ordered pairs helps you see the connection between two sets of numbers by drawing a picture of the problem.

3.1 ◆ ORDERED PAIRS

In a math game, Ann drew a rule card. She will apply that rule to any number you give her.

If your number is 2, Ann's number is $2 + 3$ or 5. If your number is 4, what is Ann's number? If your number is x, what is Ann's number?

The rule could also be given as an equation.

$$a = x + 3$$

Ann's number   Your number

Example 1: Use Ann's rule to complete the table.

Your number (x)	0	1	2	3	4	5
Ann's number (a)	3	4	5	6	7	8

$$a = x + 3 \qquad a = x + 3$$
$$= 0 + 3 \qquad = 1 + 3$$
$$= 3 \qquad = 4$$

Replace x with each number. Solve for a.

You can list these pairs of numbers in another way. In each pair, list your number first and Ann's number second.

$$(0, 3), (1, 4), (2, 5), (3, 6), (4, 7), (5, 8)$$

Since we have specified an order, these are called **ordered pairs** of numbers.

Example 2: Write the rule as an equation.
Use the rule to complete the table.

Multiply each number by 2. Then add 3.	Let x be the first number and y be the second number. $y = 2x + 3$

x	0	1	2	3	4	5	6	7	8
y	3	5	7	9	11	13	15	17	19

$$y = 2x + 3$$
$$= 2(0) + 3$$
$$= 0 + 3$$
$$= 3$$

$$y = 2x + 3$$
$$= 2(1) + 3$$
$$= 2 + 3$$
$$= 5$$

Replace x with each number. Solve for y.

Exercises

A State each rule as an equation.
Let x be the first number and y be the second number.

1. Add 7 to each number.   **2.** Subtract 2 from each number.

3. Multiply each number by 8.   **4.** Divide each number by 2.

5. Multiply each number by 3. Then subtract 2.

6. Multiply each number by 4. Then add 1.

7. Divide each number by 3. Then add 2.

Interchange the numbers in each ordered pair. Then tell what the new ordered pair means.

Example: The date 2–12 means February 12th.
The date 12–2 means December 2nd.

8. The date 5–10 means May 10th.

9. Section 3.1 means chapter 3, section 1.

10. A count of 3–2 in baseball means 3 balls, 2 strikes.

11. A volleyball score of 11–6 means the serving team has 11.

Use the rule to complete the table.

12. $y = x - 2$

x	5	6	7	8	9	10	11
y	3	4					

13. $y = 4x - 3$

x	1	2	3	4	5	6	7
y							

14. $y = \frac{x}{2} + 5$

x	2	4	6	8	10	12	14
y							

15. $y = 7x$

x	0	1	2	3	4	5	6
y							

Use the rule to complete the ordered pairs.
The values of x are given first.

16. $y = 3x + 2$

(2, 8), (3, 11), (4,   ), (5,   ), (6,   ), (7,   )

17. $y = 10x$

(3,   ), (5,   ), (7,   ), (9,   ), (11,   ), (13,   )

18. $y = x + 6$

(3,   ), (4,   ), (5,   ), (6,   ), (7,   ), (8,   )

C Discover the rule for each table.

19. length of side (s)	1	2	3	4	5	6	
perimeter (p)	4	8	12	16	20	24	

20. millimeters (m)	10	20	30	40	50	60	70
centimeters (c)	1	2	3	4	5	6	7

Row Seat

D5

Suppose this is your ticket stub.

To find your seating location, you would go to row D, then to seat 5. The letter D tells you how far to go in one direction. The number 5 tells you how far to go in another direction.

An *ordered pair* of numbers like (2, 4) can be graphed in the same way. You can use grid paper as shown below.

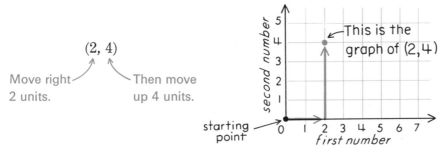

(2, 4)

Move right 2 units.   Then move up 4 units.

This is the graph of (2,4)

starting point

The red arrows show the moves. Do not draw them as part of the graph. Just draw a dot at the ending point.

Example 1:   Graph the ordered pair (3, 0).

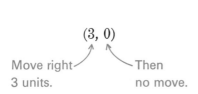

(3, 0)

Move right 3 units.   Then no move.

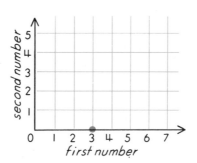

Example 2: Graph the ordered pairs.

x (first number)	0	1	2	3	4	5	6
y (second number)	3	2	6	5	4	0	1

If it helps, list the ordered pairs as follows.

(0, 3), (1, 2), (2, 6), (3, 5), (4, 4), (5, 0), (6, 1)

Graph each ordered
pair as shown in
Example 1.

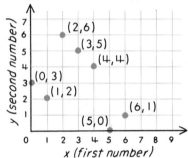

Exercises

A Tell the moves you would make to graph each ordered pair.

1. (3, 4)　　　　**2.** (5, 8)　　　　**3.** (0, 5)　　　　**4.** (3, 3)

5. (6, 2)　　　　**6.** (1, 0)　　　　**7.** (10, 7)　　　　**8.** (2, 9)

Name the ordered pair for each point.

9. A　　　　**10.** B

11. C　　　　**12.** D

13. E　　　　**14.** F

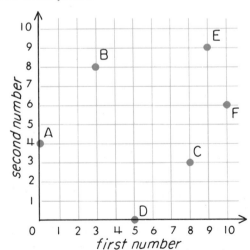

B Graph each set of ordered pairs.

15.

x	1	2	3	4	5	6
y	4	5	6	7	8	9

16.

x	0	2	4	6	8	10
y	4	3	2	3	4	5

17.

x	0	1	2	3	4	5
y	4	4	4	4	4	4

18.

x	0	1	2	3	4	5
y	0	1	2	3	4	5

19. (0, 5), (1, 4), (2, 3), (3, 2), (4, 1), (5, 0)

20. (3, 0), (3, 1), (3, 2), (3, 3), (3, 4), (3, 5)

21. (1, 2), (2, 3), (3, 4), (3, 5), (4, 6), (5, 7)

22. (1, 1), (2, 4), (3, 1), (4, 4), (5, 1), (6, 4)

C Graph the set of ordered pairs. Then join the points by line segments in the order listed.

23. (2, 0), (1, 2), (2, 1), (3, 2), (5, 3), (8, 3),

(10, 2), (9, 4), (9, 5), (10, 6), (11, 6), (12, 5),

(15, 4), (12, 4), (11, 3), (12, 2), (12, 1), (11, 0)

24. (3, 0), (2, 2), (5, 2), (5, 8), (8, 3), (6, 2), (11, 2),

(11, 11), (16, 3), (12, 2), (18, 2), (22, 4), (21, 0)

25. Make up your own list of ordered pairs for a picture. Let a friend draw the picture.

3.3 ◆ FUNCTIONS

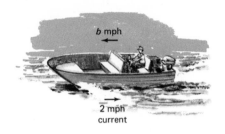

$$g = b - 2$$

ground speed · · · boat speed (in still water)

boat speed (b)	4	5	6	7	8	9
ground speed (g)	2	3	4	5	6	7

The ordered pairs in the table can be written as

$$(4, 2), (5, 3), (6, 4), (7, 5), (8, 6), (9, 7).$$

Are any values of b (*first numbers*) ever repeated?

Suppose you try 8 again. Will g still be 6?

For every value of b, there is only one value of g. Such a set of ordered pairs is called a *function.*

> A **function** is a set of ordered pairs that has only one *second number* for each *first number.*

Let's examine the graph of the function.

There is only one value of g for each value of b. So the graph of a function can *never* have one dot above another.

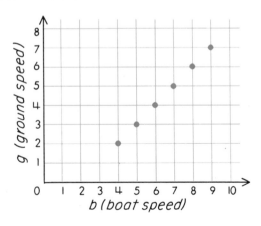

Example 1: Is (2, 3), (3, 4), (3, 5), (4, 6) a function?

$$(2, 3), \boxed{(3, 4), (3, 5),} (4, 6)$$

NO. There are two second numbers, 4 and 5, for the first number 3.

Example 2: Is (4, 6), (5, 6), (6, 6), (7, 6) a function?

YES. Every first number has only one second number.

Example 3: Is the following the graph of a function?

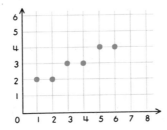

NO. The graph of a function can never have one dot above another.

Example 4: Is the following the graph of a function?

YES. No two dots are above each other.

Exercises

───────────────────────────────────────

A Is each set of ordered pairs a function? If not, tell why not.

1. (7, 7), (8, 6), (9, 5), (10, 4), (11, 3)

2. (5, 0), (6, 1), (7, 2), (7, 3), (8, 4)

3.

first number	2	4	6	8	10
second number	3	5	5	7	9

4.

first number	1	3	5	7	9
second number	1	9	25	49	81

Is each graph the graph of a function ? If not, tell why not.

5.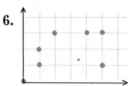

6.

B Tell whether each set of ordered pairs is a function.

7. (1, 6), (2, 7), (3, 8), (4, 9), (5, 10)

8. (5, 7), (5, 8), (6, 9), (7, 10), (8, 11)

9. (2, 4), (2, 5), (2, 6), (2, 7), (2, 8)

10.
first number	4	5	6	7	8
second number	2	2	2	2	2

11.
first number	1	2	3	4	5
second number	2	4	6	8	10

12.
first number	0	1	2	3	4
second number	0	1	2	3	4

Tell whether each graph is the graph of a function.

13.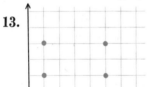

14.

15.

16.

17.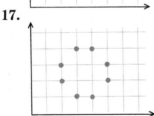

18.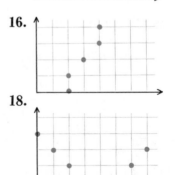

Tell whether each rule describes a function.

19. Multiply the first number by itself to get the second number.

20. The first number is always 1. The second number can be any whole number.

21. The first number can be any whole number. The second number is always 3.

22. If the first number is even, the second number is the same as the first number. If the first number is odd, the second number is the next larger whole number.

23. The second number is the same as the first number.

24. Multiply the first number by 2. Then divide by the first number to get the second number.

How Many Guests?

Suppose you invite the Uster family to dinner. That family consists of 1 grandfather, 2 fathers, 1 mother, 2 brothers, 4 sons, and 2 daughters.

Can they all ride in one car? What is the smallest possible number of guests that can arrive?

3.4 ◆ USING GRAPHS

Some superhighways have mile posts numbered 1, 2, 3, and so on, starting at a state line. An example is the Pennsylvania Turnpike, as shown below. When you pass the 140-mile post, you know you are 140 miles from the Ohio state line.

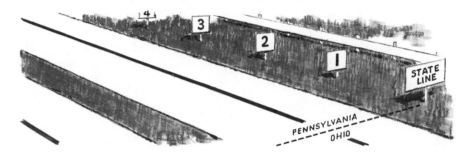

Jo noticed that she crossed the Ohio state line into Pennsylvania at 12 o'clock. At 1 o'clock she looked out the window and saw the 60-mile post.

The rest of the trip went as follows.

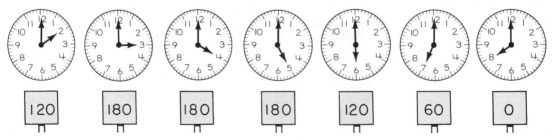

To get a better idea of the trip, put the information in a table and draw a graph.

Time elapsed (hr)	Distance from Ohio state line (mi)
0	0
1	60
2	120
3	180
4	180
5	180
6	120
7	60
8	0

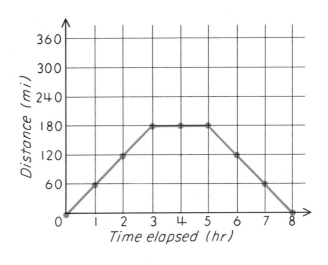

Drawing line segments between the points makes it easier to "see" the trip. The graph provides answers to several questions you might have about the trip.

Question 1: What was the car doing during the first 3 hours?

Since the graph is ↗, the car was going away from the Ohio state line.

Question 2: What was the car doing during the 4th and 5th hours?

Since the graph is →, the car was stopped.

Question 3: What was the car doing during the last 3 hours?

Since the graph is ↘, the car was going toward the Ohio state line.

Question 4: How far from the Ohio state line did the car get?

The highest dot is at 180, so the car got 180 miles from the Ohio state line.

Question 5: What was the average speed during the first 3 hours?

Since the car went 180 miles in the 3 hours, the average speed was $\frac{180}{3}$ or 60 mph.

Exercises

A Use the graph to complete the table.

1.

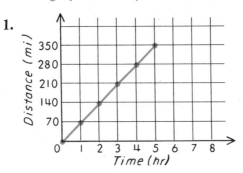

Time elapsed (hr)	Distance (mi)
0	——
1	——
2	——
3	——
4	——
5	——

2.

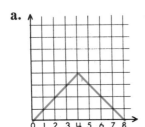

Time elapsed (hr)	Distance (mi)
0	——
1	——
2	——
3	——
4	——

B Choose one of the following to answer questions 3–8.

a.

b.

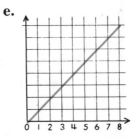

c.

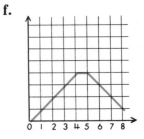

d.

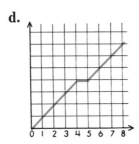

e.

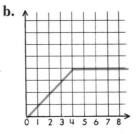

f.

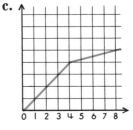

What would the graph in Exercise 2 look like if the car did the following at the end of 4 hours?

3. Stopped for 4 hours

4. Turned around and went back

5. Stopped for 1 hour and then started back

6. Stopped for 1 hour and then continued on

7. Continued on at the same speed

8. Continued on at a slower speed

Answer the following about the graph in Exercise 2.

9. How far did the car go in 4 hours?

10. What was its average speed?

11. Is the graph the graph of a function?

12. Using d for distance in miles and t for time in hours, write an equation for the graph.

C Two cars on the Pennsylvania Turnpike enter Pennsylvania from Ohio at 12 o'clock. The distance-time graphs are given below.

13. At 1 o'clock which car had traveled farther? How much farther?

14. At 1 o'clock, which car was traveling faster?

15. At what time did car B overtake car A?

16. What was the average speed of car A for the entire trip?

17. What was the average speed of car B for the entire trip?

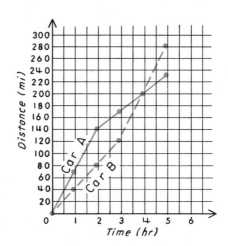

18. What was the greatest distance between the two cars? At what time did that occur?

3.5 🔷 USING FUNCTIONS

Jim heard the thunder 4 seconds after he saw the lightning. He wondered how far away the lightning was.

Sound travels about 1100 feet per second through air. So the following equation shows how *distance* and *time* are related.

distance (ft)　　　　　time (sec)

$$d = 1100\,t$$

Let's solve Jim's problem.

$$d = 1100t$$
$$= 1100 \times 4 \qquad \text{Replace } t \text{ with 4.}$$
$$= 4400$$

The lightning was 4400 feet away.

Let's make a table and a graph for $d = 1100t$.

t	d
0	0
1	1100
2	2200
3	3300
4	4400
5	5500
6	6600

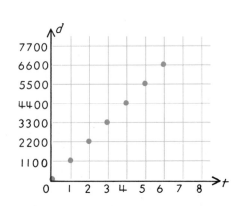

Are any values of t repeated in the table?

Suppose you try 3 again. Would d still be 3300?

Does the value of d depend on the value of t?

Is the graph the graph of a function?

Such a time-distance relationship is a function. Other functions from nature and everyday life are used in the exercises.

Exercises

A Answer these questions.

1. Jill saw lightning strike a tree that was 5500 feet away. How long after that did she hear the noise? (See the table and the graph on page 84.)

2. Light travels about 186,000 miles per second. Give an equation that tells the distance d that light will travel in t seconds.

3. How can you find the number of seconds it takes for light to travel from the sun to the earth?

B Solve these problems.

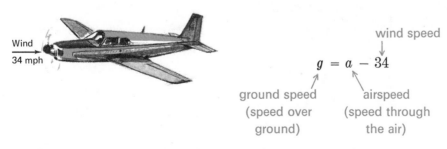

$$g = a - 34$$

ground speed (speed over ground)   airspeed (speed through the air)   wind speed

4. If your airspeed is 140 mph, find your ground speed.

5. To reach your destination on time, you must make a ground speed of 126 mph. What airspeed should you maintain?

As you leave the earth's surface, the temperature drops about 2°C. every 1000 feet.

$$T = t - 2\left(\frac{d}{1000}\right)$$

—altitude in feet

temp. at altitude

temp. on ground

6. The ground temperature was 24°C. A balloon went up 10,000 feet. What was the temperature at that altitude?

7. The ground temperature was 32°C. How high must a helicopter go to reach a temperature of 0°C.?

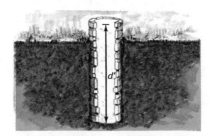

Free-falling object

$$d = 16 \times t \times t$$

distance (ft)

time (sec)

8. Jean dropped a stone in the well. It hit bottom in 2 seconds. How deep was the well?

9. A helicopter dropped a life raft. It hit the water in 10 seconds. How high was the helicopter?

Breaking strength of a rope

$$w = 5000d(d + 1)$$

weight (lb)

diameter of rope (in)

10. How many pounds could a 1″ rope support without breaking?

11. A contractor needed a rope that could lift loads up to 30,000 pounds. Would a 2″ rope do the job?

[C] Solve these problems.

12. To see n miles out to sea, your eye needs to be $\frac{2n \times n}{3}$ feet above sea level. How tall should the lighthouse be if you are to see 9 miles out to sea?

13. During a search at sea, a helicopter crew wanted to see at least 18 miles. They must be at least how high?

14. A sonar set measures the time it takes for sound waves to reach an object and return. Sound travels through water about 4800 feet per second.

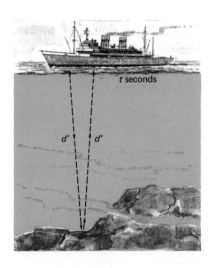

distance
(ship to
object
in feet)

time in
seconds for
"round trip"
of sound waves

$$d = \frac{4800t}{2}$$

or

$$d = 2400t$$

It took 3 seconds for the sound waves to reach the ocean floor and return. How deep is the ocean at that point?

15. A submarine was 4800 feet from the ship. How long did it take the sound waves to reach the submarine and return?

3.6 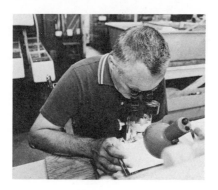 ENLARGING AND REDUCING

A biologist often makes enlarged drawings of microbes.

A draftswoman makes reduced
drawings of a building.

Example 1: Make a 1-to-2 enlargement of the square.

"1-to-2 enlargement" means that all dimensions of the new square are to be 2 times those of the original square.

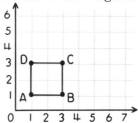

Step 1: For a 1-to-2 enlargement, multiply both numbers in each original ordered pair by 2.

Point	Original ordered pair	Point	New ordered pair
A(1, 1)		A′(2, 2)	
B(3, 1)		B′(6, 2)	
C(3, 3)		C′(6, 6)	
D(1, 3)		D′(2, 6)	

A′ is read *A prime*. Using A′ rather than some other letter makes it easy to see that point A′ corresponds to point A.

Step 2: Graph the new ordered pairs. Draw the new square.

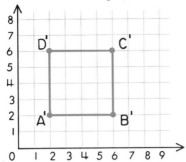

Example 2: Make a 1-to-3 reduction of the triangle.

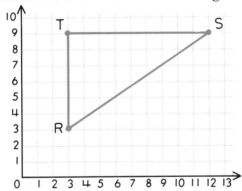

For a 1-to-3 reduction, divide both numbers in each original ordered pair by 3.

Original triangle	New triangle
R(3, 3)	R'(1, 1)
S(12, 9)	S'(4, 3)
T(3, 9)	T'(1, 3)

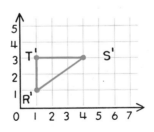

Exercises

A What would you do with the numbers in each ordered pair to make each of the following?

1. a 1-to-4 enlargement

2. a 1-to-10 enlargement

3. a 1-to-2 reduction

4. a 1-to-5 reduction

Use the drawing to make the following.

5. a 1-to-3 enlargement

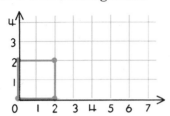

6. a 1-to-5 enlargement

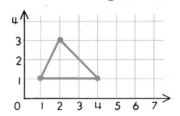

7. a 1-to-2 reduction

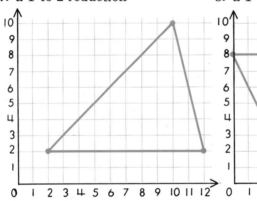

8. a 1-to-4 reduction

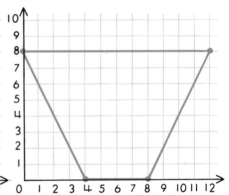

C Complete each set of ordered pairs. Graph all four triangles on the same grid.

9.

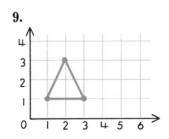

Original ordered pair	Multiply first number by 4.	Multiply second number by 4.	Multiply both numbers by 4.
(1, 1)	(4, 1)	(1, 4)	(4, 4)
(3, 1)	(___, 1)	(3, ___)	(___, ___)
(2, 3)	(___, 3)	(2, ___)	(___, ___)

a. How does multiplying only the first numbers change the shape of a figure?

b. How does multiplying only the second numbers change the shape of a figure?

c. How does multiplying both numbers change the shape of a figure?

Complete each set of ordered pairs. Graph all four triangles on the same grid.

10.

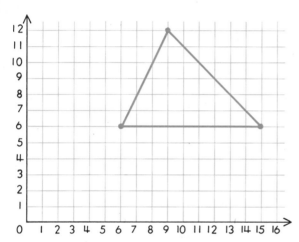

Original ordered pair	Divide first number by 3.	Divide second number by 3.	Divide both numbers by 3.
(6, 6)	(2, 6)	(6, 2)	(2, 2)
(15, 6)	(___, 6)	(15, ___)	(___, ___)
(9, 12)	(___, 12)	(9, ___)	(___, ___)

a. How does dividing only the first numbers change the shape of a figure?

b. How does dividing only the second numbers change the shape of a figure?

c. How does dividing both numbers change the shape of a figure?

3.7 ⬤ SLIDING BY GRAPHING

You can slide or move
a drawing by graphing.

Example 1: Slide the triangle 5 units to the right.

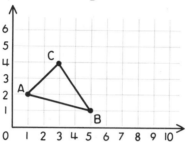

Step 1: To slide a drawing 5 units to the right, add 5 to the first number in each ordered pair.

Point	Original ordered pair	Point	New ordered pair
A(1, 2)		A′(6, 2)	
B(5, 1)		B′(10, 1)	
C(3, 4)		C′(8, 4)	

Step 2: Graph the new ordered pairs. Draw the new triangle.

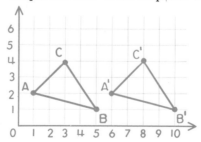

How would you slide a drawing *to the left* by graphing?

Example 2: Slide the figure 4 units down.

To slide a figure 4 units down, subtract 4 from the second number in each ordered pair.

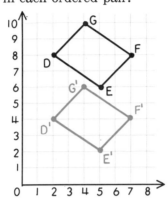

Original figure	New figure
D(2, 8)	D'(2, 4)
E(5, 6)	E'(5, 2)
F(7, 8)	F'(7, 4)
G(4, 10)	G'(4, 6)

How would you slide a figure *up* by graphing?

Exercises

A What would you do with the numbers in each ordered pair to make the following slides?

1. 6 units to the right   **2.** 5 units down

3. 3 units to the left   **4.** 7 units up

5. 2 units to the right and 5 units up

6. 4 units down and 6 units to the left

B Make the following slides by graphing.

7. 3 units to the right   **8.** 5 units to the left

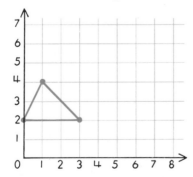   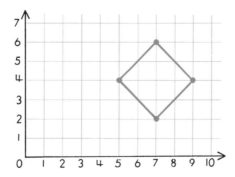

9. 4 units down

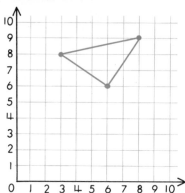

10. 6 units up

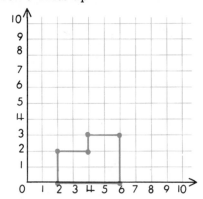

11. 4 units to the right
and 2 units down

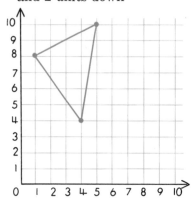

12. 5 units up and
3 units to the left

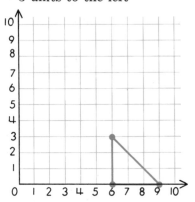

C Use graphing to make the following.

13. a 1-to-3 enlargement,
then a slide 4 units
to the right

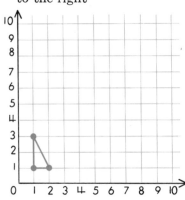

14. slide 5 units down,
then a 1-to-2 reduction

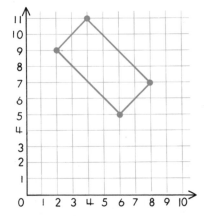

Match the correct example with each term.

1. the graph of (2, 1), (2, 3)

2. the graph of a function

3. a function

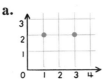

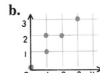

c.

d. (2, 6), (3, 7), (4, 7), (5, 8)

e. (0, 3), (1, 4), (1, 5), (2, 6)

CHAPTER REVIEW

Use the rule to complete each table.   3.1

1. $y = 2x + 5$

x	0	1	2	3	4	5
y						

2. $y = \frac{x}{3} - 1$

x	3	6	9	12	15	18
y						

Graph each set of ordered pairs.   3.2

3. (1, 3), (2, 4), (3, 5), (4, 6), (4, 7)

4.
x	0	1	2	3	4	5
y	3	4	5	2	3	1

Is each set of ordered pairs a function?

5. (0, 2), (1, 2), (2, 4), (3, 4), (4, 5)

6. (3, 4), (3, 5), (4, 6), (5, 7), (6, 8)

Tell whether each graph is the graph of a function.

7. 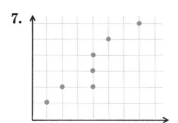 **8.**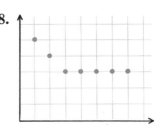

3.4 The graph shows how a stock car made a 600-mile cross-country race.

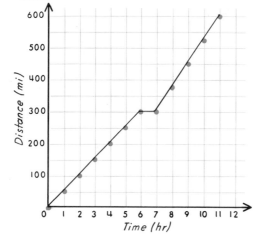

9. How far did the car go in the first 6 hours?

10. What was its average speed the first 6 hours?

11. What was the car doing during the 7th hour?

12. How far did the car go in the first 9 hours?

13. Was the car going faster during the first 6 hours or during the last 4 hours?

3.5 Solve each problem.

14. A stream is flowing at a rate of 3 mph. How long will it take a piece of driftwood to go 12 miles downstream? $r \times t = d$

15. You noticed that the ground temperature (t) at the airport was 25°C. Shortly after takeoff, the pilot said that you had climbed 12,000 feet (d). What was the outside temperature (T) then? $T = t - 2(\frac{d}{1000})$

Use the drawings to make the following.

16. a 1-to-4 enlargement

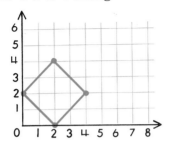

17. a 1-to-3 reduction

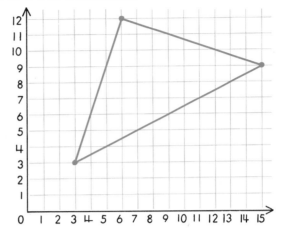

Use the drawings to make the following slides.

18. 4 units up

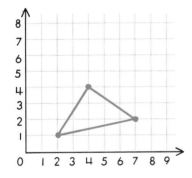

19. 5 units to the right

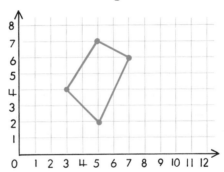

CHAPTER TEST

Use the rule to complete the ordered pairs. *x* is given first.

1. $y = 4x - 3$

x	2	3	4	5	6	7
y						

2. $y = x + 6$

$(0, \underline{\quad}), (1, \underline{\quad}), (3, \underline{\quad}), (4, \underline{\quad})$

Write the ordered pair for each lettered dot.

3. A   **4.** B

5. C   **6.** D

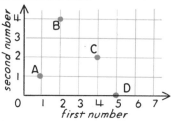

Graph each set of ordered pairs.

7. (2, 5), (2, 6), (2, 7), (2, 8)

8.

x	0	1	2	3	4	5
y	3	3	3	3	3	3

Answer these questions.

9. Is the graph for Exercises 3–6 the graph of a function?

10. Is the set of ordered pairs in Exercise 7 a function?

11. Is the set of ordered pairs in Exercise 8 a function?

12. You notice the flash of an explosion. You hear the "boom" 9 seconds later. How far are you from the explosion? ($r \times t = d$, and sound travels about 1100 feet per second.)

● Use the drawings to make the following.

13. a 1-to-3 enlargement

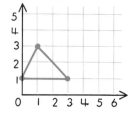

14. a 1-to-2 reduction

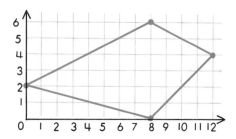

Activities for Chapter 3

Activity 1

Each dot is the graph of an ordered pair (x,y). That is, x is first and y is second. Find an equation for each graph.

1. *Hint:* Find the sum of the numbers in each ordered pair.

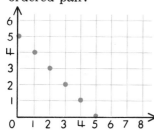

2. *Hint:* Subtract the first number from the second number.

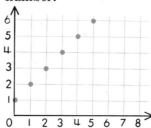

Activity 2

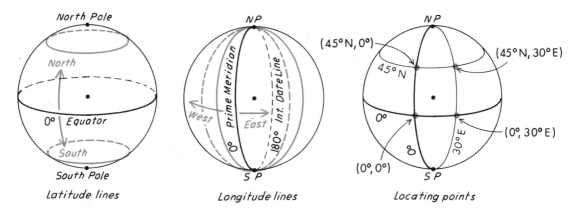

Latitude lines | Longitude lines | Locating points

Latitude and longitude lines on a globe form a grid. You can use ordered pairs to locate points on earth. The first number is *latitude*. The second number is *longitude*.

In what country is each point located? Use a globe.

1. (30°S, 135°E)   **2.** (75°N, 30°W)   **3.** (0°, 15°E)

Give an ordered pair to approximately locate each city.

4. Cairo, Egypt   **5.** Ottawa, Canada   **6.** Leningrad, USSR

Mathematics and Telephones

If there were only a few telephones in the world, connecting them to each other would be quite simple.

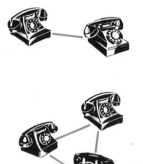
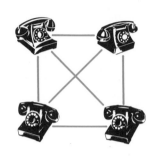

Number of telephones (t)	2	3	4	5	6	7	8
Number of connections (c)	1	3	6	10	?	?	?

You could draw diagrams to find how many connections are needed for 6, 7, 8, or more telephones. This soon becomes difficult and time consuming. So you might try to discover a formula.

Fortunately, some kind friend has discovered this formula.

$$c = \frac{t(t-1)}{2}$$

Example: For 50 telephones: $c = \dfrac{50(50-1)}{2}$

$$= \frac{50 \times 49}{2}$$

$$= 1225$$

You need 1225 connections.

How many connections are needed for

a. 100 telephones?

b. 1000 telephones?

c. the 80 million telephones in the United States?

Find the number named by each phrase.

1. $(7 + 3) \times (7 + 3)$ 2. $6(4 + 2)$ 1.1

3. $(5 \times 3) \times (5 \times 2)$ 4. $136 \div 8$

5. $84 \div 2$ 6. $65 \div 5$

7. $41 \div 3$ 8. $193 \div 5$ ES

Complete each list of multiples.

9. 3, 6, 9, 12, ____, ____, ____, ____, ____, ____

10. 7, 14, 21, ____, ____, ____, ____, ____, ____

11. 8, 16, ____, ____, ____, ____, ____, ____, ____

12. 11, 22, 33, ____, ____, ____, ____, ____, ____

13. 16, 32, 48, ____, ____, ____

14. 24, 48, ____, ____, ____

Answer each question.

15. What are the first 15 odd numbers?

16. What are the first 20 even numbers greater than 0?

Find the value of each phrase.   1.2

17. $3(x + 3)$ if $x = 17$

18. $n(n + 1)$ if $n = 6$

19. $3 \times y \times 5$ if $y = 4$

20. $x(5 + x)$ if $x = 3$

21. $n(n + 2)$ if $n = 10$

22. $\frac{a + 4}{2} - 3$ if $a = 8$

Number Theory —————————— 4

Before a race, skiers must study the snow conditions, wax their skis, check their bindings, and make other preparations.

Before progressing further in algebra, you need to know about factors, prime and composite numbers, and exponents. These and other facts about whole numbers will be studied in this chapter.

Camp Hiawatha's director has to buy tennis rackets for 48 girls. Each racket is to be shared by the same number of girls.

If the director buys 48 rackets, each girl gets a racket. If she buys 24 rackets, 2 girls share a racket. If she buys 16 rackets, 3 girls share a racket.

48, 24, and 16 are *factors* of 48.

$$48 \times 1 = 48 \qquad 24 \times 2 = 48 \qquad 16 \times 3 = 48$$

factors of 48

> If two or more numbers are multiplied, each is a **factor** of the product.

Example 1: The director bought 12 rackets. Is 12 a factor of 48?

Yes, because $12 \times 4 = 48$.

Example 2: Find all the factors of 24.

$$24 = 1 \times 24$$
$$= 2 \times 12$$
$$= 3 \times 8$$
$$= 4 \times 6$$

factors of 24

> Listing all the ways to express a number as a product gives you all the factors of the number.

An easy way to check whether one number is a factor of another is by dividing. The quotient should be a whole number.

Example 3: Is 8 a factor of 96?

96 ÷ 8 = 12, so 8 is a factor of 96.

Example 4: Is 7 a factor of 96?

$96 \div 7 = 13\frac{5}{7}$, so 7 is not a factor of 96.

▌ A number is divisible by each of its factors. ▐

Exercises

Ⓐ Find the factors of each number.

1. 6	**2.** 12	**3.** 8	**4.** 15	**5.** 21
6. 10	**7.** 18	**8.** 16	**9.** 20	**10.** 14

11. Is 7 a factor of 63?

12. Is 9 a factor of 54?

13. Is 6 a factor of 25?

14. Is 11 a factor of 11?

Ⓑ Divide to find whether 3 is a factor of each number.

15. 38	**16.** 117	**17.** 51	**18.** 144	**19.** 82

Divide to find whether 8 is a factor of each number.

20. 105	**21.** 216	**22.** 172	**23.** 87	**24.** 144

Express each number as the product of two or more of its factors.

Examples: 35 = 5 × 7   27 = 3 × 9 or 3 × 3 × 3

25. 12	**26.** 16	**27.** 36	**28.** 32	**29.** 28
30. 45	**31.** 30	**32.** 70	**33.** 48	**34.** 26

Find all the factors you can for each number.

35. 66	**36.** 29	**37.** 56	**38.** 80	**39.** 42
40. 47	**41.** 144	**42.** 81	**43.** 64	**44.** 46

45. Write 18 as the product of three factors. Use factors greater than 1.

46. Write 56 as the product of four factors. Use factors greater than 1.

47. Write 72 as the product of five factors. Use factors greater than 1.

48. Write 37 as the product of two factors.

49. A number is a perfect number if the sum of its factors (other than the number itself) is that number.

Example: $\underbrace{1 + 2 + 3}_{\text{factors of 6}} = 6$, so 6 is a perfect number.

There is another perfect number under fifty. Try to find it.

50. 496 is a perfect number. Find its factors and prove that it is perfect.

Operation: Decode

A spy intercepted this message: 426   7039   9240   91267.

The code below had previously been intercepted. It was known that the letter O is 3 and the letter A is 2. Find the number for each letter. Then decode the message given above.

CODE:

```
      LOT         ANT
    × ALL        +LOT
      LOT         OPT
      LOT
      ANT
    ASCOT
```

4.2 ◆ SHORTCUTS TO DIVISIBILITY

Since a number is divisible by each of its factors, some rules for divisibility can help you find the factors of a number.

▌ A number is divisible by 2 if its last digit is even. ▐

Example 1: Which of these numbers are divisible by 2?

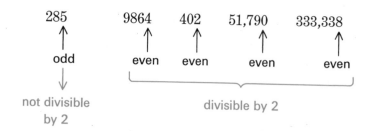

285	9864	402	51,790	333,338
↑	↑	↑	↑	↑
odd	even	even	even	even

odd → not divisible by 2

even → divisible by 2

▌ A number is divisible by 3 if the sum of its digits is divisible by 3. ▐

Example 2: Which of these numbers are divisible by 3?

285　　9864　　402　　51,790　　333,338

285　$2+8+5=15$ and $15 \div 3 = 5$

9864　$9+8+6+4=27$ and $27 \div 3 = 9$　→ divisible by 3

402　$4+0+2=6$ and $6 \div 3 = 2$

51,790　$5+1+7+9+0=22$ and $22 \div 3 = 7\frac{1}{3}$

333,338　$3+3+3+3+3+8=23$ and $23 \div 3 = 7\frac{2}{3}$　→ not divisible by 3

▌ A number is divisible by 5 if its last digit is 0 or 5.
A number is divisible by 10 if its last digit is 0. ▐

Example 3: Which of these numbers are divisible by 5? By 10?

285   9864   402   51,790   333,338

285 and 51,790 are divisible by 5.
51,790 is divisible by 10.

Exercises

A Which of these numbers are divisible by 2? By 3? By 5? By 10?

1. 84   **2.** 205   **3.** 52   **4.** 2310   **5.** 135

6. 77   **7.** 110   **8.** 291   **9.** 450   **10.** 111,111

B Which of these numbers are divisible by 2? By 3? By 5? By 10?
Use the rules for divisibility to help you.

11. 1560   **12.** 5691   **13.** 2382   **14.** 42,655

15. 12,345   **16.** 711,026   **17.** 880,800   **18.** 2,081,491

Find all the factors you can for each number.

19. 165   **20.** 96   **21.** 39   **22.** 83   **23.** 100

C To be divisible by 6, a number must be divisible by 2 and by 3.
Which of these numbers are divisible by 6?

24. 32,212   **25.** 2916   **26.** 22,440

27. 48,964   **28.** 54,162   **29.** 36,639

4.3 ◆ PRIMES AND COMPOSITES

Maria asked Joe to find the missing numbers:

2, 3, 5, 7, 11, ——, 17, ——, ——, 29.

Joe answered 13, 19, and 23. He was correct. Do you know why? The numbers Maria and Joe listed are *prime numbers*. Each number they listed has only 1 and itself as factors.

> A whole number greater than 1 that has only 1 and itself as factors is a **prime number**.

The table below shows the ways to express each number from 2 to 9 as a product of its factors.

2	3	4	5	6	7	8	9
1 × 2	1 × 3	1 × 4	1 × 5	1 × 6	1 × 7	1 × 8	1 × 9
		2 × 2		2 × 3		2 × 4	3 × 3
						2 × 2 × 2	

Notice that each of the numbers 2, 3, 5, and 7 can be expressed as a product only one way—1 times the number. The numbers 2, 3, 5, and 7 are prime numbers. The numbers 4, 6, 8, and 9 are *composite numbers*.

> All whole numbers greater than 1 that are not prime are **composite**.

Example 1 :   Show that 24 can be written as a product of primes.

$$24 = 6 \times 4 \qquad\qquad 24 = 8 \times 3 \qquad\qquad 24 = 12 \times 2$$

$$= (2 \times 3) \times (2 \times 2) \qquad = (2 \times 2 \times 2) \times 3 \qquad = (3 \times 2 \times 2) \times 2$$

$$= 2 \times 3 \times 2 \times 2 \qquad\quad = 2 \times 2 \times 2 \times 3 \qquad\quad = 3 \times 2 \times 2 \times 2$$

Notice that each way yields the same prime factors.

Every composite number can be expressed as a product of prime numbers in only one way. This product of prime numbers is the **prime factorization** of the composite number.

Factor trees aid in finding the prime factorization of a number.

Example 2: Find the prime factorization of 210.

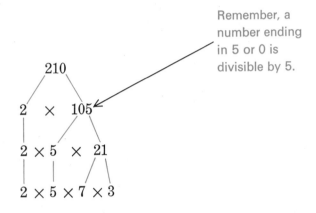

Remember, a number ending in 5 or 0 is divisible by 5.

So 210 = 2 × 5 × 7 × 3.

Example 3: Find the prime factorization of 396.

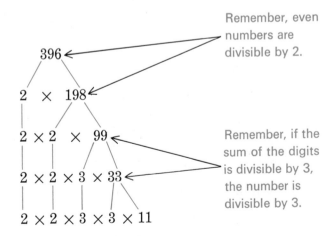

Remember, even numbers are divisible by 2.

Remember, if the sum of the digits is divisible by 3, the number is divisible by 3.

So 396 = 2 × 2 × 3 × 3 × 11.

Exercises

A Use the chart below to tell whether each number is prime or composite.

1. 10   **2.** 11   **3.** 12   **4.** 13   **5.** 14   **6.** 15   **7.** 16

10	11	12	13	14	15	16
1×10	1×11	1×12	1×13	1×14	1×15	1×16
2×5		2×6		2×7	3×5	2×8
		3×4				4×4
		$2 \times 2 \times 3$				$2 \times 2 \times 4$
						$2 \times 2 \times 2 \times 2$

B Tell whether each number is prime or composite.

8. 33   **9.** 41   **10.** 52   **11.** 30   **12.** 59   **13.** 47

14. 40   **15.** 45   **16.** 51   **17.** 49   **18.** 31   **19.** 77

Give the prime factorization of each number.

20. 18   **21.** 26   **22.** 20   **23.** 22   **24.** 25   **25.** 35

26. 17   **27.** 27   **28.** 48   **29.** 36   **30.** 39   **31.** 49

32. 40   **33.** 144   **34.** 98   **35.** 225   **36.** 126   **37.** 585

C Complete this table.

38.

Prime number	2	3	5	7	11	13	17
	2×2	3×3	5×5	7×7	11×11	13×13	17×17
Square	4	9					

39. Is 97 prime? Since 97 is between 7×7 and 11×11, you need check only for divisibility by 2, 3, 5, and 7.

Determine whether each number below is prime.

40. 143   **41.** 171   **42.** 163   **43.** 197   **44.** 221

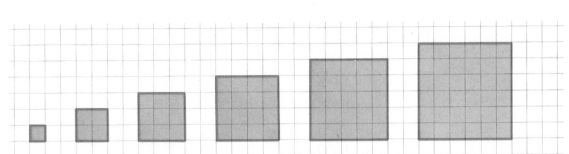

1, 4, 9, 16, 25, and 36 are **square numbers**. Each can be written as the product of two equal factors. Whenever a factor is repeated, you can write the product as a power.

Number	Equal factors	Power
1	1×1	1^2
4	2×2	2^2
9	3×3	3^2

Number	Equal factors	Power
16	4×4	4^2
25	5×5	5^2
36	6×6	6^2

$$2 \times 2 = 2^2 \quad \textit{two squared or two to the second power}$$

$$2 \times 2 \times 2 = 2^3 \quad \textit{two cubed or two to the third power}$$

$$2 \times 2 \times 2 \times 2 = 2^4 \quad \textit{two to the fourth power}$$

$$2 \times 2 \times 2 \times 2 \times 2 = 2^5 \quad \textit{two to the fifth power}$$

Base
(The number used as a factor)

2^4

Exponent
(Number of times the base is a factor)

Example 1: Write $n \times n \times n \times n \times n$ using exponents.

Since n is a factor 5 times, $n \times n \times n \times n \times n = n^5$.

Example 2: Express 3^4 as a product of factors. Then find the value of 3^4.

$$3^4 = 3 \times 3 \times 3 \times 3 = 81$$

Example 3: Find the cube of 4.

$$4^3 = 4 \times 4 \times 4 = 64$$

Example 4: Find the prime factorization of 72. Write the answer using exponents.

$$72 = 8 \times 9$$
$$= (2 \times 2 \times 2) \times (3 \times 3)$$
$$= 2^3 \times 3^2$$

Example 5: Express the prime factorization of 300 using exponents.

$300 = 3 \times 100$

$\quad = 3 \times (10 \times 10)$

$\quad = 3 \times (5 \times 2) \times (5 \times 2)$

$\quad = 3 \times (5 \times 5) \times (2 \times 2)$ Like factors have been grouped.

$\quad = 3 \times 5^2 \times 2^2$

$\quad = 2^2 \times 3 \times 5^2$ Factors have been arranged from least to greatest.

Exercises

A Read each expression. Then name the base and the exponent.

1. 6^3 **2.** 10^4 **3.** 4^{10} **4.** x^5 **5.** 11^2

Express the following using exponents.

6. $1 \times 1 \times 1 \times 1 \times 1 \times 1$ **7.** $x \times x \times x \times x \times x \times x \times x \times x$

8. $z \times z \times z \times z$ **9.** $5 \times 5 \times 5 \times 5 \times 5$

Find the square of each number.

10. 7   **11.** 8   **12.** 9   **13.** 10   **14.** 12

15. Does 2^3 equal 3^2?

16. Does 3×4 equal 4^3?

B Find the cube of each number.

17. 2   **18.** 3   **19.** 1   **20.** 5   **21.** 6   **22.** 8

Find the value of each expression.

23. 2^4 **24.** 2^5 **25.** 2^6 **26.** 1^8 **27.** 10^6

28. five to the fourth power

Express the prime factorization of each number using exponents. List the factors from least to greatest.

29. 54   **30.** 75   **31.** 88   **32.** 196   **33.** 288

34. 720   **35.** 1250   **36.** 1053   **37.** 1400   **38.** 1575

39. Does $2^2 + 3^2 = (2 + 3)^2$?

C Compute the squares of these numbers.

40. 11   **41.** 111   **42.** 1111   **43.** 11,111

44. Predict the square of 111,111.

Complete these computations.

45. $1^3 + 2^3 = (1 + \underline{\quad})^2$

46. $1^3 + 2^3 + 3^3 = (1 + 2 + \underline{\quad})^2$

47. $1^3 + 2^3 + 3^3 + 4^3 = (\underline{\quad} + \underline{\quad} + \underline{\quad} + \underline{\quad})^2$

Complete these statements. Recall that $2^5 = 32$ and $2^6 = 64$.

48. $2^2 \times 2^3 = 2^{\underline{\quad}}$

49. $(2^3)^2 = 8^2 = 2^{\underline{\quad}}$

50. $(2^2)^3 = 4^3 = 2^{\underline{\quad}}$

If you start with 1 and find the sums of consecutive odd numbers, you get an interesting pattern.

$$1 = 1$$
$$1 + 3 = 4$$
$$1 + 3 + 5 = 9$$
$$1 + 3 + 5 + 7 = 16$$

The sums are square numbers. Let's look at the square numbers to see this relationship.

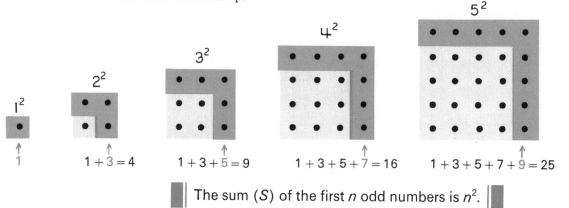

1^2
↑
1

2^2
↑
$1 + 3 = 4$

3^2
↑
$1 + 3 + 5 = 9$

4^2
↑
$1 + 3 + 5 + 7 = 16$

5^2
↑
$1 + 3 + 5 + 7 + 9 = 25$

▍ The sum (S) of the first n odd numbers is n^2. ▍

Example 1: Find the sum of the first 15 odd numbers.

$$S = n^2$$
$$= 15^2$$
$$= 15 \times 15$$
$$= 225$$

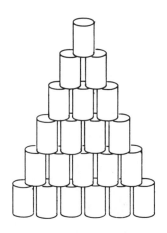

Each row in this stack of cans has one more can than the row above it. Finding the number of cans in 5 rows is the same as finding this sum: $1 + 2 + 3 + 4 + 5$. Let's see if we can find a pattern.

We can represent the cans in a row by dots.

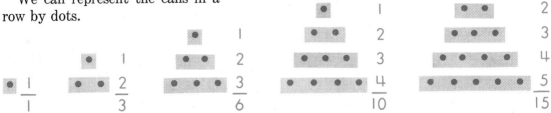

The numbers 1, 3, 6, 10, 15, and so on, are called **triangular numbers**. We have found a pattern, but not a formula. Let's look at this sum: $1 + 2 + 3 + 4 + 5 + 6$. We can add the numbers to themselves to get twice the sum we want.

$$1 + 2 + 3 + 4 + 5 + 6$$
$$\underline{6 + 5 + 4 + 3 + 2 + 1}$$
$$7 + 7 + 7 + 7 + 7 + 7$$

The numbers in the sum will each be equal to 1 more than the last number.

There are six 7's, so 6×7 is twice the sum we want. Then, $\frac{1}{2} \times 6 \times 7 = 21$ is the required sum. Let's look at the problem to find a formula.

$$\frac{1}{2} \times 6 \times 7$$

n
consecutive numbers

7 is $6 + 1$, so it is $n + 1$.

$$\frac{1}{2} \times 6 \times 7$$

$n + 1$

$$S = \frac{1}{2}n(n + 1)$$

Sum of first n numbers

> The sum (S) of the first n numbers greater than 0 is
> $$\frac{1}{2}n(n + 1).$$

Example 2: Find the number of cans in 10 rows.

$$S = \frac{1}{2}n(n + 1)$$

$$= \frac{1}{2} \times 10 \times (10 + 1)$$

$$= \frac{1}{2} \times 10 \times 11$$

$$= 55$$

Exercises

A Use the formula $S = n^2$ to find the sum of each set of numbers.

1. 1, 3, 5, 7, 9, 11

2. 1, 3, 5, 7, 9, 11, 13, 15

3. 1, 3, 5, 7, 9, 11, 13, 15, 17, 19

4. the first 9 consecutive odd numbers

5. the first 100 consecutive odd numbers

B Use the formula $S = \frac{1}{2}n(n + 1)$ to find the sum of each set of numbers.

6. 1, 2, 3, $\cdots$, 10

7. 1, 2, 3, $\cdots$, 15

8. 1, 2, 3, $\cdots$, 18

9. the numbers from 1 through 25

10. the numbers from 1 through 50

11. the numbers from 1 through 75

12. the numbers from 1 through 100

13. the numbers from 1 through 200

14. What is the 100th odd number?

15. Find the sum of each pair of consecutive triangular numbers.

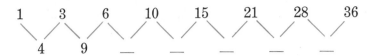

16. Draw a dot pattern for each square number in Exercise 15. Then show that a square number is the sum of two triangular numbers.

17. What is the least number greater than 1 that is both triangular and square?

18. You are to make a triangular stack of cans of B-Quick and have no cans left over. B-Quick comes only in boxes of 12 cans each. What is the smallest number of boxes you need?

C **19.** You are to make a triangular stack of cans of tomato soup and have no cans left over. The soup comes only in boxes of 24 cans each. What is the smallest number of boxes you need?

20. Compare the sum of the first 100 odd numbers (Exercise 5) and the sum of the first 100 numbers (Exercise 12). Are the sums equal? Is one about twice the other?

21. What is the sum of all the odd numbers between 1 and 100?

$S = n(n + 1)$ is the formula for finding the sum of the first n even numbers greater than 0. Find each sum.

22. 2, 4, 6, $\cdots$, 100

23. the first 150 consecutive even numbers

24. Add the answers for Exercises 21 and 22.
Is the result equal to the answer to Exercise 12?

25. $1^3 + 2^3 = 3^2$ 2nd triangular number
$1^3 + 2^3 + 3^3 = 6^2$ 3rd triangular number

Show that this pattern holds for the 4th and 5th triangular numbers.

4.6 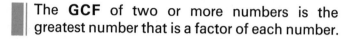 GREATEST COMMON FACTOR

When you are simplifying fractions, you often need to find the *greatest common factor (GCF)* of the numerator and the denominator.

> The **GCF** of two or more numbers is the greatest number that is a factor of each number.

Prime factorization can help you find the GCF of two or more numbers.

Example 1: Find the GCF of 36 and 54.

$$36 = 6 \times 6 = \boxed{3} \times 2 \times \boxed{3} \times \boxed{2}$$
$$54 = 9 \times 6 = \boxed{3} \times 3 \times \boxed{3} \times \boxed{2}$$

3, 3, and 2 are common factors.
3 × 3 × 2 = 18, so 18 is the GCF.

> The **GCF** of two or more numbers is the product of all their common prime factors.

Example 2: Find the GCF of 49 and 30.

$$49 = 7 \times 7$$

$$30 = 5 \times 6 = 5 \times 3 \times 2$$

There are no common prime factors. Since 1 is a factor of every number, 1 is the GCF.

Example 3: Find the GCF of 16 and 80.

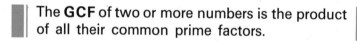

$$16 = 2 \times 8 = 2 \times 2 \times 2 \times 2$$
$$80 = 10 \times 8 = 2 \times 5 \times 2 \times 2 \times 2$$

2, 2, 2, and 2 are common factors.
2 × 2 × 2 × 2 = 16, so 16 is the GCF.

Example 4: Find the GCF of 45, 75, and 120.

$$45 = 5 \times 9 = 5 \times 3 \times 3$$
$$75 = 3 \times 25 = 3 \times 5 \times 5$$
$$120 = 10 \times 12 = 2 \times 5 \times 3 \times 2 \times 2$$

3 and 5 are common factors.
$3 \times 5 = 15$, so 15 is the GCF.

Exercises

A What are the common factors of each pair of numbers? What is the GCF of each pair?

1. $3 = 3$
$12 = 3 \times 2 \times 2$

2. $6 = 3 \times 2$
$9 = 3 \times 3$

3. $3 = 3$
$7 = 7$

4. $4 = 2 \times 2$
$10 = 2 \times 5$

5. $12 = 3 \times 2 \times 2$
$18 = 3 \times 3 \times 2$

6. $66 = 3 \times 2 \times 11$
$77 = 7 \times 11$

7. $27 = 3 \times 3 \times 3$
$39 = 3 \times 13$

8. $9 = 3 \times 3$
$16 = 2 \times 2 \times 2 \times 2$

9. $28 = 2 \times 2 \times 7$
$52 = 2 \times 2 \times 13$

B What is the GCF of each set of numbers?

10. 30 and 50

11. 36 and 45

12. 34 and 85

13. 24 and 66

14. 3 and 19

15. 42 and 116

16. 38 and 57

17. 100 and 625

18. 248 and 396

19. 4, 8, and 24

20. 27, 54, and 108

21. 90 and 126

22. 50, 78, and 112

23. 16, 96, and 108

24. 33, 42, and 90

C **25.** Find the GCF of 404, 696, and 1970.

26. Find the GCF of 128, 256, and 640.

27. If one number is prime and another number is not a multiple of that prime, what is their GCF?

4.7 ◆ LEAST COMMON MULTIPLE

24-inch cartons are being stacked next to 36-inch cartons. What is the shortest height at which the stacks will be the same height?

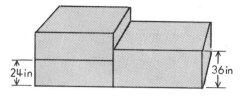

24-inch cartons

Number of cartons	1	2	3	4	5	6
Height in inches	24	48	72	96	120	144

36-inch cartons

Number of cartons	1	2	3	4	5
Height in inches	36	72	108	144	180

72 inches

144 inches

72 is the least non-zero number that is a multiple of both 24 and 36. It is the *least common multiple* (*LCM*) of 24 and 36.

> The **LCM** of a set of numbers is the least non-zero number that is a multiple of each number in the set.

Prime factorization makes it easy to find the LCM of a set of numbers.

Example 1: Find the LCM of 24 and 36.

Common factors get counted only once.

$24 = 2 \times 2 \times 3 \times 2 = 2 \times 2 \times 3 \times 2$
$36 = 2 \times 2 \times 3 \times 3 = 2 \times 2 \times 3 \quad \times 3$

$2 \times 2 \times 3 \times 2 \times 3 = 72$, so 72 is the LCM.

Example 2: Find the LCM of 15 and 45.

$15 = 5 \times 3 \quad\quad = 5 \times 3$
$45 = 5 \times 3 \times 3 = 5 \times 3 \times 3$

$5 \times 3 \times 3 = 45$, so 45 is the LCM.

Example 3: Find the LCM of 8 and 15.

$15 = 5 \times 3 \qquad = 5 \times 3$

$8 = 2 \times 2 \times 2 = \qquad 2 \times 2 \times 2$

8 and 15 have no common factors, so their LCM is 8×15.

$5 \times 3 \times 2 \times 2 \times 2 = 120$, so 120 is the LCM.

Example 4: Find the LCM of 18, 27, and 30.

$18 = 3 \times 3 \times 2 = 3 \times 3 \times 2$

$27 = 3 \times 3 \times 3 = 3 \times 3 \qquad \times 3$

$30 = 3 \times 2 \times 5 = 3 \qquad \times 2 \qquad \times 5$

$3 \times 3 \times 2 \times 3 \times 5 = 270$, so 270 is the LCM.

Exercises

A Find the LCM of each pair of numbers.

1. $4 = 2 \times 2$
$6 = 2 \qquad \times 3$

2. $7 = 7$
$21 = 7 \times 3$

3. $4 = 2 \times 2$
$15 = \qquad 3 \times 5$

4. $6 = 3 \times 2$
$48 = 3 \times 2 \times 2 \times 2 \times 2$

5. $18 = 2 \times 3 \times 3$
$24 = 2 \times 3 \qquad \times 2 \times 2$

6. $20 = 5 \times 2 \times 2$
$35 = 5 \qquad \times 7$

7. $3 = 3$
$10 = \qquad 2 \times 5$

B Find the LCM of each set of numbers.

8. 9 and 36

9. 5 and 7

10. 2, 3, 4, and 6

11. 16 and 80

12. 18 and 32

13. 25 and 49

14. 18 and 45

15. 37 and 74

16. 7, 21, and 84

17. 30 and 105

18. 39 and 26

19. 35 and 12

20. 11, 33, and 44

21. 15, 75, and 50

22. 3, 5, and 7

23. When is the LCM of a set of numbers equal to the greatest number in the set?

C Find the LCM of each set of numbers. You can leave the answer written as a product of prime factors.

24. 20, 90, and 36   **25.** 30, 40, 48, and 60   **26.** 144, 24, 18, and 72

27. 66, 96, and 54   **28.** 28, 68, 88, and 110   **29.** 38, 42, 57, and 95

30. What is the LCM of any pair of prime numbers?

Playing the Same Game

The Angle Baseball Team has many extra players. Many players do not play every day. José is the starting pitcher every fourth game. Mary plays first base every second game. Al is the shortstop every third game.

José, Mary, and Al are all in today's game. How many games before Mary and Al play in the same game again? How many games before all three play in the same game again?

Choose the best term.

1. 2 is (*a factor of, divisible by*) 10.

2. (*3 × 4, 3 × 3 × 2, 3 × 2 × 2*) is the prime factorization of 12.

3. (*13, 14, 15*) is a prime number.

4. In the expression 3^5, 3 is the (*base, exponent*).

5. 6^2 is read (*two to the sixth power, six to the second power*).

6. 8 is the (*LCM, GCF*) of 2 and 8.

7. 2 is the (*LCM, GCF*) of 2 and 8.

8. 1 is the (*LCM, GCF*) of 3 and 5.

CHAPTER REVIEW

Find all the factors you can for each number. 4.1

1. 34   **2.** 70   **3.** 30   **4.** 19   **5.** 62   **6.** 95

Divide to find whether 7 is a factor of each number.

7. 54   **8.** 98   **9.** 84   **10.** 371   **11.** 105   **12.** 121

Which of these numbers are divisible by 2 ? By 3 ? By 5 ? By 10 ? 4.2

13. 870   **14.** 3025   **15.** 192   **16.** 61,215

17. 7312   **18.** 241,013   **19.** 45,100   **20.** 9270

Tell whether each number is prime or composite. 4.3

21. 23   **22.** 51   **23.** 17   **24.** 13   **25.** 99   **26.** 39

Find the prime factorization of each number.

27. 32   **28.** 46   **29.** 56   **30.** 81   **31.** 65   **32.** 93

4.4   Express the following using exponents.

33. $5 \times 5 \times 5 \times 5 \times 5 \times 5$ **34.** $y \times y \times y$

35. $9 \times 9 \times 9 \times 9 \times 2 \times 2$ **36.** the prime factorization of 72

Find the value of each expression.

37. the cube of 9   **38.** the square of 13   **39.** 3^5 **40.** 1^7

4.5   Use a formula to find the sum of each of the following sets.

41. the numbers from 1 through 60

42. 1, 3, 5, 7, 9, 11, 13

43. the first 20 odd numbers

44. the first 20 numbers

4.6   Find the GCF of each set of numbers.

45. 63 and 84   **46.** 32 and 51   **47.** 22, 66, and 33

48. 29 and 75   **49.** 100, 50, and 6   **50.** 68 and 85

51. When is the GCF of two numbers equal to 1?

52. When is the GCF of two numbers equal to the lesser of the two numbers?

4.7   Find the LCM of each set of numbers.

53. 23 and 92   **54.** 64 and 96   **55.** 35 and 9

56. 75 and 45   **57.** 6, 50, and 100   **58.** 68 and 85

59. When is the LCM of two numbers the product of the numbers?

60. When is the LCM of a set of numbers equal to one of the numbers in the set?

Find all the factors you can for each number.

1. 11 **2.** 20 **3.** 55 **4.** 42

Which of these numbers are divisible by 2? By 3? By 5? By 10?

5. 321 **6.** 620 **7.** 1170 **8.** 4625

Tell whether each number is prime or composite.

9. 39 **10.** 19 **11.** 51 **12.** 37

Write the prime factorization of each number using exponents.

13. 60 **14.** 54 **15.** 108 **16.** 150

Find the value of each expression.

17. two to the fourth power **18.** the square of 15 **19.** 2^5 **20.** 1^6

Find the GCF of each pair of numbers.

21. 20 and 80 **22.** 8 and 15 **23.** 24 and 36

Find the LCM of each set of numbers.

24. 21 and 32 **25.** 28 and 40 **26.** 6, 9, and 18

● Use the formula $S = n^2$ to find the sum for each set.

27. the odd numbers from 1 through 19

28. the first 24 odd numbers

● Use the formula $S = \frac{1}{2}n(n + 1)$ to find the sum for each set.

29. the numbers from 1 through 30

30. the first 24 numbers

Activities for Chapter 4

Activity 1

The primes in the first row of the chart have been circled. The gray tints cover all the multiples of 2 except 2.

1. Copy the chart.

2. Two lines can cross out all the multiples of 3. One of these lines is the gray tint through 6. Draw the other line, but do not cross out 3.

3. Four diagonal lines can be drawn through all the multiples of 5. The first line has been drawn for you.

4. Draw 3 diagonal lines through all the multiples of 7 except 7.

5. Starting with 11, circle the numbers not crossed-out. The circled numbers are the primes between 1 and 100.

②	③	4	⑤	6	⑦
8	9	10	11	12	13
14	15	16	17	18	19
20	21	22	23	24	25
26	27	28	29	30	31
32	33	34	35	36	37
38	39	40	41	42	43
44	45	46	47	48	49
50	51	52	53	54	55
56	57	58	59	60	61
62	63	64	65	66	67
68	69	70	71	72	73
74	75	76	77	78	79
80	81	82	83	84	85
86	87	88	89	90	91
92	93	94	95	96	97
98	99	100			

Activity 2

Express the following numbers as the sum of 2 primes.

Example: $22 = 11 + 11$ or $19 + 3$ or $17 + 5$

1. 6   **2.** 8   **3.** 10   **4.** 12   **5.** 14   **6.** 16   **7.** 18   **8.** 20

9. Try some even numbers greater than 22.

10. Do you think that any even number greater than 2 can be expressed as the sum of two primes?

Mathematics and Space Travel

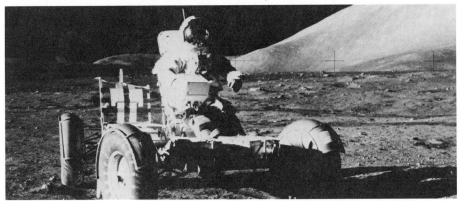

If you were in an Apollo spacecraft orbiting Earth for $2\frac{1}{2}$ days, you would make about 40 orbits and travel over 1,000,000 (1 million) miles.

You can use powers of 10 when naming large numbers.

$$10^2 = 10 \times 10 = 100$$

$$10^3 = 10 \times 10 \times 10 = 1000$$

$$10^4 = 10 \times 10 \times 10 \times 10 = 10,000$$

number of zeros

DISTANCE FROM EARTH TO SUN

$$93,000,000 \text{ miles} = 93 \times 1,000,000 \text{ miles} = 93 \times 10^6 \text{ miles}$$

6 zeros   6 zeros

Complete this table.

	Distance in miles	
59-day Skylab Mission in 1973	25,000,000	
From Earth to Moon	239,000	
From Mars to Earth		59×10^6
How far light travels in 1 year	586,000,000,000	
From Earth to nearest star (past the Sun)		25×10^{11}

Getting Ready for Chapter 5

Match each set with the best description.

1.7   **1.** whole numbers   **a.** $\{0, 2, 4, 6, 8\}$

4.2   **2.** odd numbers   **b.** $\{0, 1, 2, 3, \cdots\}$

4.3   **3.** prime numbers less than 10   **c.** $\{2, 3, 5, 7\}$

         4. composite numbers less than 10   **d.** $\{1, 3, 5, 7, 9, \cdots\}$

4.2   **5.** even numbers less than 10   **e.** $\{4, 6, 8, 9\}$

Find the value of each phrase.

1.1   **6.** $(13 + 5) - 5$ **7.** $(16 - 2) + 2$

         8. $(19 \times 4) \div 4$ **9.** $(18 \div 2) \times 2$

        10. 1×6 **11.** 218×1

        12. $15 + 0$ **13.** $0 + 275$

        14. $0 \div 1$ **15.** 3×0

        16. 0×16 **17.** $0 \div 48$

Solve each equation.

1.5   **18.** $x + 8 = 20$ **19.** $n + 16 = 22$

2.1   **20.** $9r = 63$ **21.** $7y = 56$

2.2   **22.** $y - 6 = 6$ **23.** $z - 13 = 6$

        24. $\frac{s}{7} = 6$ **25.** $\frac{p}{3} = 12$

Operations and Their Properties _____ 5

A good driver observes the "rules of the road." Using the rules is an important part of a successful trip.

The "rules of the road" in mathematics include the *properties of the operations*. You will observe these properties in this chapter. Using the properties is an important part of success in solving equations and in making computation easy.

5.1 ◆ SETS OF NUMBERS AND CLOSURE

Consider finding the sum of any two whole numbers.

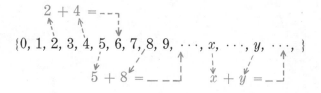

Is $2 + 4$ a whole number? Is $5 + 8$ a whole number? Sure they both are. In fact, the sum of any two whole numbers is a whole number. For this reason we say that the set of whole numbers is *closed under addition*. This idea is called the **closure property**.

> A set is closed under an operation when the *result* of the operation on any two numbers in the set *is* also *in that set*.

Example 1: Is the set of whole numbers closed under subtraction?

Check a few examples.

$$9 - 2 = 7 \qquad 4 - 0 = 4 \qquad 6 - 9 = ?$$

No, because the result of $6 - 9$ is not a whole number. Remember, only *one* example like this is needed to state that the set is not closed.

Example 2: Is the set of whole numbers closed under multiplication?

Check a few examples.

$$9 \times 2 = 18 \qquad 0 \times 4 = 0 \qquad 8 \times 6 = 48$$

Yes, since the product of any two whole numbers is in the set of whole numbers.

Example 3: Is the set of whole numbers closed under division?

Check a few examples.

$$8 \div 2 = 4 \qquad 0 \div 4 = 0 \qquad 7 \div 3 = \tfrac{7}{3}$$

No, because the result of $7 \div 3$ is not a whole number.

Exercises

A Check some examples. Then tell if the set is closed under the indicated operation.

Set	Examples			Operation
1. {1, 2, 3, 4, 5, $\cdots$}	$1 + 6$	$9 + 4$	$17 + 18$	addition
2. {1, 2, 3, 4, 5, $\cdots$}	$1 - 1$	$7 - 4$	$3 - 12$	subtraction
3. {1, 2, 3, 4, 5, $\cdots$}	4×9	19×4	16×16	multiplication
4. {1, 2, 3, 4, 5, $\cdots$}	$12 \div 3$	$8 \div 3$	$15 \div 5$	division
5. {0, 1}	0×0	0×1	1×1	multiplication
6. {0, 1}	$0 + 0$	$0 + 1$	$1 + 1$	addition
7. {1, 2}	$2 \div 1$	$1 \div 1$	$1 \div 2$	division
8. {1, 2}	$1 - 2$	$2 - 1$	$1 - 1$	subtraction

B Determine if each set is closed under addition, subtraction, multiplication, and division.

9. {even numbers} **10.** {odd numbers}

11. {prime numbers} **12.** {composite numbers}

C Identify each set as *finite* or *infinite*.

Examples: {states in U.S.} is a **finite set** because it is possible to count or list all 50 states.

{whole numbers} is an **infinite set** because it is impossible to count or list all numbers in the set.

13. {students in your class} **14.** {citizens of Japan}

15. {1, 2, 3, 4, 5, $\cdots$} **16.** {0, 5, 10, 15}

17. {even numbers} **18.** {odd numbers}

5.2 ◆ INVERSE OPERATIONS

You often do something and then undo it.

Sometimes it is impossible to undo an activity or operation.

> Operations that undo each other are called **inverse operations.**

Example 1: What is the inverse of each of the following?
(Be careful; not every operation has an inverse.)

Operation	Inverse operation
climbing up a ladder	climbing down a ladder
unlocking a window	locking a window
breaking a window	no inverse operation
subtracting 5	adding 5
dividing by 2	multiplying by 2

Example 2:   Study how inverse operations are used.

inverse
operations
↓   ↓
$(13 + 5) - 5 = 13$
↑   ↑
└----same----┘

Subtraction undoes addition.

inverse
operations
↓   ↓
$(14 - 2) + 2 = 14$
↑   ↑
└----same----┘

Addition undoes subtraction.

inverse
operations
↓   ↓
$(5 \times 3) \div 3 = 5$
↑   ↑
└----same----┘

Division undoes multiplication.

inverse
operations
↓   ↓
$(12 \div 4) \times 4 = 12$
↑   ↑
└----same----┘

Multiplication undoes division.

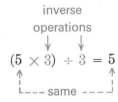

Inverse Operations

addition ⟷ subtraction
multiplication ⟷ division

Example 3:   You use inverse operations to solve equations. Knowing this allows you to omit certain steps as shown.

Long way	*Short way*
$x + 7 = 13$	$x + 7 = 13$
$x + 7 - 7 = 13 - 7$ ⎱ inverse operations	$x = 13 - 7$
$x + 0 = 13 - 7$ ⎰	$= 6$
$x = 6$	

Example 4:   Use an inverse operation to check each computation.

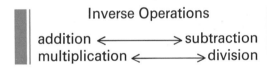

$$
\begin{array}{r} 19 \\ +38 \\ \hline 57 \end{array}
\qquad
\begin{array}{r} 139 \\ -47 \\ \hline 92 \end{array}
\qquad
\begin{array}{r} 123 \\ \times 27 \\ \hline 3321 \end{array}
\qquad
\begin{array}{r} 242 \\ 14\overline{)3388} \end{array}
$$

Check:
$$
\begin{array}{r} 57 \\ -38 \\ \hline 19 \end{array}
\qquad
\begin{array}{r} 92 \\ +47 \\ \hline 139 \end{array}
\qquad
\begin{array}{r} 123 \\ 27\overline{)3321} \end{array}
\qquad
\begin{array}{r} 242 \\ \times 14 \\ \hline 3388 \end{array}
$$

INVERSE OPERATIONS   133

Exercises

A What is the inverse of each of the following ?

1. starting a car

2. landing a plane

3. making a profit

4. walking 2 miles east

5. melting ice

6. putting on your shoes

7. adding 7

8. dividing by 3

9. subtracting 16

10. multiplying by 16

Tell how you would use an inverse operation to check each computation.

11.
$$\begin{array}{r} 43 \\ +17 \\ \hline 60 \end{array}$$

12.
$$\begin{array}{r} 26 \\ \times 4 \\ \hline 104 \end{array}$$

13.
$$\begin{array}{r} 39 \\ -16 \\ \hline 23 \end{array}$$

14.
$$25)\overline{625}$$
with 25 on top

15.
$$\begin{array}{r} 36 \\ \times 8 \\ \hline 288 \end{array}$$

16.
$$\begin{array}{r} 126 \\ -47 \\ \hline 79 \end{array}$$

17.
$$4)\overline{364}$$
with 91 on top

18.
$$\begin{array}{r} 309 \\ +76 \\ \hline 385 \end{array}$$

B Compute as indicated. Use an inverse operation to check each answer.

19.
$$\begin{array}{r} 78 \\ +26 \\ \hline \end{array}$$

20.
$$\begin{array}{r} 26 \\ \times 4 \\ \hline \end{array}$$

21. $4)\overline{76}$

22.
$$\begin{array}{r} 65 \\ -32 \\ \hline \end{array}$$

23.
$$\begin{array}{r} 39 \\ \times 12 \\ \hline \end{array}$$

24.
$$\begin{array}{r} 195 \\ -76 \\ \hline \end{array}$$

25.
$$\begin{array}{r} 352 \\ +48 \\ \hline \end{array}$$

26. $12)\overline{312}$

27. $15)\overline{930}$

28.
$$\begin{array}{r} 739 \\ +463 \\ \hline \end{array}$$

29.
$$\begin{array}{r} 406 \\ \times 9 \\ \hline \end{array}$$

30.
$$\begin{array}{r} 364 \\ -108 \\ \hline \end{array}$$

31.
$$\begin{array}{r} 946 \\ -338 \\ \hline \end{array}$$

32.
$$\begin{array}{r} 381 \\ \times 26 \\ \hline \end{array}$$

33. $4)\overline{1704}$

34.
$$\begin{array}{r} 1921 \\ +647 \\ \hline \end{array}$$

Solve each equation.

35. $x + 9 = 16$

36. $g - 8 = 17$

37. $m \times 8 = 32$

38. $k \div 3 = 8$

39. $t \times 16 = 48$

40. $b + 7 = 19$

41. $j - 9 = 25$ **42.** $n \div 5 = 65$ **43.** $r \times 8 = 64$

44. $z + 18 = 35$ **45.** $p - 6 = 14$ **46.** $s \div 6 = 46$

C Solve each equation. As shown by the examples, you must use two different inverses to solve each equation.

Examples: $(a \times 3) - 2 = 43$ $\qquad$ $(b + 2) \div 4 = 6$

$$a \times 3 = 43 + 2 \qquad\qquad b + 2 = 6 \times 4$$

$$a \times 3 = 45 \qquad\qquad b + 2 = 24$$

$$a = 45 \div 3 \qquad\qquad b = 24 - 2$$

$$= 15 \qquad\qquad\qquad\quad = 22$$

47. $(n \times 4) - 6 = 66$ **48.** $(r + 6) \div 8 = 1$

49. $(t \div 2) \times 3 = 12$ **50.** $(s - 6) \div 2 = 5$

51. $(w - 3) \times 5 = 40$ **52.** $(x + 19) - 12 = 41$

Soda Splitting

Tom and Jean want to share the soda equally. They can use only the three empty containers, the soda bottle, and the funnel. How can they do it?

5.3 ◆ COMMUTATIVE PROPERTIES

Walk 5 blocks E and 2 N.   *Walk 2 blocks N and 5 E.*

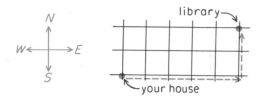

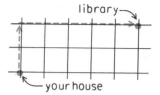

The order in which you walk from your house to the library does not affect the result. You get to the library either way.

> An operation is **commutative** if you can change the order (commute) without affecting the result.

Some operations are not commutative.

Go out and close the door.   *Close the door and go out.*

In mathematics you can commute in some operations but not in others.

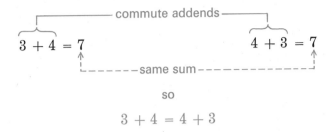

so

$$3 + 4 = 4 + 3$$

Since changing the order of any two addends does not affect their sum, we say *addition is commutative.*

Commutative Property of Addition

For any numbers *a* and *b*,
$$a + b = b + a.$$

Example 1: Is multiplication commutative?

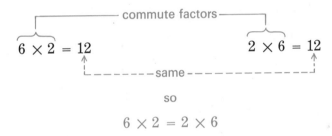

so

$$6 \times 2 = 2 \times 6$$

Yes, multiplication is commutative.

Commutative Property of Multiplication

For any numbers *a* and *b*,
$$ab = ba.$$

Example 2: Solve and check $5 + x = 7$.

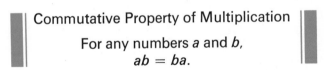

		Check
$5 + x = 7$		
$x + 5 = 7$	commute addends	$5 + x = 7$
$x = 7 - 5$	inverse operation	$5 + 2 = 7$
$= 2$		$7 = 7$

Example 3: Sometimes commuting the factors makes the computation easier.

$$
\begin{array}{r}
20 \\
\times 586 \\
\hline
120 \\
1600 \\
10000 \\
\hline
11720
\end{array}
\qquad
\begin{array}{r}
586 \\
\times 20 \\
\hline
11720
\end{array}
$$

Exercises

A Tell whether or not the following activities can be commutative.

1. Putting on your hat; putting on your coat.

2. Taking off in an airplane; starting the engine.

3. Cooking an egg; eating an egg.

4. Salting your soup; peppering your soup.

5. Taking a picture; putting film in your camera.

6. Taking a bath; taking off your clothes.

Study the examples. Tell if subtraction and division are commutative.

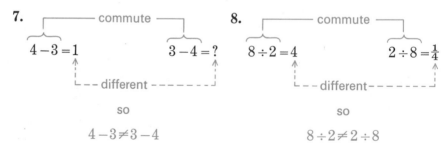

7.   commute   **8.**   commute

$4-3=1$ $3-4=?$ $8 \div 2 = 4$ $2 \div 8 = \frac{1}{4}$

different   different

so   so

$4-3 \neq 3-4$ $8 \div 2 \neq 2 \div 8$

B Solve and check each equation.

9. $5 + x = 9$ **10.** $4 + y = 10$ **11.** $8 + z = 14$

12. $m \times 3 = 15$ **13.** $t \times 7 = 49$ **14.** $r \times 6 = 42$

15. $6 + t = 14$ **16.** $k \times 9 = 72$ **17.** $11 + m = 69$

18. $z \times 8 = 96$ **19.** $13 + n = 81$ **20.** $y \times 7 = 245$

21. $18 + c = 96$ **22.** $r \times 11 = 242$ **23.** $17 + d = 91$

Compute. Whenever possible, use the commutative property to make the computation easier.

24. $\begin{array}{r} 20 \\ \times 425 \\ \hline \end{array}$ **25.** $\begin{array}{r} 300 \\ \times 625 \\ \hline \end{array}$ **26.** $\begin{array}{r} 428 \\ \times 30 \\ \hline \end{array}$ **27.** $\begin{array}{r} 200 \\ \times 856 \\ \hline \end{array}$

28. $\begin{array}{r} 142 \\ \times 72 \\ \hline \end{array}$ **29.** $\begin{array}{r} 83 \\ \times 524 \\ \hline \end{array}$ **30.** $\begin{array}{r} 40 \\ \times 6295 \\ \hline \end{array}$ **31.** $\begin{array}{r} 300 \\ \times 6675 \\ \hline \end{array}$

C For each addition sentence, write 2 subtraction sentences.
For each multiplication sentence, write 2 division sentences.

Examples: $5 + 2 = 7$ —— inverse ⟶ $7 - 2 = 5$

commute addends

$2 + 5 = 7$ —— inverse ⟶ $7 - 5 = 2$

$3 \times 6 = 18$ —— inverse ⟶ $18 \div 6 = 3$

commute factors

$6 \times 3 = 18$ —— inverse ⟶ $18 \div 3 = 6$

32. $9 + 18 = 27$ **33.** $45 + x = 72$ **34.** $95 + 67 = 162$

35. $5 \times 9 = 45$ **36.** $k \times 9 = 414$ **37.** $85 \times 72 = 6120$

5.4 ◆ ASSOCIATIVE PROPERTIES

You can add only two numbers at a time. But you often have to find the sum of three numbers. To do so, you must first group or *associate* the addends.

$$3 + 5 + 7$$

Should you begin by adding 3 and 5? Or 5 and 7? Or does it matter?

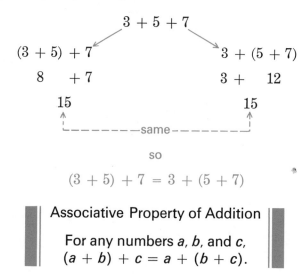

$$3 + 5 + 7$$

$(3 + 5) + 7$		$3 + (5 + 7)$
$8 \quad + 7$		$3 + \quad 12$
15		15

-------- same --------

so

$$(3 + 5) + 7 = 3 + (5 + 7)$$

> **Associative Property of Addition**
>
> For any numbers *a*, *b*, and *c*,
> $(a + b) + c = a + (b + c)$.

As you might expect, multiplication is also associative.

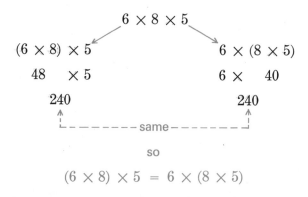

$$6 \times 8 \times 5$$

$(6 \times 8) \times 5$		$6 \times (8 \times 5)$
$48 \quad \times 5$		$6 \times \quad 40$
240		240

-------- same --------

so

$$(6 \times 8) \times 5 = 6 \times (8 \times 5)$$

> **Associative Property of Multiplication**
>
> For any numbers *a*, *b*, and *c*,
> $(ab)c = a(bc)$.

Example 1 : Tell which method of associating makes the computation easier.

$$28 + 96 + 4$$

$(28 + 96) + 4$ $28 + (96 + 4)$

124   + 4   28 +   100

128   128

$28 + (96 + 4)$ enables most people to do the addition mentally.

Example 2 : Sometimes the commutative and associative properties are both used to make the computation easier.

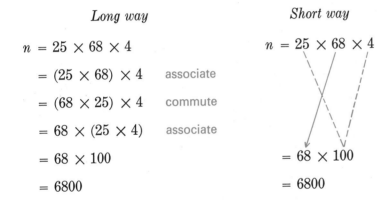

Long way	
$n = 25 \times 68 \times 4$	
$= (25 \times 68) \times 4$	associate
$= (68 \times 25) \times 4$	commute
$= 68 \times (25 \times 4)$	associate
$= 68 \times 100$	
$= 6800$	

Short way

$n = 25 \times 68 \times 4$

$= 68 \times 100$

$= 6800$

Exercises

Ⓐ Study the examples. Tell if subtraction and division are associative.

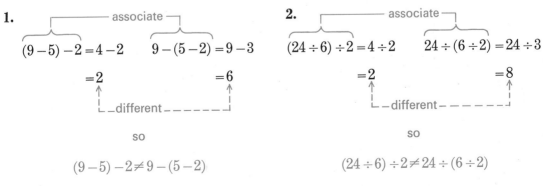

1.

associate

$(9 - 5) - 2 = 4 - 2$ $9 - (5 - 2) = 9 - 3$

$= 2$ $= 6$

different

so

$(9 - 5) - 2 \neq 9 - (5 - 2)$

2.

associate

$(24 \div 6) \div 2 = 4 \div 2$ $24 \div (6 \div 2) = 24 \div 3$

$= 2$ $= 8$

different

so

$(24 \div 6) \div 2 \neq 24 \div (6 \div 2)$

Tell how you would associate the addends or the factors to make the computation easy.

3. $30 + 60 + 18$ **4.** $72 + 91 + 9$ **5.** $54 + 6 + 27$

6. $5 \times 2 \times 9$ **7.** $12 \times 4 \times 5$ **8.** $25 \times 4 \times 16$

9. $16 + 84 + 99$ **10.** $33 \times 25 \times 8$ **11.** $4 \times 250 \times 172$

B Compute as indicated. Use the properties to make the computation as easy as possible.

12. $6 + 4 + 9$ **13.** $5 \times 40 \times 6$ **14.** $19 + 13 + 17$

15. $9 \times 4 \times 25$ **16.** $63 + 37 + 59$ **17.** $83 \times 20 \times 50$

18. $68 + 89 + 11$ **19.** $8 \times 25 \times 6$ **20.** $943 + 57 + 68$

21. $8 \times 250 \times 17$ **22.** $83 + 69 + 31$ **23.** $4 \times 25 \times 63$

24. $16 + 24 + 48$ **25.** $19 \times 50 \times 20$ **26.** $72 + 83 + 17$

C Compute as indicated. Use the properties to make the computation as easy as possible.

Examples:

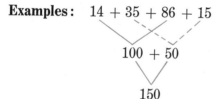

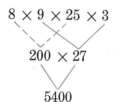

27. $26 + 53 + 74 + 10$ **28.** $132 + 68 + 46 + 14$

29. $25 \times 7 \times 4 \times 6$ **30.** $20 \times 5 \times 9 \times 6$

You already know that 0 and 1 have special properties.

$$8 + 0 = 8 \qquad 275 + 0 = 275 \qquad y + 0 = y$$

$$0 + t = t \qquad\qquad 0 + 0 = 0$$

The sum of 0 and any number is that number.

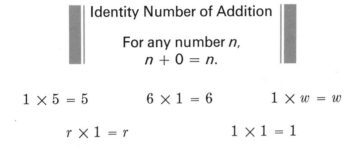

Identity Number of Addition

For any number n,
$n + 0 = n$.

$$1 \times 5 = 5 \qquad 6 \times 1 = 6 \qquad 1 \times w = w$$

$$r \times 1 = r \qquad\qquad 1 \times 1 = 1$$

The product of 1 and any number is that number.

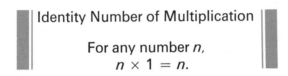

Identity Number of Multiplication

For any number n,
$n \times 1 = n$.

There are several other important ideas you must remember.

$$3 \times 0 = 0 \qquad 0 \times a = 0 \qquad 37 \times 0 = 0$$

$$0 \div 16 = 0 \qquad\qquad 0 \div 42 = 0$$

$$4 \div 4 = 1 \qquad 24 \div 24 = 1 \qquad 142 \div 142 = 1$$

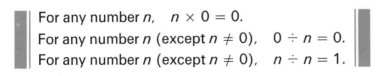

For any number n, $\quad n \times 0 = 0$.
For any number n (except $n \neq 0$), $\quad 0 \div n = 0$.
For any number n (except $n \neq 0$), $\quad n \div n = 1$.

You may wonder why zero cannot be the divisor. See what happens when you attempt to divide by zero.

These equations are checked like this.

$$6 \div 0 = x \longrightarrow x \times 0 = 6$$ No replacement makes $x \times 0 = 6$ true.

$$0 \div 0 = x \longrightarrow x \times 0 = 0$$ Every replacement makes $x \times 0 = 0$ true.

Since $6 \div 0$ does not name a number, and since $0 \div 0$ names every number, we say that division by zero is meaningless.

 Never divide by zero.

Exercises

A Find the value of each phrase.

1. 4×1
2. 1×16
3. $42 + 0$
4. $0 + 172$
5. 19×0
6. 0×16
7. $0 \div 16$
8. $0 \div 8$
9. $3 \div 3$

B Solve each equation.

10. $1 \times 16 = m$
11. $0 \div y = 0$
12. $184 + 0 = d$
13. $37 \times 0 = k$
14. $36 \div 36 = c$
15. $k \times 32 = 32$
16. $14 \div r = 1$
17. $84 \times x = 0$
18. $0 \times 189 = p$
19. $79 \times 1 = r$
20. $596 + m = 596$
21. $h \times 0 = 0$
22. $t \div 4 = 0$
23. $1 \times t = 89$
24. $196 \times c = 196$
25. $f + 0 = 296$
26. $26 \div a = 1$
27. $b \div 8 = 0$
28. $g \div 31 = 1$
29. $0 + n = 197$
30. $s \times 597 = 0$

C Find the value of each phrase without doing any written computation.

31. $32 + (9 - 9)$
32. $(19 - 18) \times 56$
33. $182 - (0 \div 4)$
34. $385 \times (284 - 283)$
35. $(14 \div 14) \times 163$
36. $24 \div [8 - (4 + 3)]$

Suppose you buy 5 tapes and 4 records at the sale price. You can figure the cost in either of these two ways.

cost per item	number of items		cost of tapes	cost of records
$3 \times (5 + 4)$			$(3 \times 5) + (3 \times 4)$	
3×9			$15 + 12$	
27			27	

same

so

$$3(5 + 4) = (3 \times 5) + (3 \times 4)$$

This relationship is useful in solving problems. It is called the *distributive property of multiplication over addition*.

> **Distributive Property**
>
> For any numbers a, b, and c,
>
> $$a(b + c) = ab + ac$$
>
> and
>
> $$ab + ac = a(b + c).$$

Example 1: Use the distributive property to help compute the cost of 6 tapes and 4 records.

$$(3 \times 6) + (3 \times 4) = 3(6 + 4)$$
$$= 3 \times 10$$
$$= 30 \qquad \text{\$30 cost}$$

The commutative property allows us to state the distributive property as $ba + ca = (b + c)a$. This pattern is helpful in solving equations.

Example 2: Solve $64a + 36a = 1800$.

$$64a + 36a = 1800$$
$$(64 + 36)a = 1800 \qquad \text{distributive property}$$
$$100a = 1800$$
$$\frac{100a}{100} = \frac{1800}{100} \qquad \text{inverse operation}$$
$$a = 18$$

Exercises

[A] What number should replace each n ?

1. $3(2 + 6) = (3 \times n) + (3 \times 6)$

2. $4(n + 8) = (4 \times 7) + (4 \times 8)$

3. $(9 \times 6) + (9 \times 5) = 9(6 + n)$

4. $(8 \times 3) + (n \times 2) = 8(3 + 2)$

5. $(14 \times 2) + (12 \times 2) = (14 + 12)n$

6. $(6 \times n) + (3 \times 2) = (6 + 3)2$

7. $(5 + 4)n = (5 \times 2) + (4 \times 2)$

8. $(16 + 12)3 = (16 \times 3) + (n \times 3)$

9. $6(9 + 12) = (n \times 9) + (6 \times 12)$

10. $(7 \times 8) + (8 \times 8) = (7 + 8)n$

B Solve.

11. $a = (9 \times 16) + (9 \times 24)$

12. $b = (8 \times 17) + (8 \times 13)$

13. $c = (6 \times 83) + (6 \times 17)$

14. $d = (5 \times 73) + (5 \times 27)$

15. $e = 6(8 + 9)$

16. $f = 5(9 + 6)$

17. $g = 8(17 + 13)$

18. $h = 12(4 + 10)$

19. $i = 14(3 + 10)$

20. $j = 9(20 + 8)$

Solve and check.

Example:
$$7x + 9x = 64$$
$$(7 + 9)x = 64$$
$$16x = 64$$
$$x = 4$$

Check:
$$7x + 9x = 64$$
$$(7 \times 4) + (9 \times 4) = 64$$
$$28 + 36 = 64$$
$$64 = 64$$

21. $7t + 2t = 72$

22. $6c + 14c = 180$

23. $7g + 8g = 195$

24. $57m + 43m = 300$

25. $16y + 34y = 2500$

26. $19n + 21n = 2000$

27. $12a + 46a = 348$

28. $37b + 23b = 420$

C Find each product as shown.

$$9 \times 72 = 9(70 + 2)$$ Rename 72 as 70 + 2.
$$= (9 \times 70) + (9 \times 2)$$ Apply the distributive property.
$$= 630 + 18$$
$$= 648$$

29. 9×82

30. 8×52

31. 6×83

32. 7×93

33. 9×63

34. 8×73

▷ VOCABULARY

Complete each sentence. Choose from these words.

associative   commutative   distributive   identity   inverse

1. Subtraction is the ____ operation of addition.

2. Zero is the ____ number of addition.

3. $7 \times 3 = 3 \times 7$ illustrates that multiplication is ____.

4. $(7 + 5) + 9 = 7 + (5 + 9)$ illustrates that addition is ____.

5. $(9 \times 6) + (9 \times 5) = 9(6 + 5)$ illustrates the ____ property of multiplication over addition.

▷ CHAPTER REVIEW

5.1   Determine if each set is closed under the operation indicated.

Set	Operation
1. {0, 1}	multiplication
2. {0, 1}	addition
3. {0, 2, 4, 6, 8, $\cdots$}	addition
4. {1, 3, 5, 7, 9, $\cdots$}	multiplication

5.2   Compute as indicated. Use an inverse operation to check each answer.

5. $\begin{array}{r} 36 \\ +12 \\ \hline \end{array}$ 6. $\begin{array}{r} 43 \\ +76 \\ \hline \end{array}$ 7. $\begin{array}{r} 428 \\ +349 \\ \hline \end{array}$

8. $\begin{array}{r} 45 \\ -23 \\ \hline \end{array}$ 9. $\begin{array}{r} 75 \\ -27 \\ \hline \end{array}$ 10. $\begin{array}{r} 429 \\ -275 \\ \hline \end{array}$

11. $\begin{array}{r} 76 \\ \times 8 \\ \hline \end{array}$ 12. $\begin{array}{r} 24 \\ \times 13 \\ \hline \end{array}$ 13. $\begin{array}{r} 579 \\ \times 43 \\ \hline \end{array}$

14. $6\overline{)438}$ 15. $7\overline{)938}$ 16. $16\overline{)864}$

Solve and check each equation. 5.3

17. $5 + x = 11$

18. $8 + y = 10$

19. $7 + m = 19$

20. $37 + t = 84$

21. $z \times 6 = 96$

22. $r \times 5 = 85$

23. $8 \times s = 120$

24. $12 \times y = 120$

Compute. Use the properties to make the computation easy. 5.4

25. $16 + 14 + 39$

26. $29 + 83 + 17$

27. $69 + 31 + 87$

28. $43 + 47 + 38$

29. $6 \times 5 \times 7$

30. $2 \times 50 \times 17$

31. $4 \times 9 \times 5$

32. $69 \times 25 \times 4$

Solve each equation. 5.5

33. $1 \times 16 = x$

34. $16 \div 16 = r$

35. $0 \times 48 = y$

36. $8 + 0 = s$

37. $575 + 0 = z$

38. $0 \div 96 = r$

39. $82 \div 82 = n$

40. $32 \times 1 = t$

Solve each equation. 5.6

41. $c = 7(19 + 21)$

42. $f = 6(12 + 6)$

43. $q = (9 \times 16) + (9 \times 34)$

44. $m = (6 \times 77) + (6 \times 23)$

45. $7r + 2r = 99$

46. $56n + 44n = 900$

CHAPTER TEST

Match each example with the property it illustrates.

1. $(6 \times 3)2 = 6(3 \times 2)$ **a.** commutative property of $\times$

2. $260 + 0 = 260$ **b.** identity number of $+$

3. $(9 \times 7) + (9 \times 4) = 9(7 + 4)$ **c.** associative property of $+$

4. $9 \times 7 = 7 \times 9$ **d.** distributive property

5. $126 + 621 = 621 + 126$ **e.** associative property of $\times$

6. $14 + (6 + 9) = (14 + 6) + 9$ **f.** identity number of $\times$

7. $1 \times 363 = 363$ **g.** commutative property of $+$

Compute as indicated.

8. $(18 \div 2) \times 2$ **9.** 1×85 **10.** 76×0

11. $85 + 0$ **12.** $0 \div 96$ **13.** $(84 - 13) + 13$

14. 295×1 **15.** $(26 \times 9) \div 9$ **16.** $26 \div 26$

17. $\begin{array}{r} 54 \\ +37 \\ \hline \end{array}$ **18.** $\begin{array}{r} 652 \\ -29 \\ \hline \end{array}$ **19.** $\begin{array}{r} 42 \\ \times 8 \\ \hline \end{array}$

20. $14\overline{)168}$ **21.** $\begin{array}{r} 579 \\ \times 43 \\ \hline \end{array}$ **22.** $16\overline{)864}$

Solve each equation.

23. $6 + x = 13$ **24.** $t \times 7 = 98$

25. $(9 \times 13) + (9 \times 17) = g$ **26.** $6r + 2r = 96$

27. $16m + 34m = 250$ **28.** $8 + k = 67$

29. $(6 \times 49) + (6 \times 51) = n$ **30.** $m - 24 = 144$

31. $(36 + 14) + 39 = r$ **32.** $4(5 \times 9) = s$

33. $(8 \times 25)7 = t$ **34.** $76 + (24 + 85) = v$

Activities for Chapter 5

Activity 1

The people in DoUbelievit Land use a three-hour clock which only has one hand. The Do-Ubelievits use this clockface and its numbers 0, 1, and 2 to do their arithmetic.

Example: Find 1 ⊕ 2. (⊕ means *add*.)

To find 1 ⊕ 2,
move 1 space;
then *move 2 spaces.*

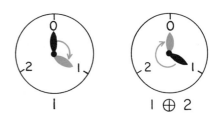

1. Copy the table. Then use a number clock to help you complete the addition table.

2. In this land, is addition commutative? Associative?

Activity 2

The DoUbelievits also use the number clock for multiplication.

Example: Find 1 ⊗ 2 and 2 ⊗ 2. (⊗ means *multiply*.)

1 ⊗ 2 means *one move of 2 spaces.*

2 ⊗ 2 means *two moves of 2 spaces each.*

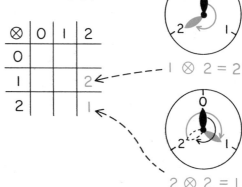

1. Copy the table. Then use a number clock to help you complete the multiplication table.

2. In this land, is multiplication commutative? Associative?

Mathematics and Transplanting Trees

A tree mover knows it is important to retain as much of the root system as possible when transplanting a tree. However, an excessively large ball adds needless weight and expense.

To compute the weight of a balled tree, use the following formula.

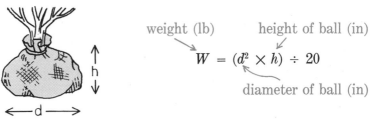

weight (lb)   height of ball (in)

$$W = (d^2 \times h) \div 20$$

diameter of ball (in)

You would proceed as follows to compute the weight of a balled tree where the diameter of the ball is $3\frac{1}{3}$ feet (40 inches) and the height of the ball is 3 feet (36 inches).

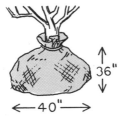

36"

←40"→

$$W = (d^2 \times h) \div 20$$
$$= (40^2 \times 36) \div 20$$
$$= 2880.$$

The weight is 2880 pounds.

Compute the weight of each balled tree indicated in the table.

Diameter of ball	Height of ball	Weight of balled tree
20 in	18 in	_____
60 in	48 in	_____
3 ft	$2\frac{1}{2}$ ft	_____

Find the prime factorization of each number.   4.3

1. 8   **2.** 9   **3.** 10   **4.** 14

5. 16   **6.** .20   **7.** 24   **8.** 25

Find the GCF of each pair of numbers.   4.6

9. $12 = 2 \times 2 \times 3$ **10.** $15 = 3 \times 5$

$18 = 2 \times 3 \times 3$ $30 = 2 \times 3 \times 5$

11. 6 and 9   **12.** 5 and 10   **13.** 3 and 7

14. 12 and 15   **15.** 21 and 28   **16.** 16 and 24

17. When is the GCF of two numbers equal to the lesser number?

18. When is the GCF of two numbers equal to 1?

Find the LCM of each pair of numbers.   4.7

19. $6 = 3 \times 2$ **20.** $5 = 5$

$8 = 2 \times 2 \times 2$ $9 = 3 \times 3$ -

21. 3 and 4   **22.** 12 and 18   **23.** 6 and 10

24. 8 and 24   **25.** 4 and 5   **26.** 7 and 35

27. When is the LCM of two numbers equal to the greater number?

28. When is the LCM of two numbers equal to the product of the two numbers?

Operations with Fractions ⸺ 6

During a lunar space mission, many important computations are made. The precision of these computations often determines the success or failure of the mission.

Fractions are an important aid to precision. In this chapter you will learn how to perform the basic operations with fractions. You will also learn how to apply your knowledge of fractions in many practical situations.

Fractions are used to indicate amounts.

TNT stock up $\frac{5}{8}$

$\frac{5}{8}$ dollar

$3\frac{3}{5}$

Average Size of U.S. Family

Fractions are also used to indicate quotients. For this reason, 0 is never a denominator.

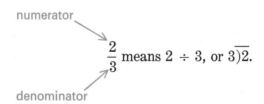

numerator

$\frac{2}{3}$ means $2 \div 3$, or $3\overline{)2}$.

denominator

Example 1: Express $7 \div 4$, $1 \div 3$, and $6 \div 1$ as fractions.

$$7 \div 4 = \frac{7}{4}$$

$$1 \div 3 = \frac{1}{3}$$

$$6 \div 1 = \frac{6}{1}$$

Any whole number divided by 1 equals itself.

$$\frac{n}{1} = n \div 1 = n$$

Example 2: Express 2, 5, and 9 as fractions.

$$2 = \frac{2}{1}$$

$$5 = \frac{5}{1}$$

$$9 = \frac{9}{1}$$

Fractions that express the same amount are **equivalent**. In the diagram, $\frac{1}{2}$, $\frac{2}{4}$, and $\frac{4}{8}$ are equivalent.

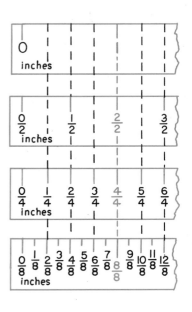

Example 3: Use the diagram to find fractions equivalent to $\frac{1}{4}$, $\frac{6}{8}$, 1, $\frac{5}{4}$, and $\frac{6}{4}$.

$$\frac{1}{4} = \frac{2}{8} \qquad \frac{6}{8} = \frac{3}{4}$$

$$1 = \frac{2}{2} = \frac{4}{4} = \frac{8}{8}$$

$$\frac{5}{4} = \frac{10}{8} \qquad \frac{6}{4} = \frac{3}{2} = \frac{12}{8}$$

The diagram shows how to add $\frac{3}{8}$ and $\frac{4}{8}$.

$$\frac{3}{8} + \frac{4}{8} = \frac{3+4}{8} = \frac{7}{8}$$

For any two fractions with the same denominator,

$$\frac{a}{c} + \frac{b}{c} = \frac{a+b}{c}.$$

Example 4: Add $\frac{3}{5}$ and $\frac{1}{5}$.

$$\frac{3}{5} + \frac{1}{5} = \frac{3+1}{5} = \frac{4}{5}$$

Exercises

A Express as fractions.

1. $1 \div 4$ **2.** $4 \div 1$ **3.** $5 \div 6$ **4.** $11 \div 2$

5. 3 **6.** 20 **7.** 6 **8.** 1

B Use the diagrams to find equivalent fractions.

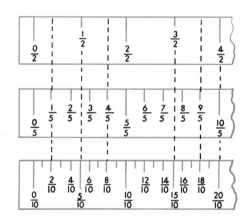

9. $\frac{1}{5} = \frac{\text{|||}}{10}$ **10.** $\frac{18}{10} = \frac{\text{|||}}{5}$

11. $\frac{8}{10} = \frac{\text{|||}}{5}$ **12.** $\frac{3}{2} = \frac{\text{|||}}{10}$

13. $\frac{1}{2} = \frac{\text{|||}}{10}$ **14.** $\frac{4}{2} = \frac{\text{|||}}{5} = \frac{\text{|||}}{10}$

Lay a ruler along the diagrams to help you find equivalent fractions.

15. $\frac{5}{6} = \frac{\text{|||}}{12}$ **16.** $\frac{18}{12} = \frac{\text{|||}}{6}$

17. $\frac{4}{6} = \frac{\text{|||}}{3} = \frac{\text{|||}}{12}$ **18.** $\frac{1}{3} = \frac{\text{|||}}{6} = \frac{\text{|||}}{12}$

19. $\frac{14}{12} = \frac{\text{|||}}{6}$ **20.** $\frac{4}{3} = \frac{\text{|||}}{6} = \frac{\text{|||}}{12}$

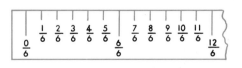

Add.

21. $\frac{1}{2} + \frac{4}{2}$ **22.** $\frac{2}{3} + \frac{3}{3}$ **23.** $\frac{2}{5} + \frac{2}{5}$ **24.** $\frac{3}{10} + \frac{6}{10}$

25. $\frac{5}{6} + \frac{2}{6}$ **26.** $\frac{4}{8} + \frac{3}{8}$ **27.** $\frac{7}{7} + \frac{2}{7}$ **28.** $\frac{6}{4} + \frac{3}{4}$

29. What whole number is equivalent to this sum: $\frac{8}{8} + \frac{8}{8} + \frac{8}{8}$?

30. For what number n is $\frac{n}{1} = \frac{n}{n}$?

C Add.

Example: $\quad \dfrac{5}{8} + \dfrac{3}{8} + \dfrac{7}{8} = \dfrac{5+3+7}{8} = \dfrac{15}{8}$

31. $\frac{2}{3} + \frac{4}{3} + \frac{2}{3}$ **32.** $\frac{4}{5} + \frac{2}{5} + \frac{3}{5}$ **33.** $\frac{1}{10} + \frac{7}{10} + \frac{5}{10}$

34. $\frac{5}{6} + \frac{1}{6} + \frac{5}{6}$ **35.** $\frac{3}{2} + \frac{1}{2} + \frac{5}{2}$ **36.** $\frac{7}{4} + \frac{3}{4} + \frac{3}{4}$

How Is the Weather?

A weather report showed that when it rained in the afternoon, it was fair in the morning. When it rained in the morning, it was fair in the afternoon. It rained on 7 days. It was fair on 5 afternoons and on 6 mornings. On how many days was the report based?

What is the area of a plot of land $\frac{2}{3}$ mile by $\frac{4}{5}$ mile?

The diagram shows a square mile separated into 15 equal parts. The $\frac{2}{3}$-mile by $\frac{4}{5}$-mile plot includes 8 of these parts. So the area of the plot is $\frac{8}{15}$ square mile.

An easy way to find the area is to multiply the width by the length.

$$\frac{2}{3} \times \frac{4}{5} =$$

Multiply numerators.

$$\frac{2}{3} \times \frac{4}{5} = \frac{2 \times 4}{} = \frac{8}{}$$

Multiply denominators.

$$\frac{2}{3} \times \frac{4}{5} = \frac{2 \times 4}{3 \times 5} = \frac{8}{15}$$

The area is $\frac{8}{15}$ square mile.

For any two fractions,

$$\frac{a}{b} \times \frac{c}{d} = \frac{ac}{bd}.$$

Example 1: Multiply $\frac{4}{9}$ by $\frac{2}{5}$.

$$\frac{4}{9} \times \frac{2}{5} = \frac{8}{45}$$

Example 2: Multiply $\frac{1}{3}$ by 2.

$$\frac{1}{3} \times \frac{2}{1} = \frac{2}{3} \qquad \text{Express each whole number as a fraction.}$$

$\frac{4}{5}$ mi

$\frac{2}{3}$ mi

I square mile

Exercises

A Multiply.

1. $\frac{1}{2} \times \frac{1}{5}$ 2. $\frac{5}{12} \times \frac{1}{2}$ 3. $\frac{1}{2} \times \frac{7}{8}$

4. $3 \times \frac{1}{4}$ 5. $\frac{1}{10} \times \frac{1}{3}$ 6. $\frac{1}{12} \times \frac{1}{3}$

7. $\frac{3}{5} \times \frac{2}{5}$ 8. $\frac{1}{3} \times \frac{1}{4}$ 9. $\frac{1}{3} \times \frac{1}{9}$

B Multiply.

10. $\frac{2}{7} \times \frac{2}{5}$ 11. $\frac{1}{4} \times \frac{7}{9}$ 12. $\frac{1}{6} \times \frac{7}{10}$

13. $\frac{1}{3} \times \frac{5}{8}$ 14. $\frac{3}{8} \times \frac{3}{4}$ 15. $\frac{3}{5} \times \frac{1}{8}$

16. $\frac{1}{7} \times \frac{3}{8}$ 17. $\frac{1}{2} \times \frac{11}{12}$ 18. $\frac{4}{5} \times \frac{1}{3}$

19. $\frac{1}{6} \times 5$ 20. $3 \times \frac{2}{7}$ 21. $\frac{9}{10} \times \frac{3}{4}$

22. $\frac{1}{5} \times \frac{2}{9}$ 23. $\frac{1}{4} \times \frac{3}{5}$ 24. $\frac{3}{10} \times 3$

25. Find $\frac{1}{2}$ of each ingredient in Eric's favorite recipe.

> *Sweet Surprise*
>
> 1 cup brown sugar
> $\frac{3}{4}$ cup sugar
> $\frac{1}{3}$ cup heavy cream
> $\frac{1}{2}$ teaspoon vanilla
> $\frac{1}{8}$ teaspoon salt
> $\frac{1}{4}$ stick bubble gum

C Find the area of each plot of land. Dimensions are given in miles.

26.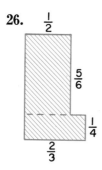

27.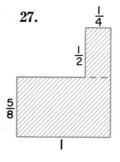

28.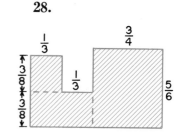

"$\frac{3}{6}$ of the doctors questioned preferred Hope Mouthwash." It would also be correct to say that $\frac{1}{2}$ of the doctors preferred Hope Mouthwash.

$$\frac{3}{6} = \frac{3 \div 3}{6 \div 3} = \frac{1}{2}$$

Since $\frac{3}{6}$ can be simplified to $\frac{1}{2}$, $\frac{3}{6}$ and $\frac{1}{2}$ are equivalent.

$\frac{1}{2}$ is a fraction *in lowest terms*.

> A fraction is **in lowest terms** if its numerator and denominator have no common whole-number factor other than 1.

Example 1: Express $\frac{8}{12}$ in lowest terms.

Step 1: Find the GCF of the numerator and denominator.

$$8 = 2 \times 2 \times 2$$
$$12 = 2 \times 2 \times 3$$
$$2 \times 2 = 4,$$
so 4 is the GCF.

Step 2: Divide the numerator and denominator by the GCF.

$$\frac{8}{12} = \frac{8 \div 4}{12 \div 4} = \frac{2}{3}$$

Example 2: Express $\frac{10}{25}$ in lowest terms.

The GCF of 10 and 25 is 5.

Long way

$$\frac{10}{25} = \frac{10 \div 5}{25 \div 5} = \frac{2}{5}$$

Short way

$$\frac{\overset{2}{\cancel{10}}}{\underset{5}{\cancel{25}}} = \frac{2}{5}$$

Example 3: Multiply. Express the answer in lowest terms.

You can simplify before you multiply.

$$\frac{5}{3} \times \frac{3}{10} = \frac{\overset{1}{\cancel{15}}}{\underset{2}{\cancel{30}}} = \frac{1}{2} \qquad \frac{\overset{1}{\cancel{5}}}{\underset{1}{\cancel{3}}} \times \frac{\overset{1}{\cancel{3}}}{\underset{2}{\cancel{10}}} = \frac{1}{2}$$

The GCF is 15.

Exercises

A Express each fraction in lowest terms. The GCF of the numerator and denominator is given in color for each fraction.

1. $\frac{3}{12}$ 3 　　　　2. $\frac{4}{8}$ 4 　　　　3. $\frac{10}{15}$ 5 　　　　4. $\frac{6}{10}$ 2

5. $\frac{7}{21}$ 7 　　　　6. $\frac{6}{9}$ 3 　　　　7. $\frac{4}{6}$ 2 　　　　8. $\frac{4}{16}$ 4

9. $\frac{5}{20}$ 5 　　　10. $\frac{2}{8}$ 2 　　　11. $\frac{6}{12}$ 6 　　　12. $\frac{4}{12}$ 4

B Express each fraction in lowest terms.

13. $\frac{9}{12}$ 　　　14. $\frac{15}{20}$ 　　　15. $\frac{6}{8}$ 　　　16. $\frac{8}{10}$ 　　　17. $\frac{7}{35}$

18. $\frac{12}{20}$ 　　　19. $\frac{2}{16}$ 　　　20. $\frac{6}{16}$ 　　　21. $\frac{5}{15}$ 　　　22. $\frac{12}{18}$

Multiply. Express each answer in lowest terms.

23. $\frac{4}{3} \times \frac{1}{2}$ 　　　24. $2 \times \frac{1}{8}$ 　　　25. $\frac{4}{3} \times \frac{3}{8}$ 　　　26. $\frac{1}{3} \times \frac{3}{5}$

27. $\frac{5}{4} \times \frac{2}{3}$ 　　　28. $\frac{5}{6} \times \frac{2}{5}$ 　　　29. $\frac{3}{2} \times \frac{4}{7}$ 　　　30. $\frac{3}{2} \times \frac{2}{9}$

31. $3 \times \frac{4}{15}$ 　　　32. $\frac{4}{5} \times \frac{5}{12}$ 　　　33. $\frac{1}{6} \times \frac{3}{4}$ 　　　34. $\frac{8}{9} \times \frac{1}{4}$

35. Gene travels a total of $\frac{4}{5}$ mile in a round trip from his home to school and back. How far is a one-way trip ($\frac{1}{2}$ of the trip)?

36. A recipe calls for $\frac{2}{3}$ cup milk. How much milk do you need for $\frac{1}{2}$ the recipe?

C The formula for finding the perimeter p of a square with side s is $p = 4s$. Find the perimeter of each of the following squares.

37. $s = \frac{3}{16}$ in 　　　38. $s = \frac{1}{12}$ ft 　　　39. $s = \frac{1}{8}$ in

The length of the bolt can be given as either $\frac{9}{4}$ or $2\frac{1}{4}$ inches.

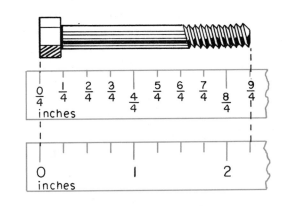

$$2\frac{1}{4} = 2 + \frac{1}{4}$$

$$= (2 \times 1) + \frac{1}{4}$$

$$= \left(\frac{2}{1} \times \frac{4}{4}\right) + \frac{1}{4}$$

$$= \frac{8}{4} + \frac{1}{4}$$

$$= \frac{9}{4}$$

Equivalent expressions

$$2\frac{1}{4} = \frac{9}{4}$$

mixed numeral   fraction

Example 1: Express $5\frac{3}{8}$ as a fraction.

Long way

$$5\frac{3}{8} = \left(\frac{5}{1} \times \frac{8}{8}\right) + \frac{3}{8}$$

$$= \frac{40}{8} + \frac{3}{8}$$

$$= \frac{43}{8}$$

$8 \times 5 = 40$

Short way

$$5\frac{3}{8} = \frac{40 + 3}{8} = \frac{43}{8}$$

Since a fraction indicates a quotient, you can divide the numerator by the denominator to find the equivalent mixed numeral.

Example 2: Express $\frac{32}{5}$ as a mixed numeral.

$$\frac{32}{5} = 32 \div 5 \longrightarrow \quad 5\overline{)\begin{array}{c} 6\frac{2}{5} \\ 32 \\ 30 \\ \hline 2 \end{array}} \qquad \frac{32}{5} = 6\frac{2}{5}$$

Example 3: Multiply $\frac{9}{4}$ by $\frac{2}{3}$. Express the answer as a mixed numeral in lowest terms (fraction in lowest terms and less than 1).

$$\overset{3}{\underset{2}{\cancel{9}}} \times \overset{1}{\underset{1}{\cancel{2}}} = \frac{3}{2} = 1\frac{1}{2}$$

Let's agree that "express the answer in lowest terms" also means "change fractions to mixed numerals whenever possible."

Exercises

A Express each of the following as a fraction.

1. $1\frac{1}{5}$ **2.** 4   **3.** $2\frac{1}{3}$ **4.** $1\frac{1}{4}$ **5.** $2\frac{1}{2}$

Express each fraction as a mixed numeral.

6. $\frac{5}{2}$ **7.** $\frac{7}{6}$ **8.** $\frac{5}{3}$ **9.** $\frac{5}{4}$ **10.** $\frac{7}{5}$

B Express each mixed numeral as a fraction.

11. $3\frac{7}{10}$ **12.** $5\frac{4}{5}$ **13.** $7\frac{1}{2}$ **14.** $4\frac{2}{3}$ **15.** $8\frac{3}{4}$

Express each fraction as a mixed numeral.

16. $\frac{11}{3}$ **17.** $\frac{16}{5}$ **18.** $\frac{28}{3}$ **19.** $\frac{31}{4}$ **20.** $\frac{43}{8}$

Multiply. Express each answer in lowest terms.

21. $\frac{1}{2} \times \frac{12}{5}$ **22.** $\frac{4}{3} \times \frac{6}{5}$ **23.** $10 \times \frac{1}{3}$

24. $\frac{5}{7} \times \frac{7}{2}$ **25.** $\frac{3}{5} \times \frac{15}{8}$ **26.** $\frac{8}{9} \times 6$

27. $5 \times \frac{7}{10}$ **28.** $\frac{5}{3} \times \frac{11}{10}$ **29.** $\frac{25}{12} \times \frac{3}{5}$

30. The table shows the average amount of certain foods that an American eats in one day. Find the amounts per week. Express each answer in lowest terms.

	Daily per capita consumption	Weekly per capita consumption
Flour	$\frac{1}{3}$ pound	
Meat	$\frac{1}{2}$ pound	
Milk	$\frac{7}{10}$ pint	
Sugar	$\frac{2}{7}$ pound	

31. On the average, each American disposes of $\frac{7}{2}$ pounds of trash a day. How much is this per week? Per year (365 days)? Express each answer in lowest terms.

[C] Multiply. Express each answer in lowest terms.

Example : $\dfrac{1}{2} \times 4 \times \dfrac{2}{3} = \dfrac{1}{\cancel{2}} \times \dfrac{4}{1} \times \dfrac{\cancel{2}}{3} = \dfrac{4}{3} = 1\dfrac{1}{3}$

32. $\frac{3}{8} \times 3 \times \frac{2}{3}$ **33.** $12 \times \frac{3}{4} \times \frac{1}{6}$ **34.** $\frac{4}{3} \times \frac{5}{4} \times \frac{2}{3}$

35. $\frac{1}{2} \times \frac{3}{4} \times \frac{5}{6}$ **36.** $\frac{3}{4} \times \frac{3}{2} \times \frac{4}{5}$ **37.** $10 \times \frac{3}{5} \times \frac{1}{4}$

Carpenter's Puzzle

A carpenter has 7 boards. Four boards are 4 feet by 1 foot. Three boards are 3 feet by 1 foot. How can these boards be fitted, without cutting, to make a perfect square?

6.5 ◆ MORE MULTIPLICATION

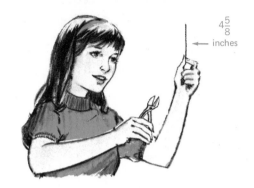

$4\frac{5}{8}$ inches

Terry wants one-half of the wire. Where should she cut?

Example 1: Find $\frac{1}{2}$ of $4\frac{5}{8}$ inches.

    Step 1: Express the mixed numeral as a fraction.

$$4\frac{5}{8} = \frac{32 + 5}{8} = \frac{37}{8}$$

    Step 2: Multiply. $\frac{1}{2} \times \frac{37}{8} = \frac{37}{16}$

    Step 3: Express the answer in lowest terms.

$$
\begin{array}{r}
2\frac{5}{16} \\
16\overline{)37} \\
32 \\
\hline
5
\end{array}
\qquad
\frac{37}{16} = 2\frac{5}{16}
$$

$\frac{1}{2}$ of $4\frac{5}{8}$ inches is $2\frac{5}{16}$ inches.

Example 2: Multiply $2\frac{5}{6}$ by 3.

$$2\frac{5}{6} \times 3 = \frac{17}{\underset{2}{6}} \times \frac{\overset{1}{3}}{1}$$

$$= \frac{17}{2} \text{ or } 8\frac{1}{2}$$

Example 3: Multiply $3\frac{1}{3} \times 1\frac{1}{2}$.

$$3\frac{1}{3} \times 1\frac{1}{2} = \frac{\overset{5}{\cancel{10}}}{\cancel{3}_{1}} \times \frac{\cancel{3}^{1}}{\cancel{2}_{1}}$$

$$= \frac{5}{1} \text{ or } 5$$

Exercises

[A] What fraction would you use in place of each mixed numeral?

1. $3 \times 4\frac{1}{2}$ 2. $1\frac{1}{2} \times 1\frac{1}{3}$ 3. $\frac{3}{5} \times 4\frac{1}{6}$

4. $2\frac{1}{3} \times 2\frac{1}{4}$ 5. $3\frac{1}{3} \times \frac{1}{5}$ 6. $2\frac{2}{9} \times 1\frac{1}{10}$

7. $8 \times 1\frac{1}{8}$ 8. $5\frac{1}{4} \times 5\frac{1}{7}$ 9. $1\frac{3}{7} \times 2\frac{4}{5}$

[B] Multiply. Express each answer in lowest terms.

10. $3 \times \frac{1}{3}$ 11. $\frac{2}{5} \times 4$ 12. $2\frac{1}{2} \times \frac{2}{3}$

13. $6 \times 2\frac{2}{9}$ 14. $1\frac{1}{2} \times \frac{1}{2}$ 15. $\frac{4}{5} \times 6\frac{1}{4}$

16. $3\frac{3}{4} \times 2$ 17. $\frac{2}{3} \times 5\frac{5}{8}$ 18. $2\frac{1}{2} \times 3\frac{1}{5}$

19. $\frac{3}{7} \times 4\frac{2}{3}$ 20. $1\frac{1}{4} \times 1\frac{1}{4}$ 21. $5 \times 2\frac{1}{10}$

22. $3\frac{1}{2} \times 2\frac{2}{3}$ 23. $2\frac{5}{8} \times 10\frac{2}{3}$ 24. $1\frac{2}{3} \times 2\frac{2}{5}$

25. $3\frac{3}{5} \times 3\frac{3}{4}$ 26. $8\frac{1}{4} \times 7\frac{1}{3}$ 27. $\frac{3}{4} \times 5\frac{1}{3}$

28. $5\frac{1}{3} \times 3\frac{3}{8}$ 29. $7\frac{1}{5} \times 4\frac{4}{9}$ 30. $4 \times 3\frac{1}{5}$

31. Sue needs $\frac{3}{4}$ yard of material to make a tie. She wants to make a tie for each of her 3 boyfriends. How much material should she buy?

32. There are 8 ounces in a cup. How many ounces are there in $\frac{1}{4}$ cup? In $\frac{2}{3}$ cup?

C The formula for finding the area of a circle is $A = \pi r^2$, where r stands for the radius and π is approximately equal to $\frac{22}{7}$.

Example:

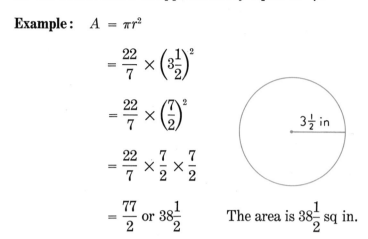

$$A = \pi r^2$$

$$= \frac{22}{7} \times \left(3\frac{1}{2}\right)^2$$

$$= \frac{22}{7} \times \left(\frac{7}{2}\right)^2$$

$$= \frac{22}{7} \times \frac{7}{2} \times \frac{7}{2}$$

$$= \frac{77}{2} \text{ or } 38\frac{1}{2}$$

The area is $38\frac{1}{2}$ sq in.

Find the area of each circle. Use $\frac{22}{7}$ for π.

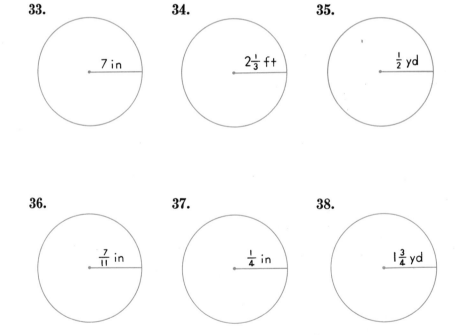

33. 7 in

34. $2\frac{1}{3}$ ft

35. $\frac{1}{2}$ yd

36. $\frac{7}{11}$ in

37. $\frac{1}{4}$ in

38. $1\frac{3}{4}$ yd

39. Which is more pizza—three 7-inch pizzas or one 14-inch pizza?

Divide $\frac{3}{4}$ yard of rope into $\frac{3}{8}$-yard pieces. How many pieces do you get? The diagram shows that $\frac{3}{4} \div \frac{3}{8} = 2$.

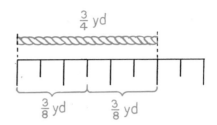

To find quotients, you can invert the divisor and multiply.

Example 1: Divide $\frac{3}{4}$ by $\frac{3}{8}$.

$$\frac{3}{4} \div \frac{3}{8} = \frac{3}{4} \times \frac{8}{3} \qquad \text{Invert and multiply.}$$

$$= \frac{\cancel{3}}{4} \times \frac{\overset{2}{\cancel{8}}}{\cancel{3}}$$

$$= \frac{2}{1} \text{ or } 2 \qquad \text{Notice that this is the same answer you got from the diagram.}$$

For any two fractions where c is not 0,

$$\frac{a}{b} \div \frac{c}{d} = \frac{a}{b} \times \frac{d}{c}.$$

Example 2: Divide $1\frac{1}{2}$ by 5.

$$1\frac{1}{2} \div 5 = \frac{3}{2} \div \frac{5}{1}$$

$$= \frac{3}{2} \times \frac{1}{5}$$

$$= \frac{3}{10}$$

Example 3: Divide $5\frac{1}{2}$ by $\frac{3}{4}$.

$$5\frac{1}{2} \div \frac{3}{4} = \frac{11}{2} \div \frac{3}{4}$$

$$= \frac{11}{\underset{1}{2}} \times \frac{\overset{2}{4}}{3}$$

$$= \frac{22}{3} \text{ or } 7\frac{1}{3}$$

Exercises

A Divide.

1. $\frac{1}{5} \div \frac{1}{2}$ 2. $\frac{1}{3} \div 3$ 3. $3 \div \frac{1}{3}$

4. $\frac{3}{2} \div \frac{1}{2}$ 5. $\frac{1}{6} \div 2$ 6. $\frac{1}{3} \div \frac{1}{4}$

B Divide. Express each quotient in lowest terms.

7. $\frac{2}{3} \div \frac{5}{6}$ 8. $5 \div 1\frac{2}{3}$ 9. $3\frac{1}{3} \div 2\frac{1}{2}$

10. $\frac{3}{4} \div 3$ 11. $1\frac{1}{5} \div 3$ 12. $3\frac{3}{4} \div \frac{5}{12}$

13. $3\frac{1}{2} \div 4\frac{1}{5}$ 14. $\frac{4}{5} \div \frac{2}{3}$ 15. $\frac{7}{10} \div 2\frac{4}{5}$

16. $4\frac{1}{2} \div 2\frac{2}{3}$ 17. $4\frac{1}{3} \div \frac{1}{9}$ 18. $2\frac{5}{8} \div 7$

19. $6 \div \frac{3}{5}$ 20. $5\frac{1}{3} \div 1\frac{3}{5}$ 21. $1\frac{1}{4} \div 1\frac{7}{8}$

22. $\frac{5}{8} \div 2\frac{1}{12}$ 23. $10 \div 4\frac{1}{6}$ 24. $2\frac{2}{9} \div \frac{5}{6}$

25. TNT stock has risen a total of $8\frac{3}{4}$ points in 5 days. What is the average daily rise for this stock?

26. Mr. Lauraitis has to find the number of panels he needs for a wall. Each panel is $1\frac{1}{3}$ feet wide. How many panels does he need for a 20-foot wall?

27. During a business trip, Mr. Levin traveled 125 miles in $2\frac{1}{2}$ hours. What was his average speed?

28. Each character typed by a pica typewriter takes $\frac{1}{10}$ inch. A character typed by an elite typewriter takes $\frac{1}{12}$ inch. How many characters are in a $7\frac{1}{2}$-inch line of pica type? Of elite type?

C Solve for *x*.

29. $\frac{1}{2} \div \frac{3}{4} \times \frac{3}{5} = x$

30. $\frac{1}{6} \times 5 \div 3\frac{1}{3} = x$

31. $2 \times 1\frac{1}{2} \div 2\frac{1}{4} = x$

32. $1\frac{3}{5} \times \frac{3}{8} \div 3 = x$

33. $4\frac{1}{2} \div 3 \div 1\frac{1}{2} = x$

34. $3\frac{3}{4} \times 2\frac{2}{3} \div 4 = x$

35. $\frac{5}{12} \div \frac{2}{3} \times 3 = x$

36. $5\frac{2}{5} \div 1\frac{4}{5} \div \frac{1}{2} = x$

The Weight of a Brick

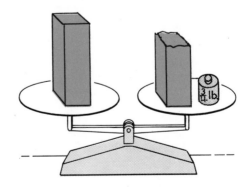

One brick weighs as much as $\frac{3}{4}$ brick and $\frac{3}{4}$ pound. How much does one brick weigh?

6.7 ◆ ADDITION AND SUBTRACTION

How much greater was Monday's gain than Tuesday's?

Stock Market Report	
Monday	Kemptronix up $\frac{7}{8}$
Tuesday	Kemptronix up $\frac{3}{8}$

Example 1: Subtract $\frac{3}{8}$ from $\frac{7}{8}$.

$$\frac{7}{8}$$
$$-\frac{3}{8}$$

Subtract numerators.
Then simplify.
$$\frac{4}{8}_2 = \frac{1}{2}$$

Monday's gain was $\frac{1}{2}$ point greater than Tuesday's.

For any two fractions with the same denominator,

$$\frac{a}{c} - \frac{b}{c} = \frac{a-b}{c}.$$

Example 2: The price before trading Monday was $17\frac{3}{4}$. What was the price of Kemptronix after Monday's trading?

$$17\frac{6}{8}$$
$$+\frac{7}{8}$$

Add numerators.
Then simplify.
$$17\frac{13}{8} = 17 + 1\frac{5}{8} = 18\frac{5}{8}$$

Use $\frac{6}{8}$ instead of $\frac{3}{4}$ because $\frac{6}{8}$ and $\frac{7}{8}$ have the same (*common*) denominator. We need common denominators to add.

Add.

Think: $\frac{13}{8} = 1\frac{5}{8}$

The price at the end of Monday's trading was $18\frac{5}{8}$.

Example 3: Add $4\frac{3}{4}$ and $3\frac{3}{4}$.

$$4\frac{3}{4}$$
$$+\ 3\frac{3}{4}$$
$$\overline{\ 7\frac{6}{4}} = 7 + 1\frac{1}{2} = 8\frac{1}{2}$$

Think: $\dfrac{\overset{3}{\cancel{6}}}{\underset{2}{\cancel{4}}} = 1\frac{1}{2}$

Example 4: The price before trading Thursday was $18\frac{3}{8}$. The price after trading was $11\frac{5}{8}$. How many points did the stock lose?

Think: $18\frac{3}{8} = 17 + \frac{8}{8} + \frac{3}{8} = 17\frac{11}{8}$

You cannot subtract numerators, so rename $18\frac{3}{8}$ as $17\frac{11}{8}$.

$$18\frac{3}{8} \longrightarrow 17\frac{11}{8}$$
$$-\ 11\frac{5}{8} \longrightarrow -\ 11\frac{5}{8}$$

Subtract numerators. Then simplify.

$$\overline{\ 6\frac{\overset{3}{\cancel{6}}}{\underset{4}{\cancel{8}}} = 6\frac{3}{4}}$$

The stock lost $6\frac{3}{4}$ points in Thursday's trading.

Exercises

A Express each mixed numeral in lowest terms.

1. $1\frac{5}{4} = 2\frac{|||}{4}$ **2.** $3\frac{11}{7} = 4\frac{|||}{7}$ **3.** $2\frac{7}{6} = 3\frac{||||}{6}$

Complete each renaming.

4. $2\frac{1}{5} = 1\frac{\text{\lVert\lVert}}{5}$
5. $4\frac{1}{6} = 3\frac{\text{\lVert\lVert}}{6}$
6. $1\frac{1}{3} = \frac{\text{\lVert\lVert}}{3}$

B Find each sum or difference. Express each answer in lowest terms.

7. $\begin{array}{r} \frac{3}{4} \\ + \frac{1}{4} \\ \hline \end{array}$
8. $\begin{array}{r} \frac{2}{3} \\ - \frac{1}{3} \\ \hline \end{array}$
9. $\begin{array}{r} \frac{7}{8} \\ - \frac{3}{8} \\ \hline \end{array}$
10. $\begin{array}{r} 1\frac{5}{6} \\ - \frac{1}{6} \\ \hline \end{array}$
11. $\begin{array}{r} 2\frac{1}{3} \\ + \frac{1}{3} \\ \hline \end{array}$

12. $\begin{array}{r} 1\frac{1}{8} \\ + \frac{7}{8} \\ \hline \end{array}$
13. $\begin{array}{r} 1\frac{1}{3} \\ - \frac{2}{3} \\ \hline \end{array}$
14. $\begin{array}{r} 2\frac{5}{12} \\ + 5\frac{5}{12} \\ \hline \end{array}$
15. $\begin{array}{r} 2\frac{2}{3} \\ + 1\frac{2}{3} \\ \hline \end{array}$

16. $\begin{array}{r} 10\frac{5}{8} \\ - 3\frac{3}{8} \\ \hline \end{array}$
17. $\begin{array}{r} 2\frac{1}{4} \\ - \frac{3}{4} \\ \hline \end{array}$
18. $\begin{array}{r} 4\frac{4}{5} \\ + 1\frac{3}{5} \\ \hline \end{array}$
19. $\begin{array}{r} 1\frac{9}{10} \\ - 1\frac{3}{10} \\ \hline \end{array}$

20. $\begin{array}{r} 3\frac{2}{5} \\ - 2\frac{3}{5} \\ \hline \end{array}$
21. $\begin{array}{r} 2\frac{5}{6} \\ + 1\frac{5}{6} \\ \hline \end{array}$
22. $\begin{array}{r} 4\frac{1}{6} \\ - 1\frac{5}{6} \\ \hline \end{array}$
23. $\begin{array}{r} 5\frac{1}{8} \\ - 2\frac{7}{8} \\ \hline \end{array}$

24. To find the plastic pipe you need, add the distance between the sockets to twice the socket depth.

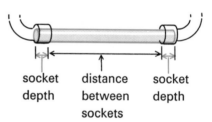

socket depth   distance between sockets   socket depth

Complete this table.

Socket depth (d) in inches	$2d$ in inches	Distance (s) between sockets in inches	Total length in inches ($2d + s$)
$\frac{3}{4}$	$2 \times \frac{3}{4} = \frac{3}{2} = 1\frac{1}{2}$	$15\frac{1}{2}$	17
$\frac{7}{8}$		$6\frac{1}{4}$	
$1\frac{1}{2}$		$10\frac{5}{16}$	
$\frac{7}{8}$		$24\frac{3}{4}$	

Example :   To subtract from 1, rename 1 as $\frac{n}{n}$.

$$1 - \frac{3}{5} = \frac{5}{5} - \frac{3}{5} = \frac{2}{5}$$

Subtract.

25. $1 - \frac{1}{4}$ **26.** $1 - \frac{5}{6}$ **27.** $1 - \frac{7}{12}$

28. English is spoken by about $\frac{1}{12}$ of the world's population. What part of the population does not speak English?

29. About $\frac{1}{18}$ of the world's population lives in the United States. What part of the world's population does not?

30. About $\frac{5}{7}$ of the earth's surface is covered with water. How much is land?

31. About $\frac{1}{10}$ of the earth's land surface is permanently covered with ice. How much is not covered with ice?

32. About $\frac{1}{16}$ of the earth's land surface is in the United States. How much is not?

C Use *cross products* to solve each equation.

Example :   Solve for x.

$$\frac{x}{21} = \frac{4}{6}$$

$$x \times 6 = 21 \times 4$$

$$x = \frac{\overset{7}{21} \times \overset{2}{4}}{\underset{1}{6_2}}$$

$$x = 14$$

$$\frac{14}{21} = \frac{4}{6}$$

33. $\frac{35}{x} = \frac{5}{6}$ **34.** $\frac{x}{33} = \frac{6}{18}$ **35.** $\frac{13}{x} = \frac{7}{14}$

36. $\frac{x}{20} = \frac{36}{45}$ **37.** $\frac{25}{x} = \frac{15}{24}$ **38.** $\frac{x}{16} = \frac{21}{28}$

6.8 ◈ LEAST COMMON DENOMINATOR

North America is responsible for about $\frac{3}{8}$ of the world's motor-vehicle production. Europe produces about $\frac{5}{12}$. What is the combined production?

Example 1:   Add $\frac{3}{8}$ and $\frac{5}{12}$.

Step 1:   Find the least common denominator by finding the LCM of the denominators.

$$8 = 2 \times 2 \times 2$$
$$12 = 2 \times 2 \qquad \times 3$$

$2 \times 2 \times 2 \times 3 = 24$, so 24 is the LCM.

Step 2:   Express each addend as an equivalent fraction with the least common denominator.

$$\frac{3}{8} = \frac{\text{IIII}}{24} \qquad\qquad \frac{5}{12} = \frac{\text{IIII}}{24}$$

$$\frac{3}{8} = \frac{3 \times 3}{24} \text{ or } \frac{9}{24} \qquad \frac{5}{12} = \frac{5 \times 2}{24} \text{ or } \frac{10}{24}$$

$$24 \div 8 = 3 \qquad\qquad 24 \div 12 = 2$$

Step 3:   Add.

$$
\begin{array}{ccc}
\frac{3}{8} & \rightarrow & \frac{9}{24} \\[4pt]
+\ \frac{5}{12} & \rightarrow & +\ \frac{10}{24} \\[4pt]
\hline
 & & \frac{19}{24}
\end{array}
$$

The combined production is $\frac{19}{24}$.

Example 2: Add $\frac{2}{5}$ and $\frac{3}{10}$.

Since 10 is a multiple of 5,
10 is the least common denominator.

$$\frac{2}{5} \longrightarrow \frac{2}{5} \times \frac{2}{2} \longrightarrow \frac{4}{10}$$

$$+\frac{3}{10} \xrightarrow{\hspace{3cm}} +\frac{3}{10}$$

$$\frac{7}{10}$$

Example 3: How far is it between exits?
Subtract $\frac{1}{4}$ from $\frac{2}{3}$.

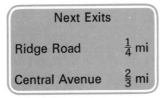

Next Exits

Ridge Road $\frac{1}{4}$ mi

Central Avenue $\frac{2}{3}$ mi

Since 3 and 4 have no common factors (except 1), 3×4, or 12, is the least common denominator.

$$\frac{2}{3} \longrightarrow \frac{2}{3} \times \frac{4}{4} \longrightarrow \frac{8}{12}$$

$$-\frac{1}{4} \longrightarrow \frac{1}{4} \times \frac{3}{3} \longrightarrow -\frac{3}{12}$$

$$\frac{5}{12}$$

The distance between the exits is $\frac{5}{12}$ mile.

Exercises

A Complete each pair of equivalent fractions.

1. $\frac{1}{4} = \frac{||||}{16}$

2. $\frac{1}{5} = \frac{||||}{15}$

3. $\frac{1}{2} = \frac{||||}{10}$

4. $\frac{1}{3} = \frac{||||}{12}$

5. $\frac{3}{4} = \frac{||||}{8}$

6. $\frac{2}{3} = \frac{||||}{6}$

For each pair of fractions, find equivalent fractions with the least common denominator.

7. $\frac{3}{8}, \frac{1}{16}$

8. $\frac{1}{10}, \frac{2}{15}$

9. $\frac{1}{5}, \frac{5}{6}$

10. $\frac{1}{6}, \frac{2}{9}$

11. $\frac{2}{3}, \frac{1}{8}$

12. $\frac{5}{24}, \frac{5}{12}$

Find each sum or difference. Express your answers in lowest terms.

13. $\begin{array}{r} \frac{1}{2} \\ +\frac{1}{4} \\ \hline \end{array}$

14. $\begin{array}{r} \frac{2}{3} \\ -\frac{1}{6} \\ \hline \end{array}$

15. $\begin{array}{r} \frac{3}{8} \\ -\frac{1}{4} \\ \hline \end{array}$

16. $\begin{array}{r} \frac{1}{6} \\ +\frac{1}{2} \\ \hline \end{array}$

17. $\begin{array}{r} \frac{1}{2} \\ -\frac{1}{3} \\ \hline \end{array}$

18. $\begin{array}{r} \frac{5}{6} \\ -\frac{3}{8} \\ \hline \end{array}$

19. $\begin{array}{r} \frac{1}{4} \\ +\frac{2}{3} \\ \hline \end{array}$

20. $\begin{array}{r} \frac{7}{8} \\ -\frac{1}{12} \\ \hline \end{array}$

21. $\begin{array}{r} \frac{1}{3} \\ +\frac{5}{8} \\ \hline \end{array}$

22. $\begin{array}{r} \frac{1}{2} \\ -\frac{2}{5} \\ \hline \end{array}$

23. $\begin{array}{r} \frac{3}{4} \\ -\frac{5}{12} \\ \hline \end{array}$

24. $\begin{array}{r} \frac{1}{6} \\ +\frac{4}{15} \\ \hline \end{array}$

25. The U.S.S.R. produces about $\frac{3}{20}$ of the world's crude oil. The Middle East produces about $\frac{2}{5}$ of the world's total. What is their combined production?

26. The Ford Motor Company makes about $\frac{1}{4}$ of the cars produced in the United States. General Motors makes about $\frac{9}{16}$. What is their combined production?

To arrange fractions in order, express the fractions as equivalent fractions with a common denominator. Then compare numerators.

Example: Which is the heaviest—$\frac{3}{4}$ oz, $\frac{2}{3}$ oz, or $\frac{5}{6}$ oz? The lightest?

12 is the LCM of 4, 3, and 6.

$$\frac{3}{4} = \frac{9}{12} \qquad \frac{2}{3} = \frac{8}{12} \qquad \frac{5}{6} = \frac{10}{12}$$

The order from least to greatest is $\frac{8}{12}, \frac{9}{12}, \frac{10}{12}$ or $\frac{2}{3}, \frac{3}{4}, \frac{5}{6}$.

The heaviest is $\frac{5}{6}$ oz and the lightest is $\frac{2}{3}$ oz.

Order each of the following sets from least to greatest.

27. $\frac{1}{2}, \frac{2}{5}, \frac{3}{10}$

28. $\frac{3}{8}, \frac{1}{4}, \frac{5}{16}$

29. $\frac{1}{6}, \frac{1}{2}, \frac{2}{3}$

30. $\frac{1}{4}, \frac{1}{5}, \frac{3}{10}$

31. $\frac{1}{4}, \frac{1}{2}, \frac{1}{3}$

32. $\frac{5}{9}, \frac{2}{3}, \frac{1}{2}$

A pattern calls for $2\frac{7}{8}$ yards for a jacket and $1\frac{1}{4}$ yards for a skirt. How much material does Nancy need to make a matching jacket and skirt?

Example 1: Add $2\frac{7}{8}$ and $1\frac{1}{4}$.

The LCM of 8 and 4 is 8.

$$2\frac{7}{8} \longrightarrow 2\frac{7}{8}$$

$$+\,1\frac{1}{4} \longrightarrow +\,1\frac{2}{8}$$

$$3\frac{9}{8} = 3 + 1\frac{1}{8} = 4\frac{1}{8} \qquad \text{Nancy needs } 4\tfrac{1}{8} \text{ yards.}$$

Example 2: Subtract $2\frac{5}{6}$ from $5\frac{1}{4}$.

The LCM of 4 and 6 is 12.

$$5\frac{1}{4} \longrightarrow 5\frac{3}{12} \longrightarrow 4\frac{15}{12}$$

$$-\,2\frac{5}{6} \longrightarrow 2\frac{10}{12} \longrightarrow -\,2\frac{10}{12}$$

$$2\frac{5}{12}$$

You cannot subtract the numerators, so rename $5\frac{3}{12}$ as $4\frac{15}{12}$.

Exercises

A Express each mixed numeral in lowest terms.

1. $2\frac{5}{3} = 3\frac{\|\|\|}{3}$ **2.** $4\frac{3}{2} = 5\frac{\|\|\|}{2}$ **3.** $6\frac{7}{5} = 7\frac{\|\|\|}{5}$

Complete each renaming.

4. $1\frac{1}{4} = \frac{\|\|\|}{4}$ **5.** $2\frac{1}{5} = 1\frac{\|\|\|}{5}$ **6.** $5\frac{2}{3} = 4\frac{\|\|\|}{3}$

Add or subtract. Express each answer in lowest terms.

7. $9\frac{1}{2}$
$+ 2\frac{1}{4}$

8. $8\frac{3}{5}$
$- 3\frac{1}{2}$

9. $2\frac{1}{10}$
$- 1\frac{2}{5}$

10. $\frac{7}{10}$
$+ 10\frac{1}{2}$

11. $7\frac{1}{8}$
$- 4\frac{3}{4}$

12. $12\frac{3}{8}$
$+ 3\frac{5}{12}$

13. $1\frac{1}{3}$
$- \frac{7}{12}$

14. $5\frac{1}{3}$
$+ 6\frac{5}{6}$

15. $5\frac{3}{4}$
$- 2\frac{4}{5}$

16. $14\frac{11}{12}$
$+ 8\frac{1}{4}$

17. $9\frac{2}{3}$
$+ 7\frac{9}{10}$

18. $6\frac{1}{6}$
$- 1\frac{4}{9}$

19. Kay cut $2\frac{5}{8}$ yards of material from a piece $4\frac{1}{2}$ yards long. How much material did she have left?

20. TNT stock was at $30\frac{1}{2}$ at the start of trading Friday. At the end of trading it was up $4\frac{3}{4}$ points. What was the price at the end of trading Friday?

21. How much oil should you add to $1\frac{1}{4}$ quarts to have 5 quarts?

C Add. Express each answer in lowest terms.

Example:
$$1\frac{2}{3} \rightarrow 1\frac{4}{6}$$
$$2\frac{1}{2} \rightarrow 2\frac{3}{6}$$
$$+ 1\frac{5}{6} \rightarrow + 1\frac{5}{6}$$
$$4\frac{12}{6} = 6$$

$$4\frac{12^{\,2}}{6_{\,1}} = 4 + 2 = 6$$

22. $4\frac{1}{2}$
$2\frac{1}{4}$
$+ 5\frac{1}{2}$

23. $3\frac{1}{2}$
$2\frac{2}{3}$
$+ 1\frac{1}{6}$

24. $\frac{5}{8}$
$2\frac{1}{4}$
$+ 3\frac{3}{8}$

25. $1\frac{3}{4}$
$2\frac{1}{3}$
$+ 1\frac{5}{12}$

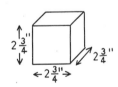

A problem might require a whole-number answer, but the result of your computation is a fraction. In such problems, the answer is usually the next greater or lesser whole number.

Example 1: Each chocolate bar weighs $2\frac{3}{4}$ ounces.
How many bars should you buy to have at least the 10 ounces needed for the recipe?

$$10 \div 2\frac{3}{4} = \frac{10}{1} \div \frac{11}{4}$$

$$= \frac{10}{1} \times \frac{4}{11}$$

$$= \frac{40}{11} \text{ or } 3\frac{7}{11}$$

RECIPE

10 oz chocolate

You can't buy $3\frac{7}{11}$ bars, and 3 bars would not be enough. So you must buy 4.

Example 2: How many small boxes will fit in one 10-inch row?

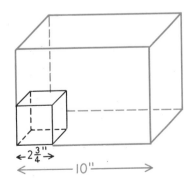

From Example 1, $10 \div 2\frac{3}{4} = 3\frac{7}{11}$.

You can't fit a box in the $\frac{7}{11}$ space. So you can fit only 3 boxes in one 10-inch row.

In the examples, the answer is not the mixed numeral that resulted from the computation.

Exercises

A The computation for each problem has a fractional result. Decide if the answer should be

   (a) the fractional result,

   (b) the next higher whole number, or

   (c) the next lower whole number.

1. Each wall panel is 4 feet wide. How many panels must you buy to panel an $18\frac{1}{2}$-foot wall?

2. A 19-inch wire is cut in half. How long is each piece?

3. How many copies of a paperback that is $\frac{5}{8}$-inch thick will fit on a 32-inch shelf?

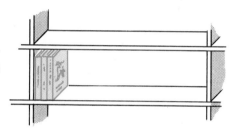

4. You're serving dinner to 11 people. How much meat should you buy, if you want to serve each person $\frac{1}{2}$ pound of meat?

5. How many $2\frac{1}{2}$-foot boards can be cut from a 12-foot board?

B Answer each question.

6. On Jane's part-time job, she works $4\frac{1}{2}$ hours a day. How many days must she work to put in at least 15 hours per week?

7. Ms. Collins is allowed to send no more than $\frac{1}{4}$ of her class to see a film. If there are 33 students in her class, what is the greatest number she can send to the film?

8. Each theater seat is $2\frac{1}{4}$ feet wide. How many seats can fit in a 15-foot row?

9. Each can holds $1\frac{1}{2}$ quarts. How many cans are needed to hold 10 quarts?

10. Sid makes $75 a week. Sid is allowed to contribute (in whole dollars) up to $\frac{1}{10}$ of his salary to a profit-sharing fund. What is the maximum amount that he can contribute per week?

11. Fruit punch comes in 3-quart ($\frac{3}{4}$-gallon) bottles. How many bottles should you buy to have enough to fill a 2-gallon punch bowl?

12. There are $2\frac{1}{4}$ cups of rice in a pound box. Chris uses $\frac{1}{2}$ cup each time he makes rice pudding. How many times can he make rice pudding from a pound box?

13. How many $3\frac{1}{8}$-inch cans will fit in one 15-inch row?

C **14.** Small boxes are arranged in layers $1\frac{1}{2}$ inches high in a carton with base dimensions of 20 by 20 inches.

The area of the base of a box is

$$1\frac{1}{2} \times 2 = \frac{3}{2} \times \frac{2}{1} \text{ or 3 sq in.}$$

The area of the base of the carton is

20×20 or 400 sq in.

A small box can be placed in the carton in either of two ways.

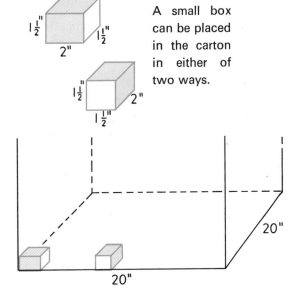

The maximum number of small boxes that fit in one layer of the carton is 133, because $400 \div 3 = 133\frac{1}{3}$.

How would you arrange the boxes to fit 133 boxes in one $1\frac{1}{2}$-inch layer?

VOCABULARY

Choose the best term.

1. 3 is the (*denominator*, *numerator*) of $\frac{3}{4}$.

2. $\frac{8}{12}$ is equivalent to ($\frac{2}{3}$, $\frac{5}{6}$, $\frac{3}{4}$).

3. ($\frac{2}{3}$, $\frac{2}{4}$, $\frac{2}{6}$) is a fraction in lowest terms.

4. 6 is equivalent to ($\frac{6}{6}$, $\frac{6}{1}$).

5. In lowest terms, $\frac{16}{6}$ is ($2\frac{1}{2}$, $2\frac{2}{3}$, $2\frac{4}{6}$).

CHAPTER REVIEW

6.1   Express as a fraction.

1. $2 \div 5$ **2.** 4 **3.** $8 \div 3$ **4.** $5 \div 2$

Add.

5. $\frac{1}{5} + \frac{1}{5}$ **6.** $\frac{2}{7} + \frac{3}{7}$ **7.** $\frac{2}{9} + \frac{5}{9}$ **8.** $\frac{3}{8} + \frac{5}{8}$

6.2   Multiply.

9. $\frac{3}{4} \times \frac{3}{4}$ **10.** $\frac{2}{3} \times \frac{4}{5}$ **11.** $\frac{5}{16} \times \frac{1}{2}$ **12.** $3 \times \frac{1}{4}$

6.3   Multiply. Express each answer in lowest terms.

13. $\frac{2}{3} \times \frac{3}{8}$ **14.** $\frac{1}{16} \times \frac{4}{5}$ **15.** $\frac{4}{3} \times \frac{3}{4}$ **16.** $3 \times \frac{1}{6}$

6.4   Express each mixed numeral as a fraction.

17. $1\frac{2}{3}$ **18.** $2\frac{1}{2}$ **19.** $1\frac{3}{5}$ **20.** $3\frac{3}{4}$

Express each fraction as a mixed numeral.

21. $\frac{10}{3}$ **22.** $\frac{9}{2}$ **23.** $\frac{7}{4}$ **24.** $\frac{11}{5}$

Multiply. Express each answer in lowest terms.

25. $\frac{4}{5} \times \frac{11}{8}$ **26.** $2 \times \frac{3}{4}$ **27.** $\frac{8}{3} \times \frac{1}{6}$

6.5   **28.** $6 \times 1\frac{1}{2}$ **29.** $1\frac{2}{3} \times \frac{3}{10}$ **30.** $2\frac{1}{2} \times 1\frac{1}{3}$

31. $2\frac{2}{5} \times 3\frac{1}{3}$ **32.** $\frac{1}{3} \times 1\frac{4}{5}$ **33.** $1\frac{1}{4} \times 4\frac{3}{5}$

Divide. Express each answer in lowest terms.   6.6

34. $\frac{5}{8} \div \frac{5}{12}$ **35.** $\frac{1}{3} \div 5$ **36.** $\frac{1}{2} \div 1\frac{1}{2}$

37. $6 \div 1\frac{1}{8}$ **38.** $1\frac{1}{2} \div 1\frac{1}{5}$ **39.** $2\frac{1}{4} \div 6$

Express each mixed numeral in lowest terms.   6.7

40. $3\frac{5}{4} = 4\frac{|||}{4}$ **41.** $2\frac{7}{5} = 3\frac{|||}{5}$ **42.** $5\frac{11}{6} = 6\frac{|||}{6}$

Complete each renaming.

43. $2\frac{2}{3} = 1\frac{|||}{3}$ **44.** $6\frac{2}{5} = 5\frac{|||}{5}$ **45.** $1\frac{1}{8} = \frac{|||}{8}$

Find each sum or difference. Express each answer in lowest terms.

46. $\begin{array}{r} 1\frac{1}{2} \\ + 2\frac{1}{2} \\ \hline \end{array}$ **47.** $\begin{array}{r} 2\frac{1}{3} \\ - 1\frac{2}{3} \\ \hline \end{array}$ **48.** $\begin{array}{r} 4\frac{2}{5} \\ + 1\frac{2}{5} \\ \hline \end{array}$ **49.** $\begin{array}{r} 5\frac{7}{8} \\ + 2\frac{5}{8} \\ \hline \end{array}$

Complete each pair of equivalent fractions.   6.8

50. $\frac{2}{3} = \frac{|||}{12}$ **51.** $\frac{3}{4} = \frac{|||}{8}$ **52.** $\frac{4}{5} = \frac{|||}{20}$

Find each sum or difference. Express your answers in lowest terms.

53. $\begin{array}{r} \frac{1}{3} \\ + \frac{1}{2} \\ \hline \end{array}$ **54.** $\begin{array}{r} \frac{3}{4} \\ - \frac{1}{6} \\ \hline \end{array}$ **55.** $\begin{array}{r} \frac{1}{4} \\ + \frac{5}{8} \\ \hline \end{array}$ **56.** $\begin{array}{r} \frac{3}{5} \\ - \frac{1}{2} \\ \hline \end{array}$

Find each sum or difference. Express your answers in lowest terms.   6.9

57. $\begin{array}{r} 2\frac{3}{5} \\ + 1\frac{3}{10} \\ \hline \end{array}$ **58.** $\begin{array}{r} 4\frac{1}{3} \\ - 3\frac{5}{6} \\ \hline \end{array}$ **59.** $\begin{array}{r} 5\frac{3}{4} \\ + 8\frac{2}{3} \\ \hline \end{array}$ **60.** $\begin{array}{r} 1\frac{1}{6} \\ - \frac{5}{8} \\ \hline \end{array}$

Answer each question.   6.10

61. Mr. Malecki's students need wire for an experiment. How many $2\frac{1}{2}$-foot pieces can he cut from a 32-foot piece?

62. Tomato juice comes in $5\frac{1}{3}$-ounce cans. How many cans should you buy if the recipe calls for 12 ounces?

63. How many $\frac{3}{4}$-dollar contributions are needed to have at least 10 dollars?

CHAPTER TEST

Express as a fraction.

1. 6

2. $4\frac{1}{2}$

3. $3 \div 2$

Express in lowest terms.

4. $\frac{5}{15}$

5. $\frac{5}{2}$

6. $\frac{10}{6}$

Compute. Express each answer in lowest terms.

7. $\frac{1}{5} \times \frac{2}{3}$

8. $\frac{2}{5} \times \frac{5}{6}$

9. $10 \times \frac{1}{4}$

10. $1\frac{1}{2} \times 1\frac{1}{3}$

11. $3 \times \frac{1}{7}$

12. $\frac{2}{3} \div \frac{1}{2}$

13. $4\frac{1}{2} \div 3$

14. $6 \div \frac{3}{8}$

15. $8\frac{1}{3} \div 3\frac{1}{3}$

Complete each pair of equivalent fractions.

16. $\frac{1}{2} = \frac{\text{\tiny||||}}{12}$

17. $\frac{2}{3} = \frac{\text{\tiny||||}}{6}$

18. $\frac{3}{4} = \frac{\text{\tiny||||}}{8}$

Express each mixed numeral in lowest terms.

19. $2\frac{4}{3} = 3\frac{\text{\tiny||||}}{3}$

20. $1\frac{7}{4} = 2\frac{\text{\tiny||||}}{4}$

21. $3\frac{11}{8} = 4\frac{\text{\tiny||||}}{8}$

Complete each renaming.

22. $2\frac{1}{4} = 1\frac{\text{\tiny||||}}{4}$

23. $6\frac{2}{5} = 5\frac{\text{\tiny||||}}{5}$

24. $5\frac{3}{10} = 4\frac{\text{\tiny||||}}{10}$

Find each sum or difference. Express each answer in lowest terms.

25. $\begin{array}{r} \frac{1}{8} \\ + \frac{3}{8} \\ \hline \end{array}$

26. $\begin{array}{r} 10\frac{1}{3} \\ - 8\frac{2}{3} \\ \hline \end{array}$

27. $\begin{array}{r} 2\frac{5}{6} \\ - 2\frac{1}{6} \\ \hline \end{array}$

28. $\begin{array}{r} 6\frac{5}{8} \\ + 5\frac{5}{8} \\ \hline \end{array}$

29. $\begin{array}{r} \frac{2}{3} \\ - \frac{1}{2} \\ \hline \end{array}$

30. $\begin{array}{r} 8\frac{1}{2} \\ - 7\frac{3}{4} \\ \hline \end{array}$

31. $\begin{array}{r} 5\frac{1}{2} \\ + 3\frac{5}{6} \\ \hline \end{array}$

32. $\begin{array}{r} \frac{1}{3} \\ + \frac{1}{4} \\ \hline \end{array}$

● Answer each question.

33. How many $2\frac{1}{4}$-inch pieces of wire can be cut from a 10-inch piece?

34. How many $1\frac{1}{2}$-quart cans must you buy to have at least 8 quarts?

Activity 1

A dot grid can help your work with fractions.

The gray lines show how to locate the point for $\frac{3}{2}$. You first go up 3 for the numerator, then right 2 for the denominator.

A line is drawn connecting the point for $\frac{3}{2}$ and the ori~~gin~~. There is no poin~~t~~ between ~~ ~~ tells you ~~ ~~ terms. E~~x~~ all the po~~i~~ equivalent

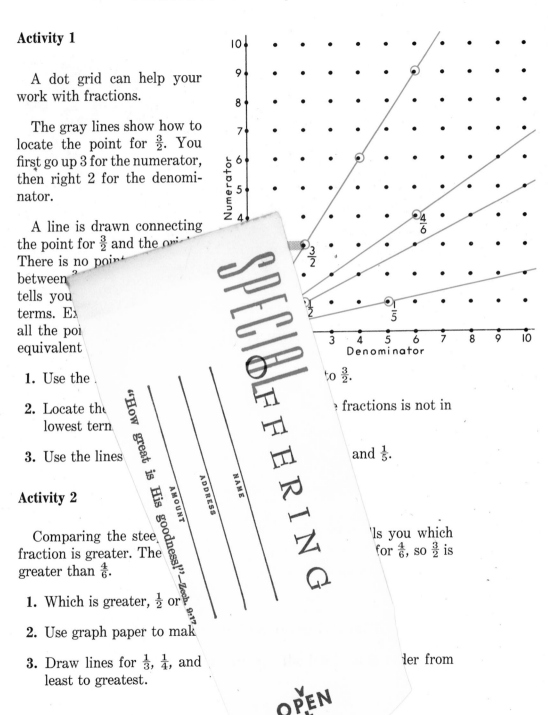

1. Use the ~~ ~~ ~~to~~ $\frac{3}{2}$.

2. Locate the ~~ ~~ fractions is not in lowest term~~s~~

3. Use the lines ~~ ~~ and $\frac{1}{5}$.

Activity 2

Comparing the stee~~p~~ ~~ ~~ ~~tel~~ls you which fraction is greater. The ~~ ~~ ~~for~~ $\frac{4}{6}$, so $\frac{3}{2}$ is greater than $\frac{4}{6}$.

1. Which is greater, $\frac{1}{2}$ or ~~ ~~

2. Use graph paper to mak~~e~~

3. Draw lines for $\frac{1}{3}$, $\frac{1}{4}$, and ~~ ~~ ~~or~~der from least to greatest.

Mathematics and Welding

Welders usually place pieces of metal they are welding $\frac{1}{16}$ to $\frac{1}{8}$ inch apart. This space is for the filler material. The finished width is found by adding the widths of the two pieces to the amount of space between the pieces.

In the example, the finished width is $14\frac{7}{8}$ inches.

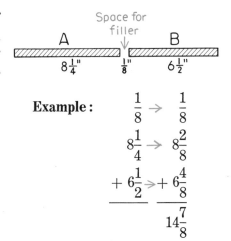

Example:

$$\frac{1}{8} \rightarrow \frac{1}{8}$$

$$8\frac{1}{4} \rightarrow 8\frac{2}{8}$$

$$+ 6\frac{1}{2} \rightarrow + 6\frac{4}{8}$$

$$\overline{\qquad 14\frac{7}{8}}$$

Find the finished width for each of the following welding jobs.

1. Piece A: $4\frac{1}{2}$ inches
   Piece B: $6\frac{1}{2}$ inches
   Filler: $\frac{1}{16}$ inch

2. Piece A: $10\frac{1}{4}$ inches
   Piece B: $10\frac{1}{4}$ inches
   Filler: $\frac{1}{8}$ inch

3. One piece of metal is $8\frac{1}{2}$ inches long. The space between the pieces is $\frac{1}{8}$ inch. If you want a total length of exactly $12\frac{1}{2}$ inches, how long should the second piece be?

What number does each letter stand for? 6.8

1. $\frac{1}{2} = \frac{a}{10}$ **2.** $\frac{2}{5} = \frac{b}{10}$ **3.** $\frac{1}{4} = \frac{c}{100}$

4. $\frac{4}{25} = \frac{d}{100}$ **5.** $\frac{9}{125} = \frac{e}{1000}$ **6.** $\frac{222}{250} = \frac{f}{1000}$

Compute. 5.2

7. $\begin{array}{r} 364 \\ +148 \\ \hline \end{array}$ **8.** $\begin{array}{r} 134 \\ -94 \\ \hline \end{array}$ **9.** $\begin{array}{r} 260 \\ 42 \\ +1486 \\ \hline \end{array}$

10. $\begin{array}{r} 36 \\ \times 8 \\ \hline \end{array}$ **11.** $\begin{array}{r} 425 \\ \times 5 \\ \hline \end{array}$ **12.** $\begin{array}{r} 34 \\ \times 25 \\ \hline \end{array}$

13. $6)\overline{504}$ **14.** $8)\overline{1928}$ **15.** $42)\overline{1512}$

16. $34 + 186 + 7$ **17.** $406 - 38$

18. 16×42 **19.** $672 \div 32$

What exponent should replace each *n*? 4.4

20. $6 \times 6 \times 6 = 6^n$ **21.** $3 \times 3 \times 3 \times 3 = 3^n$

22. $10 \times 10 \times 10 \times 10 \times 10 = 10^n$ **23.** $4 \times 10 \times 10 \times 10 = 4 \times 10^n$

Find the value of each expression. 4.4

24. 10^3 **25.** 10^2 **26.** 10^1

27. $\frac{1}{10^3}$ **28.** $\frac{1}{10^2}$ **29.** $\frac{1}{10^1}$

Operations with Decimals _____ 7

Decimals are important in your daily life. For example, you use decimals when you drive a car, buy gasoline, time a race, or check the team standings on the sports page.

In this chapter you will review the basic operations with decimals. This will enable you to use decimals when solving some of the problems you meet every day.

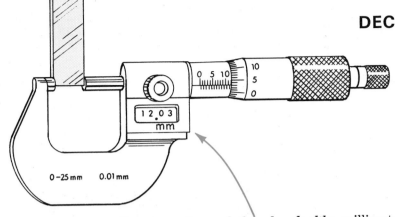

The micrometer reading is *twelve and three-hundredths* millimeters (mm). The bar is 12.03 mm wide.

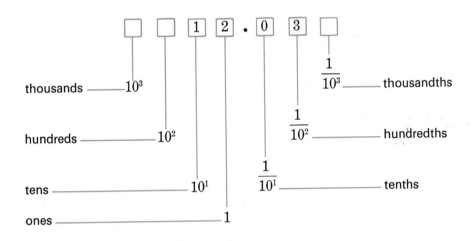

Example 1: Express 12.03 as a mixed numeral.

As you read , write .

$$12.03 = 12\frac{3}{100}$$

Example 2: Express 0.5, 5.09, and 123.456 as fractions or mixed numerals.

$$0.5 = \frac{5}{10} \text{ or } \frac{1}{2} \qquad 5.09 = 5\frac{9}{100} \qquad 123.456 = 123\frac{456}{1000} \text{ or } 123\frac{57}{125}$$

Change to lowest terms whenever possible.

Any fraction whose denominator is some power of ten (10, 100, 1000, etc.) can be written as a decimal.

Example 3 : Express $\frac{3}{10}$, $\frac{4}{100}$, and $2\frac{5}{1000}$ as decimals.

$$\frac{3}{10} = 0.3 \qquad\qquad \frac{4}{100} = 0.04 \qquad\qquad 2\frac{5}{1000} = 2.005$$

Example 4 : Express $3\frac{1}{5}$, $\frac{3}{4}$, and $\frac{1}{8}$ as decimals.

Fraction	Rename so the denominator is a power of ten.		Write as a decimal.
$3\frac{1}{5}$	=	$3\frac{2}{10}$ =	3.2
$\frac{3}{4}$	=	$\frac{75}{100}$ =	0.75
$\frac{1}{8}$	=	$\frac{125}{1000}$ =	0.125

Exercises

A Read each decimal.

1. 0.1	**2.** 1.5	**3.** 7.9	**4.** 14.6
5. 0.12	**6.** 0.02	**7.** 6.55	**8.** 35.09
9. 0.123	**10.** 0.402	**11.** 8.063	**12.** 14.839

Express the following as decimals.

13. $\frac{5}{10}$	**14.** $\frac{7}{10}$	**15.** $3\frac{9}{10}$	**16.** $17\frac{8}{10}$
17. $\frac{16}{100}$	**18.** $\frac{6}{100}$	**19.** $4\frac{37}{100}$	**20.** $43\frac{75}{100}$
21. $\frac{225}{1000}$	**22.** $\frac{25}{1000}$	**23.** $6\frac{3}{1000}$	**24.** $24\frac{502}{1000}$
25. $6\frac{9}{10}$	**26.** $6\frac{9}{100}$	**27.** $6\frac{9}{1000}$	**28.** $4\frac{75}{1000}$

B Write each decimal as a fraction or mixed numeral.

29. 0.3   **30.** 0.8   **31.** 68.9   **32.** 6.5

33. 0.17   **34.** 0.36   **35.** 9.07   **36.** 5.25

37. 0.321   **38.** 0.055   **39.** 18.009   **40.** 6.025

41. 8.6   **42.** 9.24   **43.** 16.085   **44.** 3.125

Express each of the following as a decimal.

45. $\frac{6}{10}$ **46.** $\frac{17}{100}$ **47.** $\frac{9}{1000}$ **48.** $\frac{8}{100}$

49. $3\frac{1}{2}$ **50.** $\frac{3}{4}$ **51.** $\frac{4}{5}$ **52.** $4\frac{7}{8}$

53. $\frac{3}{5}$ **54.** $16\frac{1}{4}$ **55.** $\frac{9}{25}$ **56.** $\frac{6}{125}$

57. $2\frac{5}{8}$ **58.** $\frac{33}{50}$ **59.** $12\frac{2}{5}$ **60.** $\frac{1}{8}$

C List the numbers from least to greatest.

Example : 0.362, $\frac{3}{10}$,   and $\frac{9}{25}$

0.362	0.3	0.36	Express all fractions as decimals.

0.362	0.300	0.360	Express all decimals with the same place value.

0.300	0.360	0.362	Arrange in order.
$\frac{3}{10}$	$\frac{9}{25}$	0.362	

61. 0.42, 0.34, and 0.46   **62.** 1.23, 1.038, and 1.3

63. $\frac{3}{4}$, 0.7, and $\frac{4}{5}$ **64.** $\frac{1}{2}$, $\frac{14}{25}$, and 0.506

65. $1\frac{1}{5}$, 1.165, and $1\frac{4}{25}$ **66.** $4\frac{111}{250}$, 4.44, and $4\frac{2}{5}$

67. $\frac{1}{100}$, $\frac{1}{10}$, $\frac{1}{1000}$, 10, and 1   **68.** $\frac{33}{100}$, $\frac{3}{10}$, 0.324, and 0.334

7.2 ◆ ADDITION AND SUBTRACTION

By using the following rule, you can add or subtract with decimals just as you add or subtract whole numbers.

> **Keep the decimal points aligned when adding or subtracting with decimals.**

Example 1: Ms. Bentley bought the following items. She gave the clerk a $10 bill. How much change should she get back?

These 0's call attention to the decimal points.

$1.35	milk
0.47	bread
3.44	roast
0.17	salt
+1.00	cheese

cost   6.43
tax   +0.32
total $6.75

$10.00   her $10
−6.75   total cost
$ 3.25   change

Example 2: Find the sum of 6, 0.41, 31.9, and 2.059.

Align the decimal points.

```
   6
  0.41
 31.9
+2.059
───────
40.369  ── Add. ──
```

You may write in these 0's if they help you.

```
 6.000
 0.410
31.900
+2.059
───────
40.369
```

Example 3: How much did the barometer reading change between 8 A.M. and 5 P.M.?

8:00 A.M. 29.54

5:00 P.M. 30.02

Align decimal points.

$$\begin{array}{r} 30.02 \\ -29.54 \\ \hline 0.48 \end{array}$$

Subtract as you would with whole numbers.

Exercises

[A] Answer the questions.

1. What rule must you observe when adding or subtracting with decimals?

2. How are adding whole numbers and adding with decimals alike?

3. How are subtracting whole numbers and subtracting with decimals alike?

4. Is 0.45 = .45? Why is a 0 used in cases like 0.45?

5. Is 3.2 = 3.200? Why might 0's be used in cases like 3.200?

[B] Add or subtract.

6.
$$\begin{array}{r} 3.25 \\ +4.36 \\ \hline \end{array}$$

7.
$$\begin{array}{r} 15.09 \\ +2.3 \\ \hline \end{array}$$

8.
$$\begin{array}{r} 42.3 \\ 0.42 \\ +1.093 \\ \hline \end{array}$$

9.
$$\begin{array}{r} 21.3 \\ 0.94 \\ +36 \\ \hline \end{array}$$

10.
$$\begin{array}{r} 1.45 \\ -1.05 \\ \hline \end{array}$$

11.
$$\begin{array}{r} 3.08 \\ -1.4 \\ \hline \end{array}$$

12.
$$\begin{array}{r} 13.5 \\ -0.25 \\ \hline \end{array}$$

13.
$$\begin{array}{r} 4.095 \\ -1.5 \\ \hline \end{array}$$

14.
$$\begin{array}{r} 3.425 \\ 1.5 \\ +0.93 \\ \hline \end{array}$$

15.
$$\begin{array}{r} 25.5 \\ -5.35 \\ \hline \end{array}$$

16.
$$\begin{array}{r} 44.2 \\ 9.9 \\ +9 \\ \hline \end{array}$$

17.
$$\begin{array}{r} 10.5 \\ -0.22 \\ \hline \end{array}$$

Add or subtract.

18. $36.2 + 14.85 + 1.256$

19. $3.4 - 2.45$

20. $4.2 + 4.02 + 3.5$

21. $9.6 - 3.125$

22. $0.7 + 7.7 + 7.77 + 7.777$

23. $5 - 0.25$

24. $3.6 + 5.256 + 8 + 9.25$

25. $16 - 1.75$

[C] Which figure has the greater perimeter? How much greater?

26. a.   **b.**

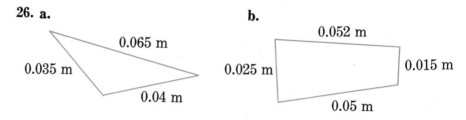

Making Money

For labor and materials, it costs "Uncle Sam" the amounts shown to produce various coins.

$0.0048

$0.0136

$0.0274

$0.0105

1. Which coin costs most to produce? Least?

2. What is the total cost of producing one coin of each kind shown?

3. How much more does it cost to produce a half dollar than a dime?

Rates between Chicago-Boston	
first 3 minutes	$1.15
every minute after	$0.35

Multiplying with decimals is like multiplying whole numbers. You must remember, however, where to place the decimal point.

Example 1: Penelope calls from Chicago and talks to her friend in Boston for ten minutes. What will the call cost?

first 3 minutes ⟶ $1.15 - - - - - - -

next 7 minutes at ⟶ 7 × 0.35
$0.35 per minute

$$\begin{array}{r} 0.35 \\ \times 7 \\ \hline 2.45 \end{array}$$

$$\begin{array}{r} \$1.15 \\ +2.45 \\ \hline \$3.60 \end{array} \quad \text{cost}$$

Example 2: When multiplying with decimals, how do you determine the number of digits after the decimal point in the answer?

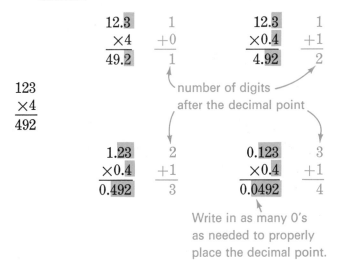

$$\begin{array}{r} 12.3 \\ \times 4 \\ \hline 49.2 \end{array} \quad \begin{array}{r} 1 \\ +0 \\ \hline 1 \end{array} \qquad \begin{array}{r} 12.3 \\ \times 0.4 \\ \hline 4.92 \end{array} \quad \begin{array}{r} 1 \\ +1 \\ \hline 2 \end{array}$$

$$\begin{array}{r} 123 \\ \times 4 \\ \hline 492 \end{array}$$

number of digits
after the decimal point

$$\begin{array}{r} 1.23 \\ \times 0.4 \\ \hline 0.492 \end{array} \quad \begin{array}{r} 2 \\ +1 \\ \hline 3 \end{array} \qquad \begin{array}{r} 0.123 \\ \times 0.4 \\ \hline 0.0492 \end{array} \quad \begin{array}{r} 3 \\ +1 \\ \hline 4 \end{array}$$

Write in as many 0's
as needed to properly
place the decimal point.

Exercises

A Tell where the decimal point should be placed in each answer.

1. 56.7	**2.** 5.67	**3.** 0.567	**4.** 0.0567
×12	×12	×12	×12
6804	6804	6804	6804

5. 56.7	**6.** 5.67	**7.** 0.567	**8.** 0.567
×1.2	×0.12	×1.2	×0.12
6804	6804	6804	6804

9. 0.025	**10.** 0.025	**11.** 0.025	**12.** 0.025
×6	×0.6	×0.06	×0.006
150	150	150	150

B Multiply.

13. 75	**14.** 3.2	**15.** 0.21	**16.** 3.8
×0.5	×7	×0.9	×0.5

17. 0.421	**18.** 5.18	**19.** 30.9	**20.** 0.42
×1.2	×0.42	×5.4	×0.25

21. 12.3	**22.** 42.1	**23.** 6.05	**24.** 0.0031
×2.4	×0.25	×0.02	×6

25. 4.012×3.1 **26.** 6.2×0.25 **27.** 3.1×3.1

28. 6×19.5 **29.** 7.5×0.75 **30.** 0.3×0.16

C Compute.

31. $0.7(4.2) + 0.7(5.8)$ **32.** $0.7(4.2 + 5.8)$

33. $1.5(0.03) + 1.5(6.97)$ **34.** $1.5(0.03 + 6.97)$

35. $8.2(6.25) + 8.2(0.75)$ **36.** $8.2(6.25 + 0.75)$

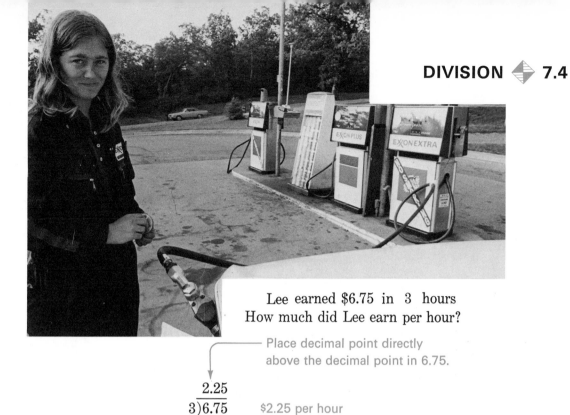

Lee earned $6.75 in 3 hours
How much did Lee earn per hour?

Place decimal point directly
above the decimal point in 6.75.

$$\begin{array}{r} 2.25 \\ 3\overline{)6.75} \end{array}$$ $2.25 per hour

Divide as you
would whole numbers.

Example 1: Lee earned $15 for 4 hours work. What was Lee paid
per hour?

$$4\overline{)15}$$ $$\begin{array}{r} 3.75 \\ 4\overline{)15.00} \end{array}$$ $3.75 per hour

A decimal point is   Use 0's after the decimal
understood to be here.   point as needed.

Example 2: Divide 2.3 by 8.

$$8\overline{)2.3}$$ $$\begin{array}{r} 0.2875 \\ 8\overline{)2.3000} \end{array}$$

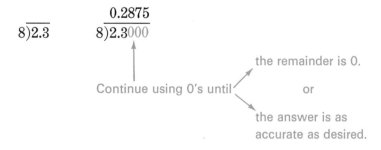

Continue using 0's until   the remainder is 0.

or

the answer is as
accurate as desired.

DIVISION   199

Exercises

A Tell where the decimal point should be placed in each answer.

$$\begin{array}{r} 1\,2 \\ \textbf{1. }8\overline{)9.6} \end{array} \qquad \begin{array}{r} 12 \\ \textbf{2. }8\overline{)0.96} \end{array} \qquad \begin{array}{r} 12 \\ \textbf{3. }8\overline{)0.096} \end{array} \qquad \begin{array}{r} 120 \\ \textbf{4. }8\overline{)960} \end{array}$$

$$\begin{array}{r} 5\,32 \\ \textbf{5. }16\overline{)85.12} \end{array} \qquad \begin{array}{r} 12 \\ \textbf{6. }24\overline{)2.88} \end{array} \qquad \begin{array}{r} 1\,6 \\ \textbf{7. }12\overline{)19.2} \end{array} \qquad \begin{array}{r} 12 \\ \textbf{8. }13\overline{)0.156} \end{array}$$

B Divide.

9. $7\overline{)8.61}$ **10.** $8\overline{)99.2}$ **11.** $6\overline{)0.21}$ **12.** $5\overline{)6.3}$

13. $3\overline{)3.069}$ **14.** $2\overline{)9.006}$ **15.** $6\overline{)0.0312}$ **16.** $8\overline{)338.4}$

17. $16\overline{)6.72}$ **18.** $12\overline{)15.6}$ **19.** $43\overline{)53.75}$ **20.** $55\overline{)0.165}$

21. $28.26 \div 9$ **22.** $0.258 \div 6$ **23.** $45.6 \div 5$

24. $12.045 \div 3$ **25.** $103.02 \div 6$ **26.** $3.045 \div 7$

27. $45.6 \div 12$ **28.** $6.76 \div 26$ **29.** $0.456 \div 38$

C Solve the problem.

30. Mary Ann put 15 Easter seals on a page that measures 21.5 by 27.9 centimeters. What is the area of the page not covered by these Easter seals?

Easter seal

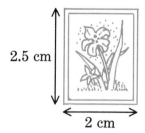

2.5 cm

2 cm

$$\begin{array}{r} 9 \\ 6\overline{)54} \end{array} \qquad \begin{array}{r} 9 \\ 6.0\overline{)54.0} \end{array} \qquad \begin{array}{r} 9 \\ 6.00\overline{)54.00} \end{array} \qquad \begin{array}{r} 9 \\ 6.000\overline{)54.000} \end{array}$$

If you move the decimal points the same number of places in both a divisor and a dividend, the answer is unchanged. You use this idea when changing a division problem so the divisor is a whole number.

$$1.2\overline{)0.96} \qquad\qquad 1.2\overline{)0.9\,6} \qquad\qquad \begin{array}{r} 0.8 \\ 1.2\overline{)0.9\,6} \end{array}$$

Change so divisor   Divide.
is a whole number.

Example 1: How would you change each division problem so the divisor is a whole number?

$$0.3\overline{)4.5} \qquad\qquad 0.43\overline{)76.841} \qquad\qquad 1.2\overline{)75}$$

$$0.3\overline{)4.5} \qquad\qquad 0.43\overline{)76.84\,1} \qquad\qquad 1.2\overline{)75.0}$$

Example 2: Divide. Check each answer.

$$2.4\overline{)76.8} \qquad\qquad 0.9\overline{)0.63} \qquad\qquad 0.34\overline{)2.7268}$$

Step 1: $\quad 2.4\overline{)76.8} \qquad\qquad 0.9\overline{)0.6\,3} \qquad\qquad 0.34\overline{)2.72\,68}$

Step 2: $\quad \begin{array}{r} 32 \\ 2.4\overline{)76.8} \end{array} \qquad\qquad \begin{array}{r} 0.7 \\ 0.9\overline{)0.6\,3} \end{array} \qquad\qquad \begin{array}{r} 8.02 \\ 0.34\overline{)2.72\,68} \end{array}$

Check:
$$\begin{array}{r} 32 \\ \times 2.4 \\ \hline 76.8 \end{array} \qquad\qquad \begin{array}{r} 0.7 \\ \times 0.9 \\ \hline 0.63 \end{array} \qquad\qquad \begin{array}{r} 8.02 \\ \times 0.34 \\ \hline 2.7268 \end{array}$$

Exercises

A How would you change each division problem so the divisor is a whole number?

1. $0.2\overline{)8.4}$ **2.** $8.1\overline{)9.72}$ **3.** $0.56\overline{)14}$

4. $2.4\overline{)0.6}$ **5.** $3.4\overline{)0.0068}$ **6.** $0.87\overline{)23.49}$

7. $0.002\overline{)0.016}$ **8.** $0.014\overline{)0.084}$ **9.** $0.09\overline{)0.225}$

Where should the decimal point be placed in each answer?

10. $0.6\overline{)7.2}$ → 12 **11.** $0.18\overline{)1.116}$ → 62 **12.** $1.3\overline{)0.0338}$ → 26

B Divide. Check each answer.

13. $0.6\overline{)15.24}$ **14.** $0.4\overline{)9.04}$ **15.** $0.5\overline{)0.0125}$

16. $0.08\overline{)4.984}$ **17.** $0.003\overline{)0.01896}$ **18.** $0.07\overline{)0.168}$

19. $1.2\overline{)0.384}$ **20.** $0.13\overline{)0.0169}$ **21.** $2.5\overline{)0.9}$

22. $0.014\overline{)0.0448}$ **23.** $0.18\overline{)0.0756}$ **24.** $1.8\overline{)4.68}$

25. $2.2\overline{)7.92}$ **26.** $3.4\overline{)0.136}$ **27.** $0.14\overline{)9.1}$

28. $2.94 \div 0.7$ **29.** $1.62 \div 0.06$

30. $0.0144 \div 0.12$ **31.** $1.44 \div 1.2$

32. $8.704 \div 3.4$ **33.** $0.315 \div 0.015$

C Solve each equation.

34. $7.5r = 317.25$ **35.** $4.19s = 1.0475$

36. $3.5t + 6.8 = 7.675$ **37.** $0.12v + 0.19 = 0.91$

38. $0.5a + 2.6 = 2.95$ **39.** $0.08b + 3.09 = 4.1028$

40. $1.2c - 0.25 = 1.19$

41. $0.6d - 0.55 = 1.49$

42. $3.2e - 0.9 = 0.7$

43. $0.006f - 0.152 = 1$

44. $7.2g - 16.5 = 163.5$

45. $0.25x + 4.85 = 5$

46. $1.3m - 22.5 = 11.3$

47. $0.12y + 2.5 = 3.256$

One Inch of Rain

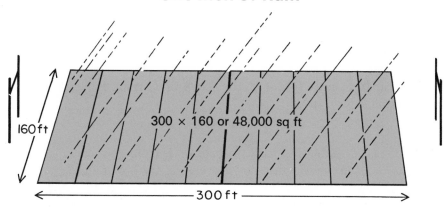

300×160 or $48{,}000$ sq ft

160 ft

300 ft

A 1-inch rainfall over a football field $\Big\}$ - - - is equal to - - - $\Big\{$ $48{,}000 \times \frac{1}{12}$ or 4000 cubic feet of water.

 1 cu ft of water weighs about 62.4 lb.

 1 gal of water weighs about 8.34 lb.

Compute as indicated.

A 1-inch rainfall over a football field $\Big\}$

weighs - - - $\Big\{$ $4000 \times$ 62.4 or _____ pounds.

is equal to - - $\Big\{$ $249{,}600 \div$ 8.34 or about _____ gallons of water.

Let's assume you average 21.5 gallons of water for your daily bath. How many days would you be able to bathe with 29,928 gallons of water—the amount from a 1-inch rainfall over a football field?

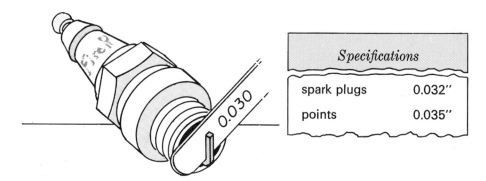

Specifications	
spark plugs	0.032″
points	0.035″

For a car to operate properly, the spark plugs must be "gapped" to the manufacturer's specifications.

Example 1: Assume the spark plug shown is from your car. Must the gap be increased or decreased? By how much?

Since 0.032″ is larger than 0.030″, you must increase the gap.

specifications ⟶ 0.032

your plug ⟶ −0.030

0.002　　increase gap

The formula for the area of a circle is $A = \pi r^2$.

Example 2: Find the area of the circle. Use 3.14 for π.

r　1.3 cm

$A = \pi r^2$

$= 3.14(1.3)^2$

$= 3.14(1.69)$

$= 5.3066$

The area is 5.3066 square centimeters or 5.3066 cm².

The gauge number of sheet metal refers to the thickness of a sheet to the nearest thousandth of an inch.

Gauge number	Uncoated carbon and low-alloy steel	Aluminum, brass, and copper
28	0.015	0.012
26	0.018	0.016
24	0.024	0.020
22	0.030	0.025
20	0.036	0.032
18	0.048	0.040
16	0.060	0.051
14	0.075	0.064
12	0.105	0.081

Example 3: The stack of sheet metal shown is made up of 28-gauge, low-alloy steel. How many pieces of 28-gauge steel would there be in that stack?

$$\begin{array}{r} 140 \\ 0.015\overline{)2.100} \end{array}$$

140 sheets

Exercises

A Use the chart above to help you answer each question.

1. Which is thicker, a 24-gauge sheet of low-alloy steel or of aluminum? By how much?

2. How would you find the combined thickness of a 22-gauge, a 16-gauge, and a 14-gauge sheet of copper?

3. A 20-gauge sheet of brass is twice as thick as you want. How would you find the gauge you want?

4. How would you find the combined thickness of eight pieces of 16-gauge, low-alloy steel?

B Solve each problem.

Average Growth Rate of Fish in Illinois

Species	age in years						
	1	2	3	4	5	6	7
	total length in inches						
Largemouth bass	6.3	9.0	11.6	13.5	15.8	17.4	18.9
Smallmouth bass	5.6	8.2	10.6	12.7	14.5	16.3	—
Bluegill	3.2	4.6	5.7	6.6	7.4	8.4	—
White crappie	5.3	7.2	8.3	10.6	12.2	—	—
Pumpkinseed sunfish	3.5	4.4	5.3	5.6	6.4	—	—
Channel catfish	6.4	9.6	12.6	14.3	16.7	18.5	21.0

(Note: The lengths are the average midsummer size at each year of age.)

5. At five years of age, what is the difference in length between the longest fish and the shortest fish?

6. At five years of age, which fish has increased the most in length since one year of age? By how much?

7. At five years of age, which fish has increased most in length since three years of age? By how much?

8. Which of the fish at least double in length between the 1st and 4th year of growth?

9. The three pieces of sheet metal are to be laminated (put together). What will the total thickness be? (Refer to the chart on page 205 to obtain the thickness of each gauge.)

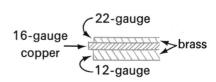

10. How many miles was the rental truck driven?

in **4 2 1 0 4**
out **3 8 4 2 9**

11. The rental agreement called for $35 a day plus $0.34 a mile. If you kept the truck two days and drove the miles indicated, what would the cost be?

12. The rainiest spot on earth is reported to be Mount Waialeale, Hawaii, with an average annual rainfall of 471.68 inches. How much more rain falls there than in Honolulu which has an average annual rainfall of 21.89 inches?

13. Phoenix, Arizona, has an average annual rainfall of 7.2 inches and Mobile, Alabama, 68.13 inches. How much greater is the rainfall at Mobile?

14. How much change would you get from your gas purchase if you paid with a $20 bill?

GOOD GAS

$ **8.7 2**
Total Sale
1 6.0
Gallons

15. How much did the gasoline cost per gallon?

C These coins are to be placed on a coin card that measures 12 by 15 centimeters. How much of the surface of the card will still be visible? (Use 3.14 for π.)

16.

0.95 cm

1.05 cm

1.2 cm

0.9 cm

1.5 cm

7.7 ⬤ SCIENTIFIC NOTATION

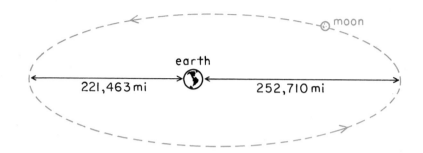

Another way to write the minimum distance between the moon and the earth is 2.21463×10^5 miles.

$$221463 = 2.21463 \times 100000 = \underbrace{2.21463 \times 10^5}$$

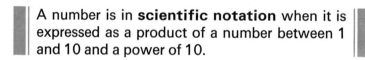

Scientific notation ⟶

> A number is in **scientific notation** when it is expressed as a product of a number between 1 and 10 and a power of 10.

Scientific notation is easy once you understand how the powers of 10 and the exponents are related.

$$1000 = \quad 10 \times 10 \times 10 \quad = 10^3$$

$$100 = \quad 10 \times 10 \quad = 10^2$$

$$10 = \quad 10 \quad = 10^1$$

$$1 = \quad 1 \quad = 10^0$$

$$\frac{1}{10} = \quad \frac{1}{10^1} \quad = 10^{-1}$$

$$\frac{1}{100} = \quad \frac{1}{10 \times 10} = \frac{1}{10^2} \quad = 10^{-2}$$

$$\frac{1}{1000} = \quad \frac{1}{10 \times 10 \times 10} = \frac{1}{10^3} = 10^{-3}$$

Example 1: Express 6000 and 0.03 in scientific notation.

A number between 1 and 10

$$6000 = 6 \times 1000 = 6 \times 10^3$$

$$0.03 = 3 \times \frac{1}{100} = 3 \times 10^{-2}$$

A power of 10

Example 2: Express 351.6, 0.0085, 0.0135, and 4065 in scientific notation.

Number	Move decimal point	Multiply by	Scientific notation
351.6	left 2	10^2	3.516×10^2
0.0085	right 3	10^{-3}	8.5×10^{-3}
0.0135	right 2	10^{-2}	1.35×10^{-2}
4065	left 3	10^3	4.065×10^3

Exercises

A What exponent should replace each n?

1. $50 = 5 \times 10^n$ **2.** $500 = 5 \times 10^n$ **3.** $5000 = 5 \times 10^n$

4. $3000 = 3 \times 10^n$ **5.** $60 = 6 \times 10^n$ **6.** $400 = 4 \times 10^n$

7. $0.2 = 2 \times 10^n$ **8.** $0.02 = 2 \times 10^n$ **9.** $0.002 = 2 \times 10^n$

10. $0.004 = 4 \times 10^n$ **11.** $0.7 = 7 \times 10^n$ **12.** $0.06 = 6 \times 10^n$

13. $800 = 8 \times 10^n$ **14.** $0.008 = 8 \times 10^n$ **15.** $80 = 8 \times 10^n$

16. If you move the decimal point to the left, do you multiply by a positive or a negative power of 10?

17. If you move the decimal point to the right, do you multiply by a positive or a negative power of 10?

B Express each number in scientific notation.

18. 3142

19. 34.21

20. 546,204

21. 59,603

22. 541.2

23. 608

24. 0.0134

25. 0.00142

26. 0.123

27. 0.25

28. 0.0004

29. 0.0304

Express each maximum and minimum distance in scientific notation.

Planet	Distance from sun (in miles)	
	maximum	minimum
30. Mercury	43,355,000	28,566,000
31. Venus	67,653,000	66,738,000
32. Earth	94,452,000	91,342,000
33. Mars	154,760,000	128,830,000
34. Jupiter	506,710,000	459,940,000
35. Saturn	935,570,000	836,700,000
36. Uranus	1,866,800,000	1,698,800,000
37. Neptune	2,817,400,000	2,769,600,000
38. Pluto	4,600,000,000	2,760,000,000

C Solve.

39. The astronomical unit of distance is the light year. A light year is approximately six million million miles. Express a light–year in scientific notation.

40. An electron has a mass of 9.107×10^{-28} grams. Express this as a decimal.

Who Hears the Music First?

The music travels to A via sound waves at 340 meters per second.

The music travels to B via radio waves at 299,780 kilometers per second.

To find the time it takes for the music to reach A, divide the distance by the rate.

$$time = \frac{distance}{rate} = \frac{30}{340}$$

$$\approx 0.088235$$

1. It takes about _____ second for the music to reach A.

2. In scientific notation this would be _____.

To find the time it takes for the music to reach B, divide the distance by the rate.

$$time = \frac{distance}{rate} = \frac{3000}{299780}$$

$$\approx 0.010007$$

3. It takes about _____ second for the music to reach B.

4. In scientific notation this would be _____.

5. Who hears the music first? By how much of a second?

▷ VOCABULARY

Choose the best term.

1. The decimal for three and three tenths is (0.33, 3.3, $3\frac{3}{10}$).

2. The 1 in (3.412, 3.142, 3.421) is in the thousandths place.

3. The 1 in (3.412, 3.142, 3.421) is in the tenths place.

4. When (*adding*, *multiplying*) with decimals, always keep the decimal points aligned.

5. When you multiply 3.1 by 0.05, there should be (*one*, *two*, *three*) places after the decimal point in the answer.

6. To divide 20.544 by 3.21, use ($2054.4 \div 321$, $3210 \div 20544$).

▷ CHAPTER REVIEW

7.1   Express each decimal as a fraction or mixed numeral.

1. 0.7   **2.** 0.5   **3.** 2.9   **4.** 3.25

5. 1.035   **6.** 0.08   **7.** 5.42   **8.** 3.6

Express the following as decimals.

9. $\frac{5}{10}$ **10.** $6\frac{8}{10}$ **11.** $\frac{9}{100}$ **12.** $4\frac{125}{1000}$

13. $2\frac{1}{4}$ **14.** $\frac{3}{8}$ **15.** $6\frac{1}{2}$ **16.** $\frac{4}{5}$

7.2   Add or subtract.

17. $68.2 + 25.4$ **18.** $73.4 - 26.6$

19. $3.1 + 2.42 + 0.196$ **20.** $13.12 - 4.221$

21. $0.31 + 25 + 4.1$ **22.** $3.1 - 2.54$

7.3   Multiply.

23. 0.2×3.61 **24.** 4.1×0.41

25. 6.8×26

26. 42.3×2.1

27. 0.04×3.02

28. 6.14×0.35

Divide.

7.4

29. $21.24 \div 6$

30. $3.72 \div 3$

31. $86.4 \div 27$

32. $0.336 \div 14$

33. $4.32 \div 18$

34. $1104.6 \div 42$

35. $5.06 \div 0.2$

36. $1.944 \div 0.6$

7.5

37. $28.8 \div 1.2$

38. $0.8 \div 0.25$

39. $0.02496 \div 0.008$

40. $9 \div 0.36$

Solve each problem.

7.6

41. Paul's batting average is 0.221 and Ellen's is 0.188. Who had the higher average? By how much?

42. A car averages 10.9 kilometers per liter of gasoline. At that rate, how many kilometers could the car travel on 30.2 liters?

Express each of the following in scientific notation.

7.7

43. 300,000

44. 42,650

45. 38,750,000

46. 0.004

47. 0.0012

48. 0.00095

CHAPTER TEST

Write each decimal as a fraction or mixed numeral. Write each fraction or mixed numeral as a decimal.

1. 0.9

2. 3.25

3. 0.035

4. $\frac{19}{1000}$

5. $\frac{3}{5}$

6. $5\frac{3}{4}$

Compute.

7. $54.6 + 25.43$

8. $42.63 - 1.5$

9. $12 + 3.42 + 1.6$

10. $6.124 - 3.5$

11. 3.6×0.8

12. 4.25×1.8

13. 30.5×0.04

14. $7.5 \div 6$

15. $40.8 \div 12$

16. $0.72 \div 0.02$

17. $3.5 \div 1.4$

18. $1.125 \div 0.5$

Solve each problem.

19. If you stacked 6 bars like this on top of one another, what would the total height be?

20. How much greater is the length of the bar than its width?

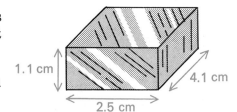

1.1 cm

4.1 cm

2.5 cm

21. Ellen paid $5.46 for 8.4 gallons of gasoline. How much did the gasoline cost per gallon?

22. Express nineteen trillion (19 followed by 15 zeros) in scientific notation.

Activities for Chapter 7

Activity 1

Use a micrometer to measure various objects, including the thickness of the cover of this book, the thickness of a page in this book, and so on.

Compare the measurements with your friends.

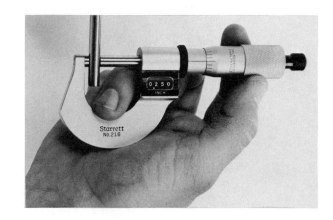

Activity 2

Find and display five examples where decimals are used. Some sources you might check are car, truck, and cycle manuals, almanacs, and the sports columns in newspapers.

Activity 3

Replace each ● with the correct numeral.

1.
```
    2.6
  ×●.4
  -----
    104
     ●●
  -----
   8.84
```

2.
```
    42.45
   ×3.●
  -------
    4245
   ●●●●●
  --------
  ●●●.●●●
```

3.
```
       ●●.●●
     ×0.56
  ---------
      ●●●●
      6170
  ---------
    ●.●●●●
```

4.
```
      0.2●
  ●)1.82
    1 4
    ----
     ●●
     ●●
    ----
      0
```

5.
```
         ●.●
  2.4)8.40
       ● ●
      -----
      1 20
      ●●●
      -----
        ●
```

6.
```
        1.●●
  ●●●)3.936
      3 2
      ----
       ●●
       ●●
      ----
        ●●
        ●●
       ----
         ●
```

Mathematics and Typesetting

A typesetter uses units of measure called *picas* and *points.*

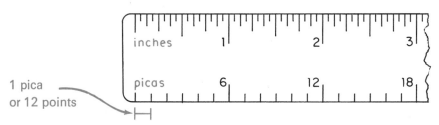

1 pica
or 12 points

1. How many points are equal to 1 pica? 6 picas? 8.5 picas?

2. How many picas are equal to 1 inch? 2 inches? 3.5 inches?

A typesetter needs to know how many characters (letters and spaces) will fit on a line of type. For example, the length of this line of type is 28 picas. The typeface used to set this copy has a character count of 2.44 (that is, there are 2.44 characters per pica).

length of line (in picas)		character count (of typeface used)		number of characters per line
28	×	2.44	=	68.32

3. If you use the typeface on this page, how many characters would there be in a line 15 picas long? 30 picas long? 25.5 picas long?

4. Typeface *X* has 1.45 characters per pica. How many characters would there be in a line 28 picas long? 20.5 picas long?

Match each item with the best description.

1. $\{0, 1, 2, 3, \cdots\}$ **a.** ordered pair   3.1

2. $(1, 2)$ **b.** inverse of $4 \times 3 = 12$ 5.2

3. $12 \div 3 = 4$ **c.** set of whole numbers   1.7

4. $\{1, 2, 3, 4, \cdots\}$ **d.** inverse of $3 + 4 = 7$ 5.2

5. $7 - 4 = 3$ **e.** $n \div 6$ 2.1

6. $\frac{n}{6}$ **f.** set of whole numbers greater than 0   1.7

Compute as indicated.   1.1

7. $15 + 23$ 8. 13×13

9. $48 - 26$ 10. $32 \div 4$

11. 0×83 12. $0 \div 227$

Solve each equation.

13. $x + 7 = 16$ 14. $x + 9 = 14$ 1.5

15. $4x = 20$ 16. $2m = 14$ 2.1

17. $n - 7 = 6$ 18. $\frac{n}{6} = 7$ 2.2

19. $2m + 7 = 9$ 20. $3y - 28 = 20$ 2.8

21. $\frac{n}{6} + 3 = 9$ 22. $\frac{n}{4} - 7 = 6$

Graph each ordered pair.   3.2

23. $(0, 6)$ 24. $(6, 0)$

25. $(0, 0)$ 26. $(6, 6)$

Integers ———————————— 8

When an airplane is climbing, we say it is changing altitude in a positive direction. When it is descending, it is changing altitude in a negative direction.

When graphing whole numbers on a number line, you used "to the right" as the positive direction. You used "to the left" as the negative direction.

In this chapter you will use *positive numbers* for distances in the positive direction and *negative numbers* for distances in the negative direction. Also, you will learn how to perform operations on positive and negative numbers.

WHOLE NUMBERS AND THEIR OPPOSITES 8.1

On a number line, opposites are the same distance from 0—but in opposite directions.

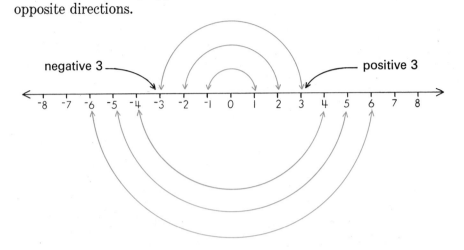

Example 1:   How do you read ⁻2?

⁻2 is read as *negative two*.

Example 2:   What is the opposite of ⁻3? Of 5?

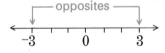   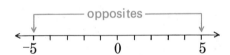

> ‖ The whole numbers and their opposites make up the set of numbers called the **integers**. ‖

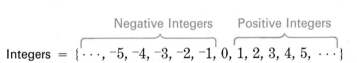

$$\text{Integers} = \{\cdots, {}^-5, {}^-4, {}^-3, {}^-2, {}^-1, 0, 1, 2, 3, 4, 5, \cdots\}$$

A ⁻ is always used when naming a negative integer.

negative sixteen   ⁻16

A ⁺ may be used when naming a positive integer.

positive sixteen   ⁺16 or 16

Exercises

A Name the opposite of each number.

1. 2	**2.** +28	**3.** ⁻17	**4.** 438
5. ⁻2	**6.** ⁻28	**7.** 86	**8.** 0

9. Which integer is neither positive nor negative?

10. Which integer is its own opposite?

B Complete the table below.

	Activity	Integer	Activity	Integer
11.	down 3 fathoms	⁻3	up 3 fathoms	_____
12.	250 miles north	+250	_____	⁻250
13.	five meters forward	+5	_____	⁻5
14.	up 6 floors	+6	down 6 floors	_____
15.	100 feet above sea level	+100	_____	⁻100
16.	$1000 profit	_____	$1000 loss	⁻1000
17.	8-yard loss	⁻8	8-yard gain	_____
18.	increase of 10°	_____	decrease of 10°	⁻10
19.	70 kilometers west	_____	70 kilometers east	+70

C Name the opposite of each number.

20. 0.38	**21.** +1.96	**22.** $2\frac{2}{3}$	**23.** ⁻a
24. ⁻0.47	**25.** ⁻$\frac{3}{4}$	**26.** +$5\frac{1}{2}$	**27.** +b

Which number in each pair is greater?

28. 0 or 10	**29.** 0 or ⁻10	**30.** ⁻10 or 10
31. ⁻12 or 4	**32.** ⁻12 or ⁻7	**33.** ⁻12 or ⁻16

You can show addition of whole numbers on a number line.

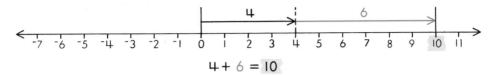

$$4 + 6 = 10$$

You can use the same techniques to find sums of integers.

Example 1: Show $^-4 + 6$ on a number line.

Step 1: The first addend is $^-4$, so start at 0 and draw an arrow 4 units to the left (negative direction).

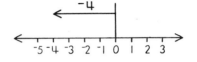

Step 2: The second addend is 6, so start at $^-4$ and draw an arrow 6 units to the right (positive direction).

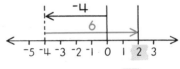

Step 3: The sum is given at the head of the second arrow.

$$^-4 + 6 = 2$$

Example 2: Show $4 + ^-6$ on a number line.

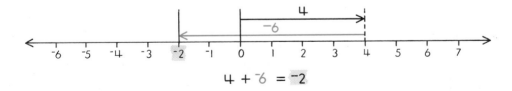

$$4 + ^-6 = ^-2$$

Example 3: Show $^-4 + ^-6$ on a number line.

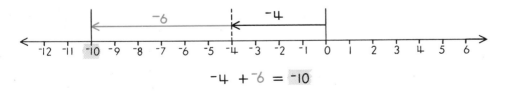

$$^-4 + ^-6 = ^-10$$

Exercises

A State an addition sentence for each drawing.

1.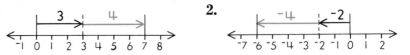

2.

3.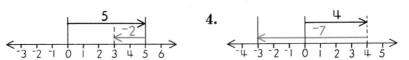

4.

B Find each sum. Use a number line to help you.

5. $6 + 5$	**6.** $^-3 + ^-6$	**7.** $^-9 + 4$
8. $8 + ^-7$	**9.** $^-6 + ^-3$	**10.** $2 + ^-9$
11. $6 + ^-1$	**12.** $8 + ^-8$	**13.** $^-6 + 2$
14. $^-2 + 9$	**15.** $5 + 5$	**16.** $^-3 + 7$
17. $3 + ^-7$	**18.** $3 + 7$	**19.** $^-6 + 6$
20. $^-4 + ^-4$	**21.** $5 + ^-4$	**22.** $^-7 + 3$
23. $^-1 + 7$	**24.** $9 + ^-5$	**25.** $8 + ^-3$

C Use a number line to help you find each sum.

Example: $1 + 2 + 3$

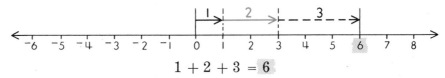

$$1 + 2 + 3 = 6$$

26. $2 + 3 + 4$	**27.** $6 + ^-1 + ^-3$	**28.** $10 + ^-8 + 5$
29. $^-3 + 4 + ^-6$	**30.** $7 + 7 + 3$	**31.** $^-1 + 1 + 8$
32. $^-2 + 3 + ^-4$	**33.** $6 + ^-7 + 1$	**34.** $2 + ^-3 + 2$
35. $^-7 + ^-5 + 4$	**36.** $^-2 + ^-4 + ^-3$	**37.** $^-6 + 5 + ^-3$

The **absolute value** of a number is the number of units that number is from 0 on the number line.

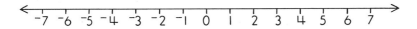

Number	Units from 0 on the number line	Absolute value
+4 or 4	4	4
-3	3	3
5	5	5
-5	5	5

You can use the idea of *absolute value* to find the sum of integers.

Example 1: How do you add integers with the same sign?

Add the absolute values.

The result has the same sign as the addends.

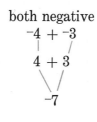

both negative

$-4 + -3$

$4 + 3$

-7

both positive

$+4 + +3$

$4 + 3$

$+7$

$$-4 + -3 = -7 \qquad +4 + +3 = +7$$

Example 2: How do you add integers with different signs?

Find the difference of the absolute values.

The result has the same sign as the addend with the greater absolute value.

$-4 + +3$

$4 - 3$

-1

$+4 + -3$

$4 - 3$

$+1$

$$-4 + +3 = -1 \qquad +4 + -3 = +1$$

Example 3: How do you add ⁻4, 6, and ⁻5?

Take your choice of which integers to add first.

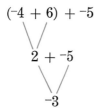

(⁻4 + 6) + ⁻5

2 + ⁻5

⁻3

⁻4 + (6 + ⁻5)

⁻4 + 1

⁻3

Exercises

A State the absolute value of each integer.

1. +16

2. ⁻24

3. 325

4. ⁻96

5. 0

6. ⁻1978

Tell whether the sum is positive or negative.

7. 18 + 48

8. ⁻63 + ⁻49

9. 73 + ⁻8

10. ⁻16 + 13

11. 16 + ⁻34

12. ⁻83 + 149

B Find each sum.

13. 16 + 12

14. ⁻17 + ⁻18

15. 23 + ⁻14

16. 32 + ⁻49

17. ⁻18 + 39

18. ⁻47 + 21

19. 37 + 48

20. ⁻23 + ⁻36

21. 88 + ⁻72

22. ⁻17 + 12

23. 103 + ⁻111

24. ⁻15 + 18

25. ⁻619 + 832

26. 173 + ⁻846

27. ⁻496 + 327

28. 792 + ⁻628

29. ⁻485 + 969

30. 278 + ⁻475

31. ⁻1692 + 1968

32. 1795 + ⁻492

33. 672 + 896

34. ⁻849 + ⁻782

35. 6742 + ⁻4385

36. ⁻6275 + 4675

Find each sum.

37. $(2 + 4) + 3$ **38.** $(^-2 + 4) + 6$ **39.** $(8 + ^-5) + 3$

40. $6 + (5 + ^-7)$ **41.** $^-4 + (^-3 + 2)$ **42.** $^-5 + (7 + ^-8)$

43. $2 + ^-7 + ^-4$ **44.** $^-2 + ^-5 + ^-7$ **45.** $^-6 + 5 + ^-8$

C Which of $>$, $=$, or $<$, should replace each 〰 so a true sentence results?

46. $^-7 + ^-3$ 〰 $^-3 + ^-7$ **47.** $^-16 + 7$ 〰 $^-7 + 16$

48. $(5 + ^-7) + 9$ 〰 $5 + (^-7 + 9)$ **49.** $^-16 + 7$ 〰 $7 + ^-16$

50. $^-83 + 55$ 〰 $^-55 + 83$ **51.** $^-9 + ^-6$ 〰 $^-19 + 16$

52. $^-8 + (6 + ^-9)$ 〰 $(^-8 + 6) + ^-9$ **53.** $^-27 + 53$ 〰 $^-53 + 27$

Who Won?

At the end of 8 innings, the Tigers led the Yankees 7 to 6. There was a bases-loaded home run in the ninth inning and the final score was 10 to 9.

How many runs did the Tigers score in the ninth?

How many runs did the Yankees score in the ninth?

Who won the ball game?

8.4 ◆ SUBTRACTING INTEGERS

Subtracting 2 from 6 gives the same answer as adding ⁻2 to 6.

It appears that subtracting a number is equivalent to adding its opposite. Let's try another example.

Again the pattern holds. Many other examples lead us to the following conclusion.

▌ To subtract an integer, add its opposite. ▐

Example 1: How do you subtract 6 from ⁻1?

Add its
opposite.

$$^-1 - 6 = {}^-1 + {}^-6$$
$$= {}^-7$$

Example 2: How do you subtract ⁻7 from ⁻2?

Add its
opposite.

$$^-2 - {}^-7 = {}^-2 + 7$$
$$= 5$$

Exercises

A Give an addition phrase for each of the following.

  1. $6 - 7$ **2.** $8 - {}^-5$ **3.** $9 - {}^-12$

  4. ${}^-5 - 6$ **5.** ${}^-4 - {}^-2$ **6.** $19 - 15$

B Find each difference.

  7. $15 - 19$ **8.** ${}^-6 - 8$ **9.** ${}^-12 - 17$

  10. $11 - {}^-5$ **11.** ${}^-11 - 3$ **12.** $4 - 10$

  13. ${}^-8 - {}^-12$ **14.** $26 - {}^-14$ **15.** ${}^-11 - {}^-33$

  16. ${}^-6 - {}^-5$ **17.** ${}^-16 - {}^-4$ **18.** ${}^-8 - 32$

  19. ${}^-18 - 16$ **20.** ${}^-12 - 12$ **21.** ${}^-38 - 54$

  22. ${}^-518 - 303$ **23.** $219 - {}^-118$ **24.** $416 - {}^-303$

  25. $1776 - {}^-1865$ **26.** ${}^-1069 - 433$ **27.** ${}^-600 - {}^-439$

C Find the value of each phrase.

  28. $(7 - 3) - 5$ **29.** $7 - (3 - 5)$

  30. ${}^-5 - (7 - 8)$ **31.** $({}^-5 - 7) - 8$

  32. $({}^-4 - 3) - {}^-2$ **33.** ${}^-4 - (3 - {}^-2)$

  34. $({}^-5 - {}^-6) - 7$ **35.** ${}^-5 - ({}^-6 - 7)$

  36. ${}^-4 - ({}^-5 - {}^-6)$ **37.** $({}^-4 - {}^-5) - {}^-6$

A Number Trick

Choose a number. Add 3. Multiply the sum by 2. Subtract 4 from the product. Divide the difference by 2. Finally, add the opposite of the number you started with. What is your answer? (Regardless of the number you start with, your answer should always be 1.)

8.5 ◆ MULTIPLYING INTEGERS

You already know how to multiply positive integers. That's just like multiplying whole numbers.

How can you find a product like $3 \times {}^-4$?

Think of multiplication as repeated addition. Thus, $3 \times {}^-4$ can be shown on a number line as follows.

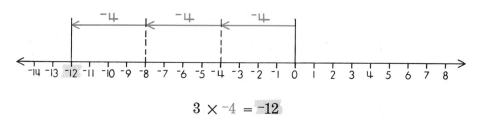

$$3 \times {}^-4 = {}^-12$$

How can you find a product such as $^-4 \times 3$?

Since you can change the order of the factors without changing the product,

$$3 \times {}^-4 = {}^-4 \times 3.$$

Since $3 \times {}^-4 = {}^-12$, certainly $^-4 \times 3 = {}^-12$.

The examples above suggest the following rule.

> If two integers have *different* signs, then their product is *negative*.

Example 1: Multiply 8 by $^-9$.

$$8 \times {}^-9 = {}^-(8 \times 9)$$
$$= {}^-72$$

Example 2: Multiply $^-14$ by 6.

$$^-14 \times 6 = {}^-(14 \times 6)$$
$$= {}^-84$$

Exercises

A Tell whether the product is positive or negative.

1. 3×4

2. $^{-}3 \times 4$

3. $3 \times ^{-}4$

4. $6 \times ^{-}5$

5. $5 \times ^{-}7$

6. $^{-}19 \times 18$

7. $^{-}42 \times 79$

8. 8×79

9. $^{-}85 \times 69$

B Find each product. Use number-line drawings if they help.

10. 7×3

11. $3 \times ^{-}6$

12. $^{-}6 \times 4$

13. $^{-}3 \times 7$

14. 9×14

15. $5 \times ^{-}8$

16. $7 \times ^{-}3$

17. $^{-}5 \times 8$

18. 8×17

Find each product.

19. $8 \times ^{-}10$

20. $^{-}9 \times 7$

21. $7 \times ^{-}11$

22. $9 \times ^{-}7$

23. $^{-}13 \times 12$

24. $^{-}16 \times 22$

25. $84 \times ^{-}3$

26. $11 \times ^{-}11$

27. $^{-}76 \times 6$

28. $38 \times ^{-}19$

29. $^{-}42 \times 17$

30. $64 \times ^{-}83$

31. $8 \times ^{-}119$

32. $^{-}476 \times 12$

33. $692 \times ^{-}48$

C Compute as indicated.

34. $8(^{-}7) + 8(6)$

35. $8(^{-}7 + 6)$

36. $9(^{-}7) + 9(^{-}8)$

37. $9(^{-}7 + ^{-}8)$

38. $^{-}5(17) + ^{-}5(17)$

39. $^{-}5(17 + 17)$

40. $12(8 + ^{-}13)$

41. $6(18 + ^{-}24)$

42. $^{-}18(24 + 37)$

43. $19(12 + ^{-}19)$

44. $^{-}32(18 + 17)$

45. $24(^{-}32 + 18)$

8.6 ◆ MORE ABOUT MULTIPLYING INTEGERS

To learn how to find the product of two negative integers, consider the following pattern.

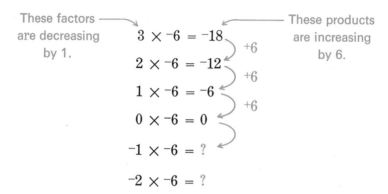

These factors are decreasing by 1.

$3 \times {}^-6 = {}^-18$
$2 \times {}^-6 = {}^-12$
$1 \times {}^-6 = {}^-6$
$0 \times {}^-6 = 0$
$^-1 \times {}^-6 = ?$
$^-2 \times {}^-6 = ?$

These products are increasing by 6.

+6
+6
+6

For the pattern to continue, you have the following.

$$^-1 \times {}^-6 = 6$$

$$^-2 \times {}^-6 = 12$$

Many other examples lead us to this conclusion.

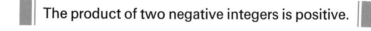

The product of two negative integers is positive.

Example 1: Multiply $^-5$ by $^-75$.

$$^-5 \times {}^-75 = 5 \times 75$$

$$= 375$$

Example 2: How do you multiply $^-3$, 4, and $^-6$?

Take your choice of which integers to multiply first.

$$(^-3 \times 4) \times {}^-6 \qquad \text{or} \qquad {}^-3 \times (4 \times {}^-6)$$

Then proceed as follows to find the product.

$$(^-3 \times 4) \times {}^-6 = {}^-12 \times {}^-6 \qquad {}^-3 \times (4 \times {}^-6) = {}^-3 \times {}^-24$$

$$= 72 \qquad\qquad\qquad\qquad = 72$$

Exercises

A Tell whether each product is positive or negative.

1. 7×6 **2.** $18 \times {}^-6$ **3.** ${}^-16 \times 18$

4. ${}^-48 \times {}^-27$ **5.** ${}^-76 \times 7$ **6.** ${}^-83 \times {}^-72$

B Find each product.

7. ${}^-7 \times {}^-6$ **8.** ${}^-9 \times {}^-10$ **9.** ${}^-8 \times {}^-4$

10. ${}^-12 \times {}^-13$ **11.** ${}^-15 \times {}^-17$ **12.** ${}^-11 \times {}^-16$

13. ${}^-19 \times {}^-20$ **14.** ${}^-23 \times {}^-23$ **15.** ${}^-18 \times {}^-18$

Find each product.

16. ${}^-4 \times {}^-5 \times {}^-6$ **17.** $11 \times {}^-4 \times {}^-5$

18. ${}^-8 \times 6 \times {}^-2$ **19.** $8 \times 7 \times {}^-6$

20. ${}^-14 \times {}^-4 \times {}^-8$ **21.** $1 \times {}^-8 \times {}^-19$

22. ${}^-25 \times {}^-25 \times 25$ **23.** ${}^-72 \times {}^-73 \times 43$

24. $48 \times {}^-99 \times {}^-101$ **25.** $18 \times {}^-19 \times {}^-21$

C Find each product.

26. $7 \times 6 \times 3$ **27.** $8 \times {}^-7 \times 5$

28. ${}^-7 \times {}^-4 \times 2$ **29.** ${}^-6 \times {}^-7 \times {}^-8$

30. ${}^-7 \times 4 \times {}^-9$ **31.** ${}^-8 \times 7 \times {}^-17 \times {}^-5$

32. ${}^-17 \times {}^-4 \times {}^-8 \times {}^-3$ **33.** ${}^-8 \times {}^-17 \times {}^-13 \times 3$

Use your answers to 26–33 to decide if the following statements are true or false.

34. If there is an *even number of negative factors*, then the product is *positive*.

35. If there is an *odd number of negative factors*, then the product is *negative*.

8.7 ◆ DIVIDING INTEGERS

Multiplication and division are inverse operations. You can use this relationship to discover how to divide integers.

both positive

If $3 \times 4 = 12$,   then $12 \div 4 = 3$.

If $3 \times {}^-4 = {}^-12$,   then ${}^-12 \div {}^-4 = 3$.

positive quotients

both negative

> If two integers have the *same* sign, then their quotient is *positive*.

Example 1 :   Divide ${}^-18$ by ${}^-2$.

same sign

$${}^-18 \div {}^-2 = 18 \div 2$$
$$= 9 \qquad \textit{positive quotient}$$

What if the signs are different?

different signs

If ${}^-3 \times 4 = {}^-12$,   then ${}^-12 \div 4 = {}^-3$.

If ${}^-3 \times {}^-4 = 12$,   then $12 \div {}^-4 = {}^-3$.

negative quotients

different signs

> If two integers have *different* signs, then their quotient is *negative*.

Example 2 :   Divide 28 by ${}^-4$.

different signs

$$28 \div {}^-4 = {}^-(28 \div 4)$$
$$= {}^-7 \qquad \textit{negative quotient}$$

Example 3: Solve $\frac{-84}{7} = x$.

different signs

$$\frac{-84}{7} = {}^-84 \div 7 = {}^-(84 \div 7)$$

$$= {}^-12 \qquad \textit{negative quotient}$$

Exercises

A Tell whether the quotient is positive or negative.

1. $8 \div 2$ **2.** $\frac{18}{-6}$ **3.** $^-24 \div 8$

4. $\frac{-36}{4}$ **5.** $84 \div {}^-12$ **6.** $\frac{-42}{-7}$

7. $^-48 \div {}^-16$ **8.** $\frac{96}{8}$ **9.** $78 \div {}^-3$

B Find each quotient.

10. $48 \div 16$ **11.** $16 \div {}^-4$ **12.** $^-21 \div 3$

13. $^-27 \div {}^-3$ **14.** $81 \div {}^-9$ **15.** $30 \div {}^-5$

16. $^-18 \div 6$ **17.** $72 \div {}^-8$ **18.** $^-30 \div {}^-6$

19. $^-121 \div 11$ **20.** $96 \div 16$ **21.** $91 \div 13$

22. $^-100 \div 5$ **23.** $91 \div {}^-7$ **24.** $^-70 \div 5$

Solve the following.

25. $\frac{-9}{3} = x$ **26.** $\frac{20}{-5} = x$ **27.** $\frac{-15}{-3} = x$

28. $\frac{78}{13} = x$ **29.** $\frac{-75}{5} = x$ **30.** $\frac{225}{-25} = x$

31. $\frac{-144}{-16} = x$ **32.** $\frac{-288}{9} = x$ **33.** $\frac{324}{-18} = x$

C Find the value of each phrase.

34. $9 + {}^-42 \div 3$ **35.** $^-6 \times 14 \div {}^-2$

36. $^-81 \div 9 + {}^-16$ **37.** $^-84 \div {}^-7 \times 6$

38. $16 + {}^-9 \times 4 \div 2$ **39.** $^-6 \times 12 \div 3 + {}^-5$

8.8 ◑ INTEGERS AND THE COORDINATE SYSTEM

Old Gridtown

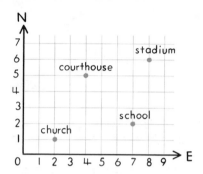

Old Gridtown had no street names. Instead, the location of each building was designated by its east and north **coordinates.**

Example 1: What are the coordinates of the school?

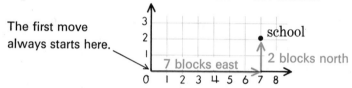

The coordinates of the school are (7, 2).

As Gridtown expanded south and west, the town leaders renamed their community "New Gridtown." They also extended their coordinate system to include negative integers.

New Gridtown

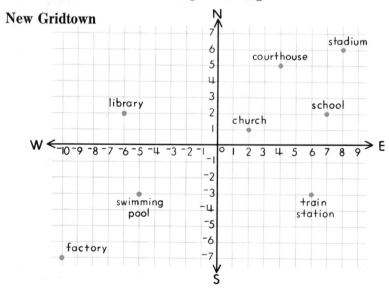

Example 2: What are the coordinates of the library?

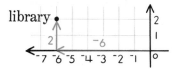

The coordinates of the library are (⁻6, 2).

Example 3: What are the coordinates of the swimming pool?

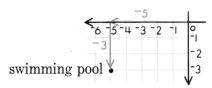

The coordinates of the swimming pool are (⁻5, ⁻3).

When two number lines are drawn perpendicular to one another, they are called **coordinate axes**. The x-axis is horizontal. The y-axis is vertical.

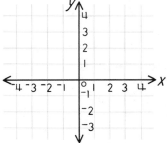

| When coordinates are given as an ordered pair, the x-coordinate is always named first.

Exercises

A Name the coordinates of each point.

1. A   2. E   3. M

4. F   5. B   6. J

7. N   8. G   9. C

10. H   11. D   12. I

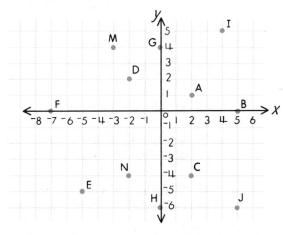

Use graph paper to draw a pair of coordinate axes. Graph the points whose coordinates are given below.

13. K(5, 6)   **14.** N(0, 0)   **15.** R(-5, -4)

16. U(-8, 2)   **17.** L(-7, -3)   **18.** P(-5, 4)

19. S(5, -4)   **20.** V(-6, 0)   **21.** M(6, 0)

22. Q(5, 4)   **23.** T(2, 1)   **24.** W(5, -2)

Use the map of New Gridtown to answer the following.

25. A gasoline station is 5 blocks due west of the origin. What are the coordinates of the gasoline station?

26. The YWCA is 6 blocks due south of the origin. What are the co-ordinates of the YWCA?

27. A laundromat is 5 blocks due east of the factory. What are the coordinates of the laundromat?

28. A grocery store is 4 blocks due north of the factory. What are the coordinates of the grocery store?

29. What are the coordinates of a building which is 6 blocks north and 3 blocks east of the church?

Use graph paper to draw a map. Locate these features on the map.

30. Wells Road (Each point has an east-west coordinate of -9.)

31. Lyles Boulevard (Each point has a north-south coordinate of -5.)

32. Richards Street (For each point, the coordinates are opposites.)

33. Collins Avenue (For each point, the coordinates are equal.)

34. Kempf Aquarium (It is located 1 block north of the intersection of Collins Avenue and Richards Street.)

35. Malecki Museum (It is located 2 blocks south of the intersection of Wells Road and Lyles Boulevard.)

Match each item with the best description.

1. 9 and ⁻9	**a.** coordinates of the origin
2. {1, 2, 3, 4, ⋯}	**b.** set of negative integers
3. 10	**c.** set of positive integers
4. 9	**d.** opposites
5. {⁻1, ⁻2, ⁻3, ⁻4, ⋯}	**e.** absolute value of ⁻10
6. (0, 0)	**f.** absolute value of 9

CHAPTER REVIEW

Name the opposite of each integer.   8.1

1. 6   **2.** ⁻7

3. 0   **4.** ⁺9

Find each sum.

5. $6 + {}^-3$ **6.** $4 + 7$ 8.2

7. ${}^-8 + 6$ **8.** ${}^-7 + {}^-5$

9. $37 + 19$ **10.** $16 + {}^-23$ 8.3

11. ${}^-18 + 37$ **12.** ${}^-15 + {}^-39$

13. $100 + {}^-100$ **14.** ${}^-75 + 95$

Find each difference.   8.4

15. ${}^-3 - 8$ **16.** ${}^-6 - {}^-8$

17. $37 - 84$ **18.** ${}^-18 - 37$

19. ${}^-76 - 38$ **20.** $39 - {}^-16$

8.5   Find each product.

21. 7×9 **22.** $4 \times {}^-7$

23. ${}^-8 \times 6$ **24.** ${}^-11 \times 7$

25. $11 \times {}^-13$ **26.** ${}^-26 \times 17$

8.6   **27.** ${}^-8 \times {}^-3$ **28.** ${}^-10 \times {}^-10$

29. ${}^-13 \times {}^-14$ **30.** ${}^-18 \times {}^-16$

8.7   Find each quotient.

31. $8 \div {}^-2$ **32.** ${}^-16 \div 8$

33. ${}^-24 \div {}^-6$ **34.** $48 \div 4$

35. $\frac{65}{{}^-13}$ **36.** $\frac{{}^-72}{4}$

37. $\frac{{}^-96}{{}^-6}$ **38.** $\frac{144}{{}^-9}$

8.8   Use the graph paper to draw a pair of coordinate axes. Graph the points whose coordinates are given below.

39. $A(6, 5)$ **40.** $B({}^-6, 3)$

41. $C({}^-6, {}^-5)$ **42.** $D(6, {}^-5)$

Find each sum.

1. $8 + {}^-6$

2. $^-7 + 8$

3. $^-16 + {}^-23$

4. $18 + {}^-26$

5. $^-48 + {}^-23$

6. $^-27 + {}^-49$

Find each difference.

7. $16 - 42$

8. $^-18 - 16$

9. $92 - {}^-16$

10. $^-84 - {}^-48$

11. $^-48 - {}^-84$

12. $^-36 - 52$

Find each product.

13. $5 \times {}^-3$

14. $^-8 \times {}^-5$

15. $^-13 \times 8$

16. $7 \times {}^-19$

17. $^-19 \times {}^-21$

18. $^-24 \times 32$

Find each quotient.

19. $18 \div {}^-3$

20. $^-48 \div 6$

21. $^-120 \div 8$

22. $^-196 \div {}^-14$

23. $\frac{^-64}{16}$

24. $\frac{360}{^-45}$

 Name the coordinates of the following points.

25. A

26. B

27. C

28. D

29. E

30. F

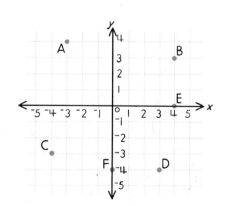

Activity 1

You can use these materials to compete in a *race:* **1.** A set of index cards, each card marked on one side only. (Make two cards for each of the numbers {⁻10, ⁻9, ⁻8, ···, 8, 9, 10}.); **2.** A number line showing the integers ⁻30 to 30; **3.** A marker or "car" for each player.

All "cars" are placed at 0, and the cards shuffled. The first "driver" in the "addition heat" takes two cards. He moves his "car" the number of units in the direction indicated by the sum of the integers on the two cards.

Example: Suppose the first player draws cards for ⁻7 and 5.

$⁻7 + 5 = ⁻2,$ *so move the "car" 2 spaces in the negative direction.*

The remaining players take their turns in a similar fashion. The "race" continues until one car crosses either of the finish lines (30 or ⁻30).

Activity 2

Races similar to that in Activity 1 can also be conducted for subtraction and multiplication. The same length of number line can be used for subtraction. However, for multiplication the number line should show the integers from ⁻150 to 150.

Mathematics and Air Conditioning

Air conditioners are often measured in British thermal units (Btu). The number of units (U) needed to cool the average house can be determined by using the formula below.

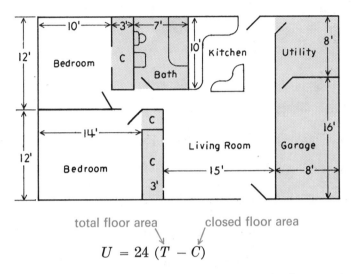

total floor area   closed floor area

$$U = 24\ (T - C)$$

Example: What size air conditioner would be required to cool the house above?

$T = 40 \times 24$
$\quad = 960$

closets   bath and closet   garage and utility

$C = (3 \times 12) + (10 \times 10) + (8 \times 24)$
$\quad = 36 + 100 + 192 \text{ or } 328$

$U = 24(960 - 328)$
$\quad = 24(632)$
$\quad = 15168$

The air conditioner should be rated 15,168 Btu or greater.

1. Determine the size air conditioner that should be installed in the house above if the utility room is to be air-conditioned.

2. Suppose the smaller bedroom above was closed off and used only occasionally. What size air conditioner would be required to cool the rest of the house?

Getting Ready for Chapter 9

Find each sum or difference.

8.3 **1.** $4 + {}^-4$ **2.** ${}^-8 + 8$

    3. $19 + {}^-3$ **4.** ${}^-23 + {}^-4$

8.4 **5.** ${}^-9 - {}^-9$ **6.** $16 - 16$

    7. ${}^-18 - 4$ **8.** $32 - {}^-19$

Find the value of each phrase when n is replaced as indicated.

8.3 **9.** $n + {}^-6$ Replace n with 15.

    10. $n + 6$ Replace n with ${}^-4$.

8.4 **11.** $n - 4$ Replace n with ${}^-5$.

    12. $n - {}^-3$ Replace n with 10.

8.6 **13.** ${}^-6n$ Replace n with ${}^-1$.

8.7 **14.** $\frac{n}{{}^-6}$ Replace n with 30.

Find each product or quotient.

8.5 **15.** $8 \times {}^-7$ **16.** $7 \times {}^-17$

8.6 **17.** ${}^-5 \times {}^-15$ **18.** ${}^-18 \times {}^-6$

8.7 **19.** $\frac{7}{7}$ **20.** ${}^-35 \div 7$

    21. $\frac{{}^-9}{{}^-9}$ **22.** $27 \div {}^-9$

8.1 Graph each set of numbers on a number line.

    23. $\{{}^-1, 0, 1, 2, 3, \cdots\}$

    24. $\{2, 1, 0, {}^-1, {}^-2, {}^-3, \cdots\}$

Sentences with Integers _____ 9

Many mathematical formulas and open sentences are used to design and operate the equipment needed for ocean exploration.

You already know how to solve open sentences involving whole numbers. In this chapter you will learn how to apply these techniques to solve open sentences involving integers.

9.1 ◆ SOLVING EQUATIONS BY ADDITION

You solved equations like $x - 4 = 12$ by adding the same number to each side.

$$x - 4 = 12$$
$$x - 4 + 4 = 12 + 4 \qquad \text{Add 4 to each side.}$$
$$x + 0 = 16$$
$$x = 16$$

The same technique is used to solve equations involving integers.

Example 1: Solve and check $x - 8 = {}^-19$.

$$x - 8 = {}^-19$$
$$x - 8 + 8 = {}^-19 + 8 \qquad \text{Add 8 to each side.}$$
$$x + 0 = {}^-11$$
$$x = {}^-11$$

Check:
$$x - 8 = {}^-19$$
$${}^-11 - 8 = {}^-19 \qquad \text{Replace } x \text{ with } {}^-11.$$
$${}^-19 = {}^-19 \qquad \text{It checks!}$$

Example 2: Solve and check $x - {}^-3 = 17$.

$$x - {}^-3 = 17$$
$$x - {}^-3 + {}^-3 = 17 + {}^-3 \qquad \text{Add } {}^-3 \text{ to each side.}$$
$$x + 0 = 14$$
$$x = 14$$

Check:
$$x - {}^-3 = 17$$
$$14 - {}^-3 = 17 \qquad \text{Replace } x \text{ with 14.}$$
$$17 = 17 \qquad \text{It checks!}$$

The set of integers will be used as the replacement set for the open sentences in this chapter.

Exercises

A To solve each equation, what would you do to each side ?

1. $n - 7 = {}^-6$ **2.** $n - {}^-4 = 6$ **3.** $k - 7 = 14$

4. $m - {}^-11 = {}^-6$ **5.** $x - 8 = 0$ **6.** $z - {}^-9 = 0$

Find the value of each phrase.

7. $n - 8$ if $n = 8$ **8.** $n - {}^-6$ if $n = {}^-6$

9. $n - 9$ if $n = 16$ **10.** $n - {}^-27$ if $n = {}^-15$

B Solve and check each equation.

11. $x - 9 = 7$ **12.** $t - 11 = {}^-6$ **13.** $x - {}^-8 = 13$

14. $r - {}^-16 = {}^-9$ **15.** $k - 3 = 19$ **16.** $t - 13 = {}^-27$

17. $x - {}^-27 = 15$ **18.** $s - {}^-17 = {}^-48$ **19.** $m - 16 = 16$

20. $b - 13 = {}^-49$ **21.** $c - {}^-9 = {}^-41$ **22.** $d - {}^-93 = 27$

23. $t - 6 = 7$ **24.** $r - {}^-7 = 14$ **25.** $s - 8 = {}^-19$

26. The launching tower was removed at *T minus 57 seconds*. The rocket engine began firing at *T minus 4 seconds*. How long was it from the time the tower was removed until firing?

27. A submarine is at the $^-100$-foot level. How far will it need to descend to get to the $^-180$-foot level?

C Solve each equation.

28. $k - ({}^-5 + 2) = {}^-6$ **29.** $t - (4 + {}^-2) = 7$

30. $n - (8 + 2) = 7$ **31.** $r - (7 - 9) = {}^-5$

32. $m - (5 - 7) = {}^-3$ **33.** $(m - 5) - 7 = {}^-3$

34. $m - (3 - 5) = 4$ **35.** $(m - 3) - 5 = 4$

9.2 ◈ SOLVING EQUATIONS BY SUBTRACTION

To solve some equations, you can subtract the same integer from each side.

Example 1: Solve $x + 3 = {}^-19$.

$$x + 3 = {}^-19$$

$$x + 3 - 3 = {}^-19 - 3 \quad \text{Subtract 3 from each side.}$$

$$x + 0 = {}^-22$$

$$x = {}^-22$$

Check: $\quad x + 3 = {}^-19$

$${}^-22 + 3 = {}^-19 \qquad \text{Replace } x \text{ with } {}^-22.$$

$${}^-19 = {}^-19 \qquad \text{It checks!}$$

Example 2: Solve $x + {}^-5 = 6$.

$$x + {}^-5 = 6$$

$$x + {}^-5 - {}^-5 = 6 - {}^-5 \quad \text{Subtract } {}^-5 \text{ from each side.}$$

$$x + 0 = 11$$

$$x = 11$$

Check: $\quad x + {}^-5 = 6$

$$11 + {}^-5 = 6 \qquad \text{Replace } x \text{ with 11.}$$

$$6 = 6 \qquad \text{It checks!}$$

Exercises

A To solve each equation, what would you do to each side?

1. $n + 7 = {}^-6$ **2.** $n + {}^-4 = 6$ **3.** $k + 9 = 14$

4. $m + {}^-11 = {}^-6$ **5.** $x + 8 = 0$ **6.** $z + {}^-9 = 0$

Find the value of each phrase.

7. $n + {}^-8$ if $n = 8$ **8.** $n + 6$ if $n = {}^-6$

9. $n + {}^-9$ if $n = 16$ **10.** $n + {}^-27$ if $n = {}^-15$

11. $n + {}^-14$ if $n = 14$ **12.** $n + 27$ if $n = {}^-16$

B Solve and check each equation.

13. $n + 3 = 9$ **14.** $m + 8 = {}^-16$ **15.** $x + {}^-9 = 8$

16. $p + {}^-9 = {}^-16$ **17.** $n + 16 = 9$ **18.** $r + {}^-6 = {}^-6$

19. $k + {}^-7 = 16$ **20.** $q + {}^-17 = {}^-9$ **21.** $x + 14 = {}^-7$

22. $x + {}^-7 = 19$ **23.** $m + 9 = {}^-32$ **24.** $k + {}^-6 = {}^-72$

Solve each problem.

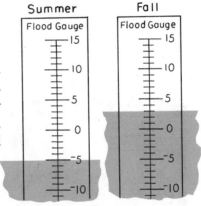

25. During the summer, Richard observed that the water level at Chandler Lake was *5 feet below normal*. By late fall, it was *3 feet above normal*. How much did the water level change during this period?

26. At dawn the temperature was $^-7°$. The temperature is $10°$ now. How much has the temperature risen since dawn?

27. Last year Mr. Buckley's blood pressure was 6 millimeters above normal. This year it is 2 millimeters below normal. How much has his blood pressure changed during the year?

28. How many feet will the submarine have to rise so that it will be at the $^-170$-foot level?

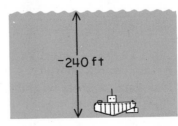

C Solve each equation as shown in the examples.

Since the sum of an integer and its opposite is 0, you need only add to each side to solve equations like $x + 3 = {}^-19$ and $x + {}^-5 = 6$.

$$x + 3 = {}^-19 \qquad\qquad x + {}^-5 = 6$$
$$x + 3 + {}^-3 = {}^-19 + {}^-3 \qquad x + {}^-5 + 5 = 6 + 5$$
$$x = {}^-22 \qquad\qquad x = 11$$

29. $x + 7 = 5$

30. $x + {}^-5 = 9$

31. $x + 9 = {}^-4$

32. $x + {}^-9 = 6$

33. $z + 7 = 6$

34. $z + {}^-7 = 9$

35. $z + 8 = {}^-9$

36. $z + {}^-8 = 16$

37. $m + 9 = {}^-7$

38. $m + 9 = {}^-4$

39. $m + 8 = 16$

40. $m + {}^-5 = 19$

Links of Chain

Hank wants the pieces of chain joined so he will have a chain 15 links long. It costs 5¢ to cut a link and 10¢ to weld it together again. What is the least possible cost to do the job? (The answer is not 60¢.)

You already know how to solve equations like $3x = 12$.

$$3x = 12$$

$$\frac{3x}{3} = \frac{12}{3} \qquad \text{Divide each side by 3.}$$

$$x = 4$$

The same technique is used to solve equations involving integers.

Example 1: Solve $3n = {}^-12$.

$$3n = {}^-12$$

$$\frac{3n}{3} = \frac{{}^-12}{3} \qquad \text{Divide each side by 3.}$$

$$n = {}^-4$$

Check: $\qquad 3n = {}^-12$

$$3({}^-4) = {}^-12 \qquad \text{Replace } n \text{ with } {}^-4.$$

$$^-12 = {}^-12$$

Example 2: Solve ${}^-5z = 15$.

$$^-5z = 15$$

$$\frac{{}^-5z}{{}^-5} = \frac{15}{{}^-5} \qquad \text{Divide each side by } {}^-5.$$

$$z = {}^-3$$

Check: $\qquad {}^-5z = 15$

$$^-5({}^-3) = 15 \qquad \text{Replace } z \text{ with } {}^-3.$$

$$15 = 15$$

Exercises

A To solve each equation, what would you do to each side ?

1. $7x = 42$ **2.** $8y = {}^-48$ **3.** ${}^-9x = 27$

4. ${}^-18z = {}^-90$ **5.** $12x = 0$ **6.** $14b = {}^-70$

Find each quotient.

7. $\frac{16}{8}$ **8.** $\frac{{}^-16}{8}$ **9.** $\frac{16}{{}^-8}$

10. $\frac{{}^-24}{{}^-6}$ **11.** $\frac{35}{{}^-7}$ **12.** $\frac{{}^-42}{{}^-6}$

B Solve and check each equation.

13. $9x = 54$ **14.** $8y = {}^-40$ **15.** ${}^-9t = 36$

16. ${}^-7n = {}^-21$ **17.** $6x = {}^-96$ **18.** $12x = 72$

19. ${}^-8t = 96$ **20.** ${}^-9k = {}^-117$ **21.** $12n = {}^-168$

22. $24z = 192$ **23.** ${}^-14s = 252$ **24.** ${}^-32p = {}^-512$

25. $27n = {}^-243$ **26.** ${}^-18t = 126$ **27.** ${}^-23n = {}^-138$

28. ${}^-17t = 153$ **29.** ${}^-16t = {}^-192$ **30.** $48n = {}^-1056$

Solve each problem.

31. A submarine left the surface of the water at a rate of ${}^-6$ feet per second. At that rate, how long would it take the submarine to reach the ${}^-180$-foot level?

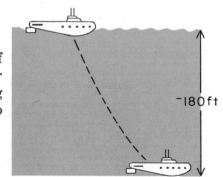

32. The stock market changed ${}^-18$ points in 3 days. What was the average change each day?

33. The Mills Company showed a change of ${}^-\$1200$ in 3 weeks. What was the average change each week?

34. In the first half, the rushing yardage for the Bears' football team was ⁻16 yards. If they had 8 rushing plays, what was the average yardage per rushing play?

C Solve each of the following.

$$\begin{aligned}
\textbf{Example:} \quad ^-7x - 3x &= 50 \\
(^-7 - 3)x &= 50 \\
^-10x &= 50 \\
\frac{^-10x}{^-10} &= \frac{50}{^-10} \\
x &= ^-5
\end{aligned}$$

35. $7z - 2z = ^-35$

36. $3n - 5n = 42$

37. $^-5k - 2k = ^-49$

38. $7x + 2x = ^-54$

39. $^-7x + 4x = 36$

40. $^-2x + ^-3x = ^-25$

Who Missed the Bus?

Jan, Laura, and Kay want to catch the 6 o'clock bus.

Jan's watch is 10 minutes fast, but she thinks it is 5 minutes slow.

Kay's watch is 5 minutes slow, but she thinks it is 10 minutes fast.

Laura thinks her watch is 10 minutes slow, but actually it is 10 minutes fast.

Each girl leaves for the bus so she can just make it if the time is what she thinks it is. Who missed the bus?

9.4 ◆ SOLVING EQUATIONS BY MULTIPLICATION

You already know how to solve equations like $\frac{n}{7} = 2$.

$$\frac{n}{7} = 2$$

$$\frac{n}{7} \times 7 = 2 \times 7 \qquad \text{Multiply each side by 7.}$$

$$n = 14$$

The same technique is used to solve equations involving integers.

Example 1: Solve $\frac{k}{3} = {}^-8$.

$$\frac{k}{3} = {}^-8$$

$$\frac{k}{3} \times 3 = {}^-8 \times 3 \qquad \text{Multiply each side by 3.}$$

$$k = {}^-24$$

Check: $\qquad \frac{k}{3} = {}^-8$

$$\frac{-24}{3} = {}^-8 \qquad \text{Replace } k \text{ with } {}^-24.$$

$${}^-8 = {}^-8$$

Example 2: Solve $\frac{m}{-2} = 15$.

$$\frac{m}{-2} = 15$$

$$\frac{m}{-2} \times {}^-2 = 15 \times {}^-2 \qquad \text{Multiply each side by } {}^-2.$$

$$m = {}^-30$$

$$Check: \quad \frac{m}{-2} = 15$$

$$\frac{-30}{-2} = 15 \qquad \text{Replace } m \text{ with } -30.$$

$$15 = 15$$

Exercises

A Find each product.

1. $8 \times {}^-7$ **2.** ${}^-8 \times {}^-7$ **3.** ${}^-8 \times 7$

4. ${}^-4 \times 9$ **5.** ${}^-5 \times 24$ **6.** ${}^-8 \times {}^-12$

Find the value of each phrase.

7. $\frac{k}{6}$ if $k = 18$ **8.** $\frac{n}{3}$ if $n = {}^-27$ **9.** $\frac{m}{-5}$ if $m = 25$

10. $\frac{p}{-4}$ if $p = {}^-24$ **11.** $\frac{x}{9}$ if $x = 54$ **12.** $\frac{t}{7}$ if $t = {}^-63$

B Solve and check each equation.

13. $\frac{n}{3} = 9$ **14.** $\frac{m}{2} = {}^-8$ **15.** $\frac{k}{-3} = 5$

16. $\frac{t}{-2} = {}^-9$ **17.** $\frac{a}{6} = 12$ **18.** $\frac{b}{5} = {}^-15$

19. $\frac{d}{-6} = 13$ **20.** $\frac{c}{-7} = {}^-21$ **21.** $\frac{x}{11} = {}^-2$

22. $\frac{n}{4} = 4$ **23.** $\frac{x}{18} = {}^-1$ **24.** $\frac{x}{-3} = {}^-12$

25. $\frac{y}{82} = 6$ **26.** $\frac{n}{101} = {}^-4$ **27.** $\frac{x}{12} = {}^-16$

28. $\frac{n}{-17} = {}^-5$ **29.** $\frac{p}{-13} = 6$ **30.** $\frac{q}{14} = {}^-13$

Solve each problem.

31. A number is divided by 3. The result is ${}^-14$. What is the number?

32. In a certain experiment, the temperature of a solution is lowered in 5 stages from 0°C. to ⁻90°C. If the temperature is lowered the same amount in each stage, what is the temperature after the first stage?

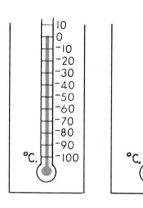

C Solve and check each equation.

Example : $\dfrac{-10}{n} = 5$

$\dfrac{-10}{n} \times n = 5 \times n$ Multiply each side by n.

$-10 = 5n$

$\dfrac{-10}{5} = \dfrac{5n}{5}$ Divide each side by 5.

$-2 = n$

Check: $\dfrac{-10}{n} = 5$

$\dfrac{-10}{-2} = 5$ Replace n with ⁻2.

$5 = 5$

33. $\dfrac{12}{n} = 6$

34. $\dfrac{^{-18}}{n} = 6$

35. $\dfrac{24}{n} = -8$

36. $\dfrac{^{-27}}{n} = -3$

37. $\dfrac{36}{n} = 9$

38. $\dfrac{42}{n} = -6$

39. $\dfrac{^{-18}}{n} = 9$

40. $\dfrac{^{-56}}{n} = -4$

41. $\dfrac{63}{n} = -9$

You can solve inequalities such as $x + 4 < {}^-7$ and $x - {}^-3 > 2$ by adding or subtracting the same number from each side.

Example 1: Solve $x + 4 < {}^-7$.

$$x + 4 < {}^-7$$

$$x + 4 - 4 < {}^-7 - 4 \quad \text{Subtract 4 from each side.}$$

$$x < {}^-11$$

Check: Try integers less than -11 in the original inequality.

Replace x with -12.	Replace x with -13.
$x + 4 < {}^-7$	$x + 4 < {}^-7$
$^-12 + 4 < {}^-7$	$^-13 + 4 < {}^-7$
$^-8 < {}^-7$ They check!	$^-9 < {}^-7$

Example 2: Solve $x - {}^-3 > 2$.

$$x - {}^-3 > 2$$

$$x - {}^-3 + {}^-3 > 2 + {}^-3 \quad \text{Add } ^-3 \text{ to each side.}$$

$$x > {}^-1$$

Check: Try integers greater than -1 in the original inequality.

Replace x with 0.	Replace x with 10.
$x - {}^-3 > 2$	$x - {}^-3 > 2$
$0 - {}^-3 > 2$	$10 - {}^-3 > 2$
$3 > 2$ They check!	$13 > 2$

Exercises

A To solve each inequality, what would you do to each side ?

1. $x + {}^-5 > 2$ 2. $y + 6 < {}^-4$ 3. $m + {}^-7 > {}^-2$

4. $n - {}^-8 < 2$ 5. $t - 6 > {}^-9$ 6. $k - {}^-19 < {}^-64$

B Solve and check each inequality.

7. $x + 5 > 4$ 8. $n + 15 < {}^-6$ 9. $a + {}^-7 > 6$

10. $t + {}^-8 < {}^-6$ 11. $z + 7 > 9$ 12. $m + 13 < {}^-19$

13. $b + {}^-8 > 14$ 14. $u + {}^-15 < {}^-17$ 15. $n + 8 < 6$

16. $k + 26 > {}^-7$ 17. $c + {}^-9 < 3$ 18. $w + {}^-11 > {}^-19$

19. $k - 5 < 3$ 20. $a - 4 > {}^-6$ 21. $t - {}^-5 < 2$

22. $v - {}^-8 > {}^-3$ 23. $j - 8 < 12$ 24. $b - 4 > {}^-3$

25. $r - {}^-11 < 13$ 26. $w - {}^-14 > {}^-19$ 27. $m - 6 > 2$

28. $c - 5 < {}^-9$ 29. $s - {}^-7 > 19$ 30. $y - {}^-23 < {}^-19$

C Try various values for x to determine whether each ⬤ should be replaced by $>$, $<$, or $=$ to make a true sentence.

31. $x + 7$ ⬤ $x + {}^-7$ 32. $x + {}^-8$ ⬤ $x - 8$

33. $x - 7$ ⬤ $x - {}^-7$ 34. $x + 6$ ⬤ $x - 6$

35. $x - 7$ ⬤ ${}^-7 + x$ 36. $x + {}^-5$ ⬤ $x - {}^-5$

37. $x + 11$ ⬤ $x - {}^-11$ 38. $x + 7$ ⬤ $7 + x$

39. $x - 2$ ⬤ $2 + x$ 40. $x + {}^-8$ ⬤ ${}^-8 + x$

You graph an open sentence such as $x + {}^-7 = {}^-9$, $x + {}^-8 < {}^-16$, or $x - {}^-3 > {}^-2$ by graphing its solution set.

Example 1: Solve $x + {}^-7 = {}^-9$. Graph the solution set.

$$x + {}^-7 = {}^-9 \qquad\qquad \textit{Check:} \quad x + {}^-7 = {}^-9$$

$$x + {}^-7 - {}^-7 = {}^-9 - {}^-7 \qquad\qquad {}^-2 + {}^-7 = {}^-9$$

$$x + 0 = {}^-2 \qquad\qquad\qquad {}^-9 = {}^-9$$

$$x = {}^-2$$

The solution set is $\{{}^-2\}$.

Graph the solution set.

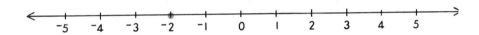

Example 2: Solve $x + {}^-8 < {}^-16$. Graph the solution set.

$$x + {}^-8 < {}^-16 \qquad\qquad \textit{Check:} \quad x + {}^-8 < {}^-16$$

$$x + {}^-8 - {}^-8 < {}^-16 - {}^-8 \qquad\qquad {}^-9 + {}^-8 < {}^-16 \qquad \text{Try } x = {}^-9.$$

$$x + 0 < {}^-8 \qquad\qquad\qquad {}^-17 < {}^-16$$

$$x < {}^-8$$

The solution set is $\{{}^-9, {}^-10, {}^-11, \cdots\}$.

Graph the solution set.

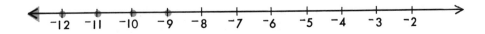

Example 3 : Solve $x - {}^-3 > {}^-2$. Graph the solution set.

$$x - {}^-3 > {}^-2 \qquad\qquad \textit{Check:} \quad x - {}^-3 > {}^-2$$

$$x - {}^-3 - 3 > {}^-2 - 3 \qquad\qquad {}^-4 - {}^-3 > {}^-2 \quad \text{Try } x = {}^-4.$$

$$x + 0 > {}^-5 \qquad\qquad\qquad {}^-1 > {}^-2$$

$$x > {}^-5$$

The solution set is $\{{}^-4, {}^-3, {}^-2, \cdots\}$.

Graph the solution set.

Exercises

A Match each set with its graph.

1. 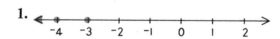   **a.** $\{3\}$

2.   **b.** $\{{}^-3, {}^-2, {}^-1, 0, \cdots\}$

3.   **c.** $\{{}^-3\}$

4.   **d.** $\{{}^-3, {}^-4, {}^-5, {}^-6, \cdots\}$

B Solve each equation. Graph its solution set.

5. $x + {}^-2 = 5$ **6.** $3x = {}^-6$ **7.** $\frac{k}{3} = {}^-2$

8. $5x = 35$ **9.** $\frac{y}{6} = 2$ **10.** ${}^-4x = {}^-32$

11. $x + {}^-3 = {}^-5$ **12.** $y + 7 = {}^-5$ **13.** $\frac{k}{9} = {}^-1$

14. $\frac{m}{{}^-7} = {}^-1$ **15.** ${}^-7x = 14$ **16.** $n + {}^-7 = {}^-7$

Solve each inequality. Graph its solution set.

17. $z + 3 < 5$ **18.** $x - {}^-5 > 7$ **19.** $m - 4 < {}^-1$

20. $n - {}^-5 > {}^-2$ **21.** $k + 7 > 2$ **22.** $p + {}^-8 < 2$

23. $t + 1 > {}^-5$ **24.** $q - {}^-2 < {}^-3$ **25.** $r + 8 < 2$

26. $x - {}^-8 > 0$ **27.** $n + 6 < {}^-7$ **28.** $p - {}^-4 > {}^-5$

C Solve each of the following. Graph the solution set.

Example: Solve $x + 2 \geq {}^-1$. (The symbol $\geq$ means *greater than or equal to*.) Graph the solution set.

$$x + 2 \geq {}^-1$$
$$x + 2 - 2 \geq {}^-1 - 2$$
$$x \geq {}^-3$$

Graph the integers greater than or equal to ${}^-3$.

29. $x + {}^-7 \geq 4$ **30.** $x - {}^-5 \leq 3$

31. $x - 6 \leq {}^-5$ **32.** $z + {}^-6 \geq {}^-8$

33. $m + 6 \geq {}^-9$ **34.** $t - 6 \geq 5$

35. $r + {}^-5 \leq {}^-8$ **36.** $w - {}^-5 \leq {}^-10$

9.7 ⊜ SOLVING INEQUALITIES BY MULTIPLICATION

If each side of a true inequality is multiplied by a *positive* integer, the resulting inequality is also true.

$$^-3 > ^-4 \qquad\qquad 6 < 10 \qquad\qquad ^-5 < 2$$

$$^-3 \times 5 > ^-4 \times 5 \qquad 6 \times 5 < 10 \times 5 \qquad ^-5 \times 5 < 2 \times 5$$

$$^-15 > ^-20 \qquad\qquad 30 < 50 \qquad\qquad ^-25 < 10$$

Notice what happens when each side of an inequality is multiplied by a *negative* integer.

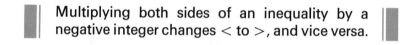

$$^-3 > ^-4 \qquad\qquad\qquad\qquad\qquad ^-5 < 2$$

$$^-3 \times ^-5 < ^-4 \times ^-5 \quad \text{Multiplying by } ^-5 \qquad ^-5 \times ^-5 > 2 \times ^-5$$

$$15 < 20 \qquad\qquad \begin{array}{l}\text{changes the}\\ \text{inequality sign.}\end{array} \qquad 25 > ^-10$$

> **Multiplying both sides of an inequality by a negative integer changes $<$ to $>$, and vice versa.**

You can use multiplication as follows to solve inequalities.

Example 1: Solve $\frac{n}{4} < ^-6$.

$$\frac{n}{4} < ^-6$$

$$\frac{n}{4} \times 4 < ^-6 \times 4 \qquad \begin{array}{l}\text{Multiply both sides by 4.}\\ \text{Keep the same inequality sign.}\end{array}$$

$$n < ^-24$$

Check: Try integers less than $^-24$ in the original inequality.

Replace n with $^-28$.   Replace n with $^-32$.

$$\frac{n}{4} < ^-6 \qquad\qquad\qquad \frac{n}{4} < ^-6$$

$$\frac{^-28}{4} < ^-6 \qquad\qquad\qquad \frac{^-32}{4} < ^-6$$

$$^-7 < ^-6 \quad \text{They check!} \quad ^-8 < ^-6$$

Example 2: Solve $\frac{n}{-3} > 4$.

$$\frac{n}{-3} > 4$$

$$\frac{n}{-3} \times {}^-3 < 4 \times {}^-3 \qquad \text{Multiply both sides by } {}^-3.$$
$$\qquad\qquad\qquad\qquad \text{Change the inequality sign.}$$

$$n < {}^-12$$

Check: Try integers less than $^-12$ in the original inequality.

Replace *n* with $^-15$.   Replace *n* with $^-18$.

$$\frac{n}{-3} > 4 \qquad\qquad\qquad \frac{n}{-3} > 4$$

$$\frac{-15}{-3} > 4 \qquad\qquad\qquad \frac{-18}{-3} > 4$$

$$5 > 4 \quad \text{They check!} \qquad 6 > 4$$

Exercises

[A] Tell whether the inequality sign will change when both sides are multiplied by the number given.

1. $^-5 < 8$ 7 **2.** $10 > 7$ $^-3$

3. $^-10 > {}^-15$ 4 **4.** $^-8 < 2$ $^-4$

5. $\frac{x}{-4} < 7$ $^-4$ **6.** $\frac{x}{7} < {}^-5$ 7

Multiply both sides of each inequality by the number indicated. Then write the resulting inequality.

7. $6 > 4$ 3 **8.** $10 > 7$ $^-4$

9. $8 > {}^-2$ $^-7$ **10.** $^-11 < 10$ $^-2$

11. $^-6 < 0$ 5 **12.** $5 > 3$ $^-3$

13. $\frac{x}{4} < {}^-8$ 4   **14.** $\frac{x}{=6} > {}^-7$ ${}^-6$

15. $\frac{x}{=7} < 10$ ${}^-7$ **16.** $\frac{x}{9} > 9$ 9

B Solve and check each inequality.

17. $\frac{x}{4} < {}^-9$ **18.** $\frac{m}{=4} > 8$ **19.** $\frac{k}{6} < 8$

20. $\frac{x}{=9} > {}^-2$ **21.** $\frac{x}{3} < {}^-2$ **22.** $\frac{n}{=9} > 8$

23. $\frac{t}{11} < 12$ **24.** $\frac{x}{5} > {}^-9$ **25.** $\frac{n}{=8} < 7$

26. $\frac{m}{5} > 7$ **27.** $\frac{x}{=6} < {}^-4$ **28.** $\frac{t}{=16} > 7$

29. $\frac{a}{=15} > {}^-4$ **30.** $\frac{n}{18} > {}^-9$ **31.** $\frac{d}{=18} < 16$

32. $\frac{b}{=13} < {}^-13$ **33.** $\frac{c}{35} > {}^-7$ **34.** $\frac{f}{=15} < {}^-32$

C Should >, <, or = replace each ▒ to make each sentence true ?

35. ${}^-6 < 2$ **36.** $4 > {}^-3$

     ${}^-6 \times 0$ ▒ 2×0 4×0 ▒ ${}^-3 \times 0$

37. $8 > 7$ **38.** ${}^-5 < {}^-3$

     8×0 ▒ 7×0 ${}^-5 \times 0$ ▒ ${}^-3 \times 0$

39. What is the effect of multiplying both sides of a true inequality by 0?

Divide each side of a true inequality by a *positive* integer. The resulting inequality is also true.

$$6 < 10 \qquad\qquad 4 > {}^-4 \qquad\qquad {}^-8 > {}^-12$$

$$\frac{6}{2} < \frac{10}{2} \qquad\qquad \frac{4}{2} > \frac{{}^-4}{2} \qquad\qquad \frac{{}^-8}{2} > \frac{{}^-12}{2}$$

$$3 < 5 \qquad\qquad 2 > {}^-2 \qquad\qquad {}^-4 > {}^-6$$

Notice what happens when both sides of a true inequality are divided by a *negative* integer.

$$6 < 10 \qquad\qquad\qquad {}^-8 > {}^-12$$

Dividing by ${}^-2$ changes the inequality sign.

$$6 \div {}^-2 > 10 \div {}^-2 \qquad\qquad {}^-8 \div {}^-2 < {}^-12 \div {}^-2$$

$${}^-3 > {}^-5 \qquad\qquad\qquad 4 < 6$$

> **Dividing both sides of an inequality by a negative integer changes > to < and vice versa.**

Example 1: Solve $3n < {}^-12$.

$$3n < {}^-12$$

$$\frac{3n}{3} < \frac{{}^-12}{3} \qquad \text{Divide each side by 3.}$$
$$\text{Keep the same inequality sign.}$$

$$n < {}^-4$$

Check: Try integers less than ${}^-4$ in the original inequality.

Replace n with ${}^-5$. \qquad Replace n with ${}^-10$.

$$3n < {}^-12 \qquad\qquad\qquad 3n < {}^-12$$

$$3 \times {}^-5 < {}^-12 \qquad\qquad 3 \times {}^-10 < {}^-12$$

$${}^-15 < {}^-12 \quad \text{They check!} \quad {}^-30 < {}^-12$$

Example 2:   Solve $-4n > 20$.

$$-4n > 20$$

$$\frac{-4n}{-4} < \frac{20}{-4} \qquad \text{Divide each side by } -4.$$

Change the inequality sign.

$$n < -5$$

Check: Try integers less than -5 in the original inequality.

Replace n with -6.   Replace n with -10.

$$-4n > 20 \qquad\qquad\qquad -4n > 20$$

$$-4 \times -6 > 20 \qquad\qquad -4 \times -10 > 20$$

$$24 > 20 \qquad \text{They check!} \qquad 40 > 20$$

Exercises

A Tell whether the inequality sign will change when both sides are divided by the given number.

1. $6 < 8$ 2   **2.** $14 > 10$ -2

3. $-8 > -12$ -4 **4.** $-12 < -6$ 6

5. $-4x > 8$ 4   **6.** $3x < -9$ 3

Divide both sides of each inequality by the number indicated. Then write the resulting inequality.

7. $8 > 4$ 2   **8.** $15 < 25$ -5

9. $36 < 64$ -4 **10.** $12 > -4$ -4

11. $-14 > -16$ 2   **12.** $-18 < -12$ -6

13. $3x > 15$ 3   **14.** $-5x < 25$ -5

15. $-6x < 24$ -6 **16.** $10x > -10$ 10

Solve and check each inequality.

17. $6x < 48$ **18.** $7x > {}^-42$ **19.** ${}^-9x < 81$

20. ${}^-3x < 6$ **21.** $8x > 16$ **22.** $5x > {}^-15$

23. ${}^-10x > {}^-100$ **24.** ${}^-2x < 12$ **25.** $4x < {}^-64$

26. $9x > {}^-108$ **27.** ${}^-6x < 36$ **28.** ${}^-11x < {}^-121$

29. $16x > 256$ **30.** ${}^-2x > {}^-24$ **31.** ${}^-4x < 196$

32. ${}^-8x < 24$ **33.** ${}^-24x < 72$ **34.** $13x < {}^-52$

C Solve and check each inequality.

35. $2x + 3x > 15$ **36.** $7x - 2x < 25$ **37.** $3(4x) < 72$

38. $\frac{8x}{2} < 60$ **39.** ${}^-5x + 2x < 9$ **40.** $5x - 8x > 36$

41. ${}^-3(2x) < 54$ **42.** $\frac{9x}{3} > {}^-54$ **43.** $4x - 7x < {}^-54$

44. ${}^-3(2x) > {}^-36$ **45.** $8x - 5x < {}^-39$ **46.** $15x - 36x > {}^-84$

Crossing the River

Two 100-pound boys and a 200-pound man wish to cross a river. Their boat is safe for 200 pounds or less. How can they cross the river using the boat?

9.9 ● GRAPHING INEQUALITIES

Graphing inequalities like $^-3x < 15$ and $\frac{n}{^-4} > ^-16$ is no different than graphing other types of inequalities.

Example 1: Solve $^-3x < 15$. Graph the solution set.

$$^-3x < 15 \qquad\qquad Check:\quad ^-3x < 15$$

$$\frac{^-3x}{^-3} > \frac{15}{^-3} \qquad\qquad ^-3 \times 0 < 15 \quad \text{Try } x = 0.$$

$$x > ^-5 \qquad\qquad\qquad 0 < 15$$

The solution set is $\{^-4, ^-3, ^-2, ^-1, \cdots\}$.

Graph the solution set.

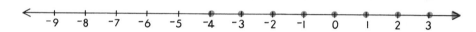

Example 2: Solve $\frac{n}{^-4} > ^-16$. Graph the solution set.

$$\frac{n}{^-4} > ^-16 \qquad\qquad Check:\quad \frac{n}{^-4} > ^-16$$

$$\frac{n}{^-4} \times ^-4 < ^-16 \times ^-4 \qquad\qquad \frac{40}{^-4} > ^-16 \quad \text{Try } n = 40.$$

$$n < 64 \qquad\qquad\qquad ^-10 > ^-16$$

The solution set is $\{63, 62, 61, \cdots\}$.

Graph the solution set.

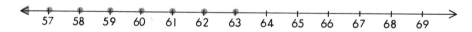

Exercises

A To solve each inequality, what would you do to each side?

1. $6x < 24$ **2.** $\frac{x}{5} > 6$ **3.** $^-5y > 20$

4. $\frac{x}{^-5} < 27$ **5.** $9m < ^-36$ **6.** $\frac{m}{7} < ^-32$

Solve each inequality. Graph the solution set.

7. $7x > 21$ **8.** $\frac{n}{7} < 16$ **9.** $-6z < 42$

10. $\frac{n}{-7} > 13$ **11.** $8k > {}^-48$ **12.** $\frac{h}{9} < {}^-3$

13. $-6m < {}^-66$ **14.** $\frac{t}{-8} > {}^-2$ **15.** $12a < 72$

16. $\frac{m}{7} > 2$ **17.** $-13b > 52$ **18.** $\frac{n}{-9} < 2$

19. $17t < {}^-85$ **20.** $\frac{p}{6} > {}^-5$ **21.** $-19d > {}^-76$

22. $\frac{r}{-3} < {}^-6$ **23.** $-2k < 24$ **24.** $\frac{q}{-4} > {}^-5$

C Solve. Graph each solution set.

Example: $-3x \geq {}^-21$

$$\frac{-3x}{-3} \leq \frac{-21}{-3}$$ Divide each side by $^-3$.
Change $\geq$ to $\leq$.

$$x \leq 7$$

Graph the set of integers less than or equal to 7.

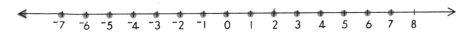

25. $-7n \leq 21$ **26.** $-5m \geq {}^-35$ **27.** $-8k \leq 48$

28. $\frac{n}{-4} \geq 2$ **29.** $\frac{k}{-6} \leq {}^-2$ **30.** $\frac{t}{-7} \geq 1$

31. $-5z \leq 45$ **32.** $\frac{m}{-9} \geq 0$ **33.** $-9t \leq {}^-81$

34. $\frac{m}{-8} \leq {}^-2$ **35.** $-6y \geq 36$ **36.** $\frac{n}{-7} \geq 2$

9.10 ◆ TWO–STEP EQUATIONS

You can solve two-step equations with integers the same way you solved two-step equations with whole numbers.

Example 1: Solve $3n + {}^-7 = {}^-19$.

$$3n + {}^-7 = {}^-19$$

$$3n + {}^-7 - {}^-7 = {}^-19 - {}^-7 \quad \text{Subtract } {}^-7 \text{ from each side.}$$

$$3n = {}^-12$$

$$\frac{3n}{3} = \frac{{}^-12}{3} \quad \text{Divide each side by 3.}$$

$$n = {}^-4$$

Check: $\quad 3n + {}^-7 = {}^-19$

$$3({}^-4) + {}^-7 = {}^-19 \quad \text{Replace } n \text{ with } {}^-4.$$

$$^-12 + {}^-7 = {}^-19$$

$$^-19 = {}^-19$$

Example 2: Solve $\frac{n}{{}^-6} + 9 = {}^-3$.

$$\frac{n}{{}^-6} + 9 = {}^-3 \qquad\qquad \textit{Check:} \quad \frac{n}{{}^-6} + 9 = {}^-3$$

$$\frac{n}{{}^-6} + 9 - 9 = {}^-3 - 9 \qquad\qquad \frac{72}{{}^-6} + 9 = {}^-3$$

$$\frac{n}{{}^-6} = {}^-12 \qquad\qquad\qquad {}^-12 + 9 = {}^-3$$

$$\frac{n}{{}^-6} \times {}^-6 = {}^-12 \times {}^-6 \qquad\qquad {}^-3 = {}^-3$$

$$n = 72$$

Example 3: Solve $\frac{k-6}{3} = {}^-12$.

$$\frac{k-6}{3} = {}^-12 \qquad\qquad Check: \quad \frac{k-6}{3} = {}^-12$$

$$\frac{k-6}{3} \times 3 = {}^-12 \times 3 \qquad\qquad \frac{{}^-30 - 6}{3} = {}^-12$$

$$k - 6 = {}^-36 \qquad\qquad\qquad \frac{{}^-36}{3} = {}^-12$$

$$k - 6 + 6 = {}^-36 + 6 \qquad\qquad\qquad {}^-12 = {}^-12$$

$$k = {}^-30$$

Exercises

A Tell the steps that you would use to solve each equation.

1. $2n + {}^-7 = 7$ **2.** $\frac{m}{6} + {}^-7 = 2$

3. $\frac{k-9}{{}^-4} = 6$ **4.** $^-2k + 7 = 9$

5. $\frac{x}{{}^-7} + 5 = {}^-2$ **6.** $3t + {}^-9 = {}^-18$

B Solve and check each equation.

7. $2k + {}^-5 = {}^-9$ **8.** $\frac{m}{8} + {}^-5 = 6$ **9.** $\frac{k-5}{4} = 6$

10. $\frac{k}{{}^-6} + 8 = 4$ **11.** $5n - 7 = 18$ **12.** $\frac{n + {}^-7}{6} = 9$

13. $\frac{m+5}{{}^-4} = 16$ **14.** $\frac{m}{8} - 6 = {}^-14$ **15.** $^-6x + {}^-9 = {}^-27$

16. $^-4t + 8 = 40$ **17.** $\frac{x + {}^-5}{3} = 7$ **18.** $\frac{r}{{}^-9} - 5 = 10$

19. $\frac{t}{5} + {}^-7 = {}^-14$ **20.** $8m + {}^-7 = 41$ **21.** $\frac{x-8}{{}^-16} = 5$

22. $\frac{x+9}{4} = {}^-5$ **23.** $\frac{m}{{}^-11} - 7 = {}^-9$ **24.** $^-7t + {}^-9 = 33$

C Solve.

25. $7 + 2x = {}^-5$ **26.** $^-7 + 3x = {}^-10$

27. $5 + {}^-4x = 13$ **28.** $3 + {}^-5x = {}^-17$

29. $2n + (3 + {}^-2) = 7$ **30.** $(3m + 3) + {}^-7 = 14$

VOCABULARY

Give the letter of the best ending for each sentence.

1. To solve $x + {}^-3 = 6$,

2. To solve $3x > {}^-5$,

3. Multiplying both sides of $\frac{x}{3} > {}^-5$ by 3

4. To solve $y - 5 = {}^-8$,

5. Dividing both sides of ${}^-3x < {}^-8$ by ${}^-3$

a. does not change the inequality sign.

b. subtract ${}^-3$ from each side.

c. divide each side by 3.

d. changes the inequality sign.

e. add 5 to each side.

CHAPTER REVIEW

Solve and check each equation.

9.1

1. $x - 9 = 4$

2. $n - {}^-4 = 7$

3. $t - {}^-18 = {}^-18$

4. $r - 11 = {}^-7$

9.2

5. $x + {}^7 = 6$

6. $n + {}^-4 = 7$

7. $k + 9 = {}^-16$

8. $m + {}^-1 = {}^-6$

9.3

9. $8x = 72$

10. $6y = {}^-48$

11. ${}^-7x = 84$

12. ${}^-5m = {}^-35$

9.4

13. $\frac{n}{3} = 6$

14. $\frac{n}{2} = {}^-7$

15. $\frac{m}{{}^-4} = 7$

16. $\frac{k}{{}^-8} = {}^-12$

9.5

Solve and check each inequality.

17. $y + 7 < 4$

18. $n + 5 < {}^-6$

19. $k + {}^-9 > 16$

20. $p - {}^-11 > {}^-14$

Solve each open sentence. Graph each solution set. 9.6

21. $x + {}^-4 = 9$ **22.** $y - 6 = {}^-17$

23. $5x = {}^-20$ **24.** ${}^-4y = 24$

25. $\frac{k}{6} = {}^-9$ **26.** $\frac{m}{{}^-7} = 40$

27. $x - {}^-7 > 5$ **28.** $y + 6 < {}^-9$

Solve and check each inequality. 9.7

29. $\frac{x}{4} < {}^-6$ **30.** $\frac{m}{{}^-3} > 8$

31. $\frac{t}{6} > 8$ **32.** $\frac{y}{{}^-2} < {}^-9$

33. $6x > 54$ **34.** $7t < {}^-35$ 9.8

35. ${}^-7x < 84$ **36.** ${}^-9w > {}^-108$

Solve each inequality. Graph each solution set. 9.9

37. $7x > 28$ **38.** $6n < {}^-42$

39. ${}^-4n < {}^-36$ **40.** $\frac{n}{7} > 12$

41. $\frac{n}{{}^-6} > 13$ **42.** $\frac{n}{{}^-9} < {}^-13$

Solve and check each equation. 9.10

43. $3x + {}^-5 = 10$ **44.** ${}^-5x - 3 = {}^-8$

45. $\frac{x}{5} + 3 = 7$ **46.** $\frac{x + {}^-8}{{}^-2} = 5$

CHAPTER TEST

Solve and check each equation.

1. $x + {}^-4 = 17$

2. $3x = {}^-15$

3. $\frac{n}{7} = {}^-8$

4. $y + {}^-7 = {}^-13$

5. $^-5x = 45$

6. $\frac{k}{{}^-3} = 14$

7. $x - 9 = {}^-14$

8. $^-12x = {}^-48$

9. $2x + 5 = {}^-15$

10. $\frac{x}{3} - {}^-7 = 28$

Solve and check each inequality.

11. $x - 4 < {}^-7$

12. $\frac{n}{5} < {}^-6$

13. $3y < {}^-12$

14. $x + {}^-3 > 2$

15. $n + {}^-7 < 6$

16. $x - {}^-4 > 5$

17. $^-5k < {}^-35$

18. $\frac{n}{{}^-3} > {}^-5$

19. $2x > 14$

20. $\frac{n}{{}^-3} > 7$

Solve each open sentence. Graph the solution set.

21. $x - {}^-5 > {}^-3$

22. $\frac{n}{3} = {}^-14$

23. $^-3k = 18$

24. $x + {}^-8 = 7$

25. $\frac{n}{{}^-3} < 4$

26. $4m > {}^-16$

Activity 1

A *magic square* is shown in **A**. The sum of the numbers in each row, in each column, and along each diagonal is the same.

Complete **B**, **C**, and **D** so they are magic squares.

A   B   C   D

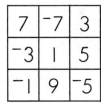

Activity 2

You can find the sum of a set of consecutive integers as follows.

$$\{-10, -9, -8, -7, -6, -5, -4, -3, -2, -1, 0, 1, 2, 3, 4, 5, 6, 7\}$$

Step 1: Add the first and the last number. $-10 + 7 = -3$

Step 2: Multiply the result by the number of numbers. $-3 \times 18 = -54$

Step 3: Divide that result by 2. The sum is -27. $-54 \div 2 = -27$

Find these sums.

1. the first 25 negative integers

2. the first 10 negative odd integers

3. the even integers from -4 through 20

Mathematics and Power Lines

Metal expands and contracts according to changes in temperature.

A certain amount of slack must be left when power lines are strung during warm weather. Otherwise, there is danger that in colder weather, the wires will contract and break.

The following formula can be used to compute the change in the length of a copper wire due to temperature changes.

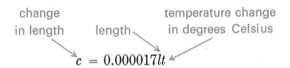

$$c = 0.000017lt$$

Example: At 20°C. a copper wire is 200 m long. What will be the change in length if the temperature drops to 0°C?

$$c = 0.000017lt$$

$$= 0.000017(200)(-20)$$

$$= -0.068$$

The wire will be 0.068 m, or 68 mm, shorter.

1. At 30°C. a copper wire is 35 m long. How much longer will the wire be at 50°C?

2. At 30°C. a copper wire is 40 m long. How much shorter will the wire be at -20°C?

Express as a fraction. 6.4

1. $1\frac{3}{4}$ **2.** $2\frac{1}{5}$ **3.** $1\frac{2}{7}$

Multiply. Express each answer in lowest terms. 6.3

4. $2 \times \frac{3}{2}$ **5.** $6 \times \frac{1}{6}$ **6.** $\frac{3}{4} \times 4$

Solve each equation.

7. $5x = 30$ **8.** $6x = 24$ 2.1

9. $3x = 36$ **10.** $2x = 46$

11. $\frac{n}{4} = 10$ **12.** $\frac{x}{3} = 7$ 2.2

13. $\frac{x}{2} = 9$ **14.** $\frac{n}{6} = 5$

15. $x + {}^-5 = 10$ **16.** $x + {}^-12 = 23$ 9.1

17. $3n = -12$ **18.** $10x = -90$ 9.3

19. $5x + 1 = 16$ **20.** $3x - 14 = 13$ 2.8

21. $2n + 1 = 25$ **22.** $\frac{n}{2} + 4 = 21$

23. $n + (n + 1) = 29$ **24.** $n + (n + 2) = 26$ 5.4

25. $3x + 5x = 16$ **26.** $6x + 4x = 50$ 5.6

Divide.

27. $0.25 \div 4$ **28.** $0.35 \div 20$ 7.4

29. $31.5 \div 5$ **30.** $2.8 \div 7$

31. $68 \div 0.17$ **32.** $39 \div 2.6$ 7.5

33. $102 \div 0.85$ **34.** $12 \div 0.4$

Problem Solving ———————— 10

If you want to enter the legal profession as a clerk, secretary, or lawyer, you will have to learn a special legal language. Work in many professions involves mathematical language.

In this chapter you will learn how to use mathematical language to write equations for problems. You can then use what you have learned about equations to find the answers to the problems.

Algebra is a kind of shorthand. You are already familiar with many terms of this shorthand—for example, $2 + 3$, $3y$, and $\frac{x}{2}$.

Example 1: Translate into algebra. To translate into algebra means to express words as symbols.

four plus seven	$4 + 7$
six divided by eleven	$\frac{6}{11}$ or $6 \div 11$
eight more than nine	$9 + 8$

Notice that *more than* and *plus* tell you to add. *Increased by* and *added to* are also common expressions for addition.

Sometimes you need to be careful that the order of the terms is correct.

four minus a number n

$$4 - n$$

Subtract four from a number n.

$$n - 4$$

Algebra can be used to represent many kinds of relationships. An expression like *five times the length* can be written as $5l$.

Example 2: Translate into algebra.

10 mph more than the speed limit s	$s + 10$
$6 less than the price p	$p - 6$

Exercises

A Tell what symbols you would use for the italicized words.

1. six *more than* nine

2. five *less* two

3. ten *times* eleven

4. thirty *decreased by* fifteen

5. one *divided by* two

6. *one-half of ten*

7. six plus *twice the cost c*

8. *double a number n*

B Translate into algebra.

9. 7 more than 20

10. the product of 8 and 9

11. height h decreased by 100

12. 12 divided by 4

13. one-third of a number n

14. profit p less tax t

15. the amount of copper c plus the amount of nickel n

16. 33 years older than Gloria's age a

17. 20 feet higher than the height h of the Eiffel Tower

18. 50 feet deeper than the depth d of the diving bell

19. 10 mph slower than the speed s of sound

20. 2 hours more than time t

C Translate into algebra.

Example : In a football game, a team gained
5 yards, then lost 12 yards. $5 + {}^{-}12$

21. In a card game, Mike had a 30-point set (loss) followed by 25- and 15-point gains.

22. A stock was at $23\frac{1}{2}$ before Monday's trading. The stock lost $\frac{5}{8}$ point on Monday and gained $\frac{3}{4}$ point on Tuesday.

23. A 500-foot dive was followed by a 200-foot rise toward the surface.

Ms. Fox showed her son Fred this number trick.

a. Think of your age.   15

b. Add 4. $15 + 4 = 19$

c. Multiply by 2. $19 \times 2 = 38$

d. Subtract 6. $38 - 6 = 32$

e. Divide by 2. $32 \div 2 = 16$

Ms. Fox said that the result is always one more than the age you start with. You can use algebra to see why this trick always works.

Example 1:

a. Age a

b. Add 4. $a + 4$

c. Multiply by 2. $2(a + 4) = 2a + 8$

d. Subtract 6. $2a + 8 - 6 = 2a + 2$

e. Divide by 2. $\dfrac{2a + 2}{2} = \dfrac{2(a + 1)}{2} = a + 1$

Working in steps can help you with complicated statements.

Example 2:   Translate into algebra.

The charity drive made five dollars more than twice the amount needed.

the amount needed a

twice the amount needed $2a$

five more than twice
the amount needed $2a + 5$

Exercises

A Give the result of the following computations.

1. Multiply $n + 1$ by 3.

2. Add 2 to $x - 1$.

3. Add 3 to $3a + 4$.

4. Divide $4x - 2$ by 2.

5. Subtract 6 from $n + 10$.

6. Double $\frac{n}{2}$.

B Use algebra to show how each trick works.

7. a. Pick a number.

  b. Add 6.

  c. Subtract 1.

  d. Multiply by 2.

  e. Subtract 10.

  f. Divide by 2.

  g. Your result should be the number you started with.

8. a. Pick a number.

  b. Add 2.

  c. Multiply by 6.

  d. Subtract 3.

  e. Divide by 3.

  f. Subtract 1.

  g. Divide by 2.

  h. Subtract the number picked.

  i. Your result should be 1.

Translate into algebra.

9. \$2 plus half the cost c

10. 5 hours less than time t

11. Subtract twice the speed s from 6.

12. Add the width w to one-third of the height h.

13. Multiply a number n by 3, then add 11.

14. Divide a number n by 4, then add 2.

15. 5 times the weight w plus half the distance d

C Translate into algebra.

Example: one-fifth of *the sum* of the cost c and 4 $\frac{1}{5}(c + 4)$

16. twice *the sum* of 5 and 4

17. $\frac{1}{2}$ *the difference* of z and 5

18. 3 times *the sum* of 2 and 3

19. 7 minus *the product* of 2 and n

Many English sentences can be translated directly into algebra.

Example 1: Translate into algebra.

Twice a number n plus three is fifteen.

$$2n \quad + \quad 3 \quad = \quad 15$$

In other situations, you must start by saying what the variable represents.

Example 2: Translate into algebra.

A 48-inch board is separated into two pieces.

One piece is 8 inches longer than the other.

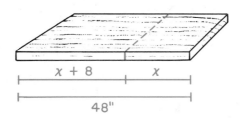

Let $\quad x =$ length of shorter piece

Then $\quad x + 8 =$ length of longer piece

The sum of the lengths is 48 inches. $\quad x + (x + 8) = 48$

Example 3: Translate into algebra.

Bob is 6 years older than twice Jim's age. Bob is 42.

Let $\quad a =$ Jim's age

Then $\quad 2a + 6 =$ Bob's age

Bob's age is 42. $\quad 2a + 6 = 42$

Exercises

A Tell how you would represent each quantity.

1. One number is five times a second number.

    a. first number   **b.** second number

2. One carton weighs 50 pounds less than a second carton.

    a. weight of first carton   **b.** weight of second carton

3. Arlene is 3 years older than her brother Paul.

    a. Arlene's age   **b.** Paul's age

4. One number is 2 less than twice a second number.

    a. first number   **b.** second number

B Translate into algebra.

5. Twenty-one is six more than a number.

6. 15 is subtracted from $\frac{1}{2}$ a number. The result is 11.

7. Twelve is $\frac{2}{3}$ of Mario's age.

8. The perimeter of a rectangle is 30 inches. The length of one side is twice the other.

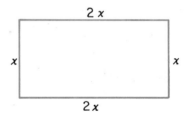

9. One shirt costs two dollars more than a second shirt. The total cost of the two shirts is twenty-four dollars.

10. Jan has saved \$235. This is \$5 less than $\frac{1}{2}$ the amount she needs for her vacation.

11. One number is 3 times a second number. The sum of the two numbers is 20.

12. Ann is 15 years old. This is 6 less than half her father's age.

13. The cost of an adult ticket is $0.50 more than a student ticket. The cost of 2 adult and 3 student tickets is $6.00.

14. The difference between two numbers is 3. Their sum is 15.

15. Stuart and Evie played 20 games of rummy. Evie won 2 more games than Stuart did.

16. The Detroit Pistons beat the Chicago Bulls by 20 points. Their combined score was 210 points.

17. 52 students were placed in two classes. There were 4 more students in Ms. Krol's class than in Mr. Luster's class.

C Translate these sentences into inequalities.

Example: Twice a number is greater than 10.

$$n = \text{number}$$

$$2n > 10$$

18. 45 is less than 3 times a number.

19. Rich is older than Karen. Karen is 27.

20. One-third of a number is less than 15.

21. The sum of 11 and a number is greater than 36.

22. $5.00 is more than what Diane wants to spend.

23. Aretha scored more points in the game than Cora. Cora scored 18 points.

24. Mark spent less than $6.00 on the gift.

10.4 ◆ HOW GREAT IT IS

The longest recorded life-span for a domestic cat is 36 years. This is $1\frac{1}{3}$ times the record for a dog. What is the longest recorded life-span for a dog?

x = dog's life-span

$1\frac{1}{3}x$ = cat's life-span

$1\frac{1}{3}x = 36$

$\frac{4}{3}x = 36$ Change $1\frac{1}{3}$ to $\frac{4}{3}$.

$3 \times \frac{4}{3}x = 3 \times 36$ Multiply each side by 3.

$4x = 108$

$\frac{4x}{4} = \frac{108}{4}$ Divide each side by 4.

$x = 27$ The longest recorded life-span for a dog is 27 years.

Exercises

A Tell what you would do to solve each equation.

1. $x + {}^-12 = 21$

2. $\frac{1}{3}y = 8$

3. $\frac{2}{5}n = 6$

4. $2\frac{1}{2}z = 2$

B Give an equation for each problem. Then solve the problem.

5. A wolf has been clocked at 35 mph. This is one-half as fast as a cheetah's top speed. How fast can a cheetah run?

6. Giant tortoises have lived to the age of about 195 years. This is 15 times as long as a rabbit's life-span. How long does a rabbit live?

7. A gazelle can attain a speed of 60 mph. This is $1\frac{1}{2}$ times as fast as a greyhound (a dog, not a bus). What is the top speed of a greyhound?

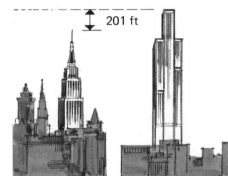

8. The Sears Building is 1451 feet high. How tall is the Empire State Building?

9. A falcon can fly 180 mph. This is about 7 times as fast as the fastest running speed for a man. What is the fastest running speed for a man? Give your answer as the nearest whole number.

10. The shortest male on record was $26\frac{1}{2}$ inches tall. This is about $\frac{1}{4}$ the height of the tallest male. How tall was the tallest male?

11. A whale can dive 12 times as far as a man can. How far can a man dive without diving equipment?

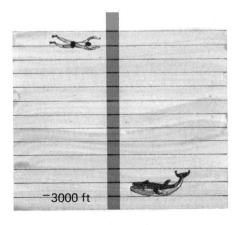

12. A golf ball has been timed at 170 mph. This is $1\frac{3}{7}$ times the fastest speed known for a hockey puck. What is the speed of a hockey puck?

13. The altitude of Death Valley is −282 feet. What is the altitude of Mt. Whitney?

C Use an equation to solve each problem. Draw diagrams to help you.

14. Two sides of a triangle have lengths of 3 and 5 inches. The perimeter is 3 times the length of the other side. Find the perimeter of the triangle.

15. The perimeter of a triangle is 520 mm. The length of side b is 3 times the length of side a. The length of side c is 120 mm longer than side a. Find the length of side a.

16. Three pieces are to be cut from a 40-inch board. One piece is to be 4 inches. The second piece is to be twice as long as the third. How long should each piece be?

17. The perimeter of a rectangle is 10 times the length of the shorter side. The longer side is 10 mm more than 3 times as long as the shorter side. How long is each side?

You have learned to solve equations involving two steps. Many problems require two-step equations.

Example 1: A punch is made from ginger ale and orange juice. Twice as much orange juice is used as ginger ale. How much of each do you need for 6 quarts of punch?

Let x = amount of ginger ale

Then $2x$ = amount of orange juice

$$x + 2x = 6$$

$$3x = 6$$

$$\frac{3x}{3} = \frac{6}{3}$$

$$x = 2 \quad \text{2 quarts of ginger ale}$$

$$2x = 4 \quad \text{4 quarts of orange juice}$$

Example 2: The sum of two consecutive integers is 17. What are the integers?

Let n = some integer

Then $n + 1$ = next integer

$$n + n + 1 = 17$$

$$2n + 1 = 17$$

$$2n + 1 - 1 = 17 - 1$$

$$2n = 16$$

$$\frac{2n}{2} = \frac{16}{2}$$

$$n = 8 \quad \text{some integer}$$

$$n + 1 = 9 \quad \text{next integer}$$

A 1. If n represents an integer, how would you represent the next two integers?

2. If n represents an even integer, how would you represent the next even integer?

3. If n represents an odd integer, how would you represent the next two odd integers?

B Give an equation for each problem. Then solve the problem.

4. One number is three times a second number. Their sum is 28. What are the numbers?

5. The sum of two consecutive integers is 65. What are the integers?

6. The sum of two consecutive even integers is 34. What are the integers?

7. To make dark orange paint, you mix red and yellow paint. You use 5 times as much red as yellow paint. How much of each should you mix to make 18 quarts of dark orange paint?

8. A car moves forward 6 feet every time a tire rotates once. How many times must a tire rotate for a car to go 1 mile (5280 feet)?

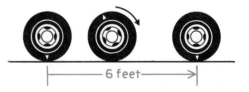

9. The sum of three consecutive integers is 57. What are the integers?

10. One number is 3 more than another. Their sum is 31. What are the numbers?

11. The perimeter of a triangle is 24 inches. Two sides are the same length. The third side is 3 inches longer than the other two. How long is each side?

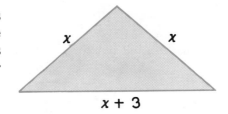

12. The sum of two consecutive odd integers is 64. What are the integers?

13. Joanne paid $15 for 2 books. One book cost $3 more than the other. How much did she pay for each book?

14. One number is 4 more than 6 times a second number. The sum of the two numbers is 39. What are the numbers?

15. A 125-centimeter board is to be cut into 3 pieces. Two of the pieces should be the same length. The third piece should be 5 centimeters longer than the other two. How long should each piece be?

16. A football field is 40 feet longer than twice its width. Its perimeter is 1040 feet. Find its dimensions.

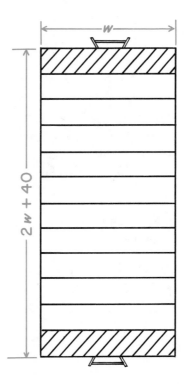

C Give an equation for each problem. Then solve the problem.

Example: Jeff bought 20 stamps for $1.90. Some were 8-cent stamps, and the others 10-cent stamps. How many of each kind of stamp did he buy?

	number	*value*
10 cent	x	$10x$
8 cent	$20 - x$	$8(20 - x)$

Total value of
stamps is $1.90, or 190¢.

$$10x + 8(20 - x) = 190$$

$$10x + 160 - 8x = 190$$

$$2x + 160 - 160 = 190 - 160$$

$$\frac{2x}{2} = \frac{30}{2}$$

$$x = 15 \qquad \text{10-cent stamps}$$

$$20 - x = 5 \qquad \text{8-cent stamps}$$

17. Sixteen nickels and dimes are worth one dollar. How many of each are there?

18. Martha sold 38 albums for a total of $130. Some albums sold for $3, and the others for $4. How many of each were sold?

19. Twenty-five sacks were placed in a carton. Some weighed 3 pounds, the others 5 pounds. They weighed a total of 89 pounds. How many of each were in the carton?

20. Bill has $2.25 in dimes and quarters. He has twice as many dimes as quarters. How many of each does he have?

An astronaut in a space suit weighs 28.9 kilograms on the moon. This is 0.17 of his weight on earth. What does he weigh on earth?

Let x = astronaut's earth weight

$0.17x = 28.9$

$$\frac{0.17x}{0.17} = \frac{28.9}{0.17}$$

$x = 170$

$$0.17\overline{)28.90} \quad \frac{1\ 70}{}$$

The astronaut in his space suit weighs 170 kilograms on earth.

Exercises

A Tell what you would do to solve each equation.

1. $0.16x = 25$

2. $11x = 0.33$

3. $3x + 2x = 0.10$

4. $2x + 1 = 13.6$

B Give an equation for each problem. Then solve .

5. Marcia figured that she would weigh 42.5 kilograms on Venus. This is 0.85 of her weight on earth. How much does she weigh on earth?

6. The lunar rover would weigh 572 kilograms on Jupiter. This is 2.6 times its weight on earth. What does it weigh on earth?

7. An Apollo spacecraft makes a 41,099-kilometer orbit in 1.46 hours. What is its speed in kilometers per hour?

8. An astronaut's space suit and backpack weigh 32.3 kilograms on Mars. This is 0.38 times their weight on earth. What do they weigh on earth?

9. The area of a triangle is 0.5 times the product of the height and the base. The area of the triangle is 120 square inches. Find the base.

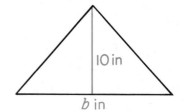

10 in

b in

10. A neighborhood recycling campaign received $1.75 for each 100 pounds of newspaper. They made $28. How many pounds of newspaper did they collect?

11. Mario's sponsors in the Walk-for-Development paid him $0.60 a mile. One sponsor offered him an additional $1.00 if he completed the walk. He completed the walk and collected a total of $10.00. How long was the walk?

12. Mrs. Chan wants to give her two children a total of $5.00 in allowances. She gives the older child $0.50 more than the younger child. How much does she give each child?

13. The perimeter of a triangle is 23.5 inches. The length of side a is twice the length of side b. The length of side c is one inch less than twice the length of side b. How long is each side?

14. In a city with serious air pollution, iron sheeting lasts only 0.4 as long as in a small town without air pollution. If it lasts 8 years in the polluted city, how many years would the iron sheeting last in the small town?

[C] Write an inequality for each problem. Then solve.

15. A number increased by 5 is greater than 12. What is the number?

16. A number increased by 6 is more than twice the number. What is the number?

17. Kathy makes $1.50 an hour. How long must she work to make more than $15.00?

18. Carl rented a car for $16.00 a day plus $0.16 a mile. If he has the car for one day, how many miles can he drive and spend less than $28.00?

An Electra and a DC-10 left JFK Airport bound for San Francisco International. The Electra left at 8:00 and averaged 450 mph. The DC-10 left at 9:00 and averaged 600 mph. When did the DC-10 catch up to the Electra?

At 9:00, when the DC-10 left, the Electra had gone 450 miles. One hour later, the DC-10 and the Electra had gone 600 and 900 miles, respectively. Putting the data into a table helps find the answer.

		Time				
		8:00	9:00	10:00	11:00	12:00
Distance from JFK (*miles*)	Electra	0	450	900	1350	1800
	DC-10	0	0	600	1200	1800

↑
The DC-10 caught up to the Electra.

Exercises

A Complete each table.

1.
Quantity	1	2	3	4	5	6	7	8
Cost (*dollars*)	5	10						

2.
Time	1:00	2:00	3:00	4:00	5:00
Distance (*miles*)	0	60	120		

3. Each year, Alice gets a $200 raise and Meg gets a $100 raise. Complete the table to find when Alice begins to earn more than Meg.

	Year 1	Year 2	Year 3	Year 4	Year 5	Year 6	Year 7
Alice's salary	$6000	$6200	$6400				
Meg's salary	$6500	$6600					

4. Mrs. Harrison made a table to show the days when three of her employees work. Complete the table for Harvey and Betty. When will Harvey, Betty, and Barbara all work the same day again?

November

	3	4	5	6	7	10	11	12	13	14	17	18	19	20	21
	M	T	W	T	F	M	T	W	T	F	M	T	W	T	F
Harvey	X		X		X		X								
Betty	X			X			X								
Barbara	X		X		X	X		X		X	X		X		X

Make a table for each problem. Then answer the question.

5. A single-engine Cessna left an airport at noon and headed north at 150 mph. A twin-engine Piper was sent from the same airport one hour later to overtake the Cessna. The Piper averaged 225 mph. When did the Piper overtake the Cessna?

6. A robber fled town in a Volkswagen at 60 mph. Five minutes later, the sheriff took off after the robber at 75 mph ($6\frac{1}{4}$ miles each 5 min). How long was it before the sheriff caught the robber?

7. A Boeing 747 and a DC-9 left O'Hare Field at the same time and headed in the same direction. The 747 averaged 600 mph. The DC-9 averaged 550 mph. How long before they were 250 miles apart?

8. Both Nick and Judy started at a salary of $8000 a year. Nick received a $200 raise at the end of each year. Judy received a $100 raise every six months. Who made the most money during the first year? The second year? (*Hint:* Show the total amount made during each 6-month period.)

9. Matt was offered two teaching jobs. One job offered $7000 a year to start, with a $200 raise each year. The second job offered $6500 a year to start, with a $300 raise each year. He took the second job. After how many years will the second job pay more per year than the first?

10. Sonya was offered a sales job. She was given this choice—$700 a month plus $2 for every $100 in sales or $600 a month plus $10 for every $100 in sales. How much must she sell each month for the second choice to be more profitable?

11. Two trains leave a station at the same time and travel in opposite directions. One train travels at an average speed of 60 mph, and the other train travels at an average speed of 40 mph. In how many hours will the trains be 300 miles apart?

12. Tara gets a homework assignment from Ms. Novak every other school day. Tara goes to the library every Monday and Wednesday to work on Mr. O'Malley's research assignment. Every third school day she has an assignment from Mr. Perez. This Monday, Tara had assignments from Ms. Novak and Mr. Perez, and she went to the library. In how many days will Tara again have to do the two assignments and go to the library on the same day?

13. Every other weekday (Monday–Friday), Sherm visits a new client. Every fourth weekday he attends a workshop. Every Thursday he completes a weekly progress report. Today Sherm visited a new client, attended a workshop, and completed his weekly progress report. In how many weeks will he have to perform all three duties again on the same day?

C Here's how an equation can be used for the first example.

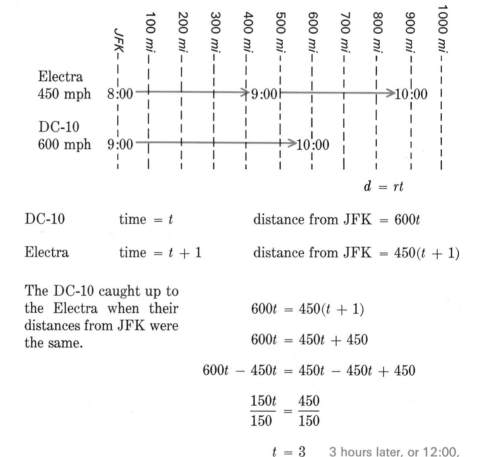

$$d = rt$$

DC-10   time $= t$ distance from JFK $= 600t$

Electra   time $= t + 1$ distance from JFK $= 450(t + 1)$

The DC-10 caught up to the Electra when their distances from JFK were the same.

$$600t = 450(t + 1)$$

$$600t = 450t + 450$$

$$600t - 450t = 450t - 450t + 450$$

$$\frac{150t}{150} = \frac{450}{150}$$

$$t = 3 \qquad \text{3 hours later, or 12:00,}$$
$$\text{the DC-10 caught up.}$$

14–16. Write equations for Exercises **5, 7,** and **11.** Then solve.

Match each item with the best description.

1. 5 less n **a.** $n - 5$

2. 5 more than n **b.** $2 + 3n$

3. 5 less than n **c.** $2n + 3$

4. 5 times n **d.** $n, \quad n + 1$

5. 3 more than twice n **e.** $5 - n$

6. 2 plus 3 times n **f.** $n, \quad n + 2$

7. consecutive integers   **g.** $5n$

8. consecutive odd integers   **h.** $n + 5$

CHAPTER REVIEW

Translate into algebra.

1. ten plus a number n 10.1

2. eight subtracted from the height h

3. six more than twice a number n 10.2

4. one minus one-half the weight w

5. Divide a number n by 4, then subtract 2.

6. One number is 4 more than a second number. The sum of the   10.3
   numbers is 26.

7. The profit is $100. This is $6 less than twice the cost.

Give an equation for each problem. Then solve.

8. Chris saved $20. This was four times the amount she needed.   10.4
   How much did she need?

9. Joe has $\frac{2}{3}$ as much money as his sister. Joe has $8. How much does his sister have?

10. Lillian says she works $1\frac{1}{2}$ times as long as Hal. If she works 54 hours a week, how many hours a week does Hal work?

10.5

11. One number is 3 less than a second number. The sum of the two numbers is 39. What are the numbers?

12. The sum of two consecutive integers is 43. What are the integers?

13. The sum of two consecutive odd integers is 52. What are the integers?

14. The sum of two numbers is 51. One number is twice the other. What are the numbers?

15. Mr. Levin is 2 years younger than 8 times his daughter's age. Mr. Levin is 38. How old is his daughter?

10.6

16. A rock sample weighs 34 kilograms on the moon. This is 0.17 of its weight on earth. What does it weigh on earth?

17. The perimeter of a square is 0.92 meter. How long is one side?

10.7

Make a table for each problem. Then answer the question.

18. A truck left town at 6:00 A.M. and headed north at 50 mph. A car left town at 7:00 A.M. and headed north at 55 mph. When did the car catch up to the truck?

19. Lynn was offered two contracts—(1) $7000 a year, with $300-a-year raises or (2) $6600 a year, with $500-a-year raises. Which contract pays more during the 4th year? During the 7th year?

20. Two trains leave a station at the same time and travel in opposite directions. One train averages 50 mph and the other train averages 45 mph. In how many hours will the trains be 475 miles apart?

Translate into algebra.

1. 6 more than n

2. n divided by 2

3. 15 subtracted from n

4. Multiply a number by 3, then subtract 5.

5. $50 is $5 less than $\frac{1}{2}$ the amount needed.

6. 25 is 3 more than twice n.

Give an equation for each problem. Then solve.

7. Art paid $10 for 2 books. One book cost $2 more than the other. How much did he pay for each book?

8. One number is three times a second number. The sum of the two numbers is 28. What are the numbers?

9. Jean finished reading 5 books for her English class. This is $\frac{1}{4}$ of the books assigned. How many books were assigned?

10. To make pale yellow paint, you mix white and yellow paint. You use 9 times as much white paint as yellow paint. How much of each should you mix to make 20 gallons of pale yellow paint?

11. The sum of two consecutive integers is 65. What are the integers?

12. An astronaut would weigh 38 kilograms on Mars. This is 0.38 of his weight on earth. What would he weigh on earth?

Make a table, then answer the question.

13. After raiding the chicken coop, a wolf ran east at 20 mph. An hour later, at 10:00, Rita rode off on her horse after the wolf at 30 mph. When did Rita catch up to the wolf?

Activities for Chapter 10

Activity 1

You can write your own number tricks.

1. Write the rule for this number trick.

    a. n

    b. $3n$

    c. $3n + 6$

    d. $3n + 6 - n = 2n + 6$

    e. $\dfrac{2n + 6}{2} = \dfrac{2(n + 3)}{2} = n + 3$

    f. $n + 3 - 3 = n$

2. Make up your own number trick. First do the algebra, then write the rule.

Activity 2

Many codes use algebra. Numbers are assigned to each letter. Then mathematical operations are performed on the numbers.

		A	B	C	D	E	F	G	H
	n	1	2	3	4	5	6	7	8
coding formula	$3n + 1$	4	7	10	13	16	19	22	25

$$3(1) + 1$$

The word "cab" would be coded as 10-4-7.

Write the coding table for the rest of the alphabet. Write the code for these words.

1. algebra   **2.** desk   **3.** parents   **4.** dance   **5.** Thursday

Mathematics and Typing

Accuracy and speed are important typing skills. For this reason, when determining your typing speed you deduct for errors.

This formula is used for a 20-minute typing test.

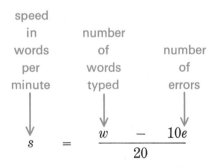

$$s = \frac{w - 10e}{20}$$

where *s* is speed in words per minute, *w* is number of words typed, and 10*e* involves the number of errors.

Find the speed for each of these scores on a 20-minute test.

1. 670 words with 5 errors
2. 720 words with 14 errors
3. 1000 words with 10 errors
4. 830 words with 7 errors

Getting Ready for Chapter 11

6.8   Rename so the denominator is 100.

     1. $\frac{1}{4}$ **2.** $\frac{2}{5}$ **3.** $\frac{1}{2}$

     4. $\frac{7}{10}$ **5.** $\frac{7}{20}$ **6.** $\frac{9}{50}$

7.1   Express as a decimal.

     7. $\frac{3}{5}$ **8.** $\frac{1}{4}$ **9.** $\frac{1}{2}$

     10. $\frac{3}{10}$ **11.** $\frac{11}{20}$ **12.** $\frac{17}{50}$

6.4   Express as a fraction or mixed numeral in lowest terms.

     13. $\frac{70}{100}$ **14.** $\frac{25}{100}$ **15.** $\frac{78}{100}$

     16. $\frac{85}{100}$ **17.** $\frac{142}{100}$ **18.** $\frac{120}{100}$

7.1   Express as a fraction in lowest terms.

     19. 0.5 **20.** 0.25 **21.** 0.68

     22. 0.75 **23.** 0.875 **24.** 0.05

     Solve.

6.5   **25.** $n = \frac{3}{5} \times 70$ **26.** $x = \frac{3}{4} \times 88$

2.1   **27.** $7w = 3 \times 56$ **28.** $15z = 4 \times 75$

7.3   **29.** $x = 0.4 \times 75$ **30.** $t = 0.75 \times 90$

Ratio and Proportion ———— 11

The strength of concrete depends in part upon the ratios of cement, water, and other materials in the mixture. Different ratios are used to produce different strengths of concrete for different purposes.

In this chapter, you will discover many useful applications of ratios, proportions, and per cents.

303

11.1 ⬥ RATIOS

Batting
average

.314

Gear
ratio

8:5

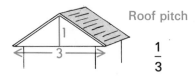

Roof pitch

$\dfrac{1}{3}$

Comparison by *ratios* is an important skill used by many people.

> The **ratio** of two numbers is a comparison by division. The ratio of *a* to *b* can be written
>
> $$a \text{ to } b \quad \text{or} \quad a{:}b \quad \text{or} \quad \frac{a}{b}.$$

Example 1:

The ratio of colored tiles to total tiles can be written

$$2 \text{ to } 5 \quad \text{or} \quad 2{:}5 \quad \text{or} \quad \frac{2}{5}.$$

The ratio of total tiles to colored tiles can be written

$$5 \text{ to } 2 \quad \text{or} \quad 5{:}2 \quad \text{or} \quad \frac{5}{2}.$$

Example 2:

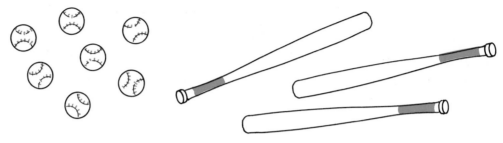

The ratio of baseballs to bats can be written

$$7 \text{ to } 3 \quad \text{or} \quad 7{:}3 \quad \text{or} \quad \frac{7}{3}.$$

The ratio of bats to baseballs can be written

$$3 \text{ to } 7 \quad \text{or} \quad 3{:}7 \quad \text{or} \quad \frac{3}{7}.$$

Of the three ways to write a ratio, the fraction is usually most convenient.

Exercises

A Give each ratio as a fraction.

1. **a.** circles to stars

   b. stars to circles

2. **a.** total squares to shaded squares

   b. shaded squares to total squares

3. a. wins to losses

b. losses to games played

c. wins to games played

GAMES PLAYED
20

WINS	LOSSES
12	8

Choose the correct ratio for each of the following.

4. 15 squares to 11 circles

$$\frac{15}{26} \qquad\qquad \frac{11}{15} \qquad\qquad \frac{15}{11} \qquad\qquad \frac{26}{15}$$

5. 2400 boys to 100 girls

$$\frac{100}{2400} \qquad\qquad \frac{2400}{2500} \qquad\qquad \frac{100}{2500} \qquad\qquad \frac{2400}{100}$$

6. 27 pounds per cubic foot

$$\frac{1}{27} \qquad\qquad \frac{27}{1} \qquad\qquad \frac{1}{28} \qquad\qquad \frac{28}{1}$$

7. 65 miles to 2 hours

$$\frac{2}{65} \qquad\qquad \frac{67}{2} \qquad\qquad \frac{2}{67} \qquad\qquad \frac{65}{2}$$

B Do the following.

Write each ratio in three different ways.

8. a. shaded parts to unshaded parts

b. unshaded parts to shaded parts

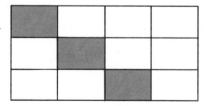

9. a. shaded sections to unshaded sections

b. unshaded sections to shaded sections

10. Draw 15 x's on your paper. Circle enough x's so the ratio of circled x's to uncircled x's is $\frac{2}{1}$.

11. A woman weighs 150 pounds. Her husband weighs 240 pounds. Write the ratio of the woman's weight to her husband's weight.

12. Write as a ratio: 1 car to 5 tires.

13. A pinch hitter was at bat 4 times and got 1 hit. What is the ratio of hits to times at bat?

14. The girls' basketball team won 7 games and lost 3. What is the ratio of games won to games played?

15. Donna received a 3 to 2 vote over Jackie for homecoming queen. Write the ratio of Jackie's votes to total votes.

16. A .190 hitter in baseball has a ratio of 190 hits to 1000 times at bat, or $\frac{190}{1000}$. Write each batting average given below as a ratio in the form of $\frac{x}{1000}$.

Stan Musial	.331	Ty Cobb	.367
Ted Williams	.344	Babe Ruth	.342
Jimmy Foxx	.325	Lou Gehrig	.340

C Guess how each ratio is found. A property of the figures is used.

$$\frac{\triangle}{\square} \quad \frac{3}{4} \qquad\qquad \frac{\pentagon}{\hexagon} \quad \frac{5}{6} \qquad\qquad \frac{\hexagon}{\triangle} \quad \frac{6}{3}$$

Use the same method to find each ratio below.

17. $\dfrac{\square}{\triangle}$ **18.** $\dfrac{\hexagon}{\square}$ **19.** $\dfrac{\square}{\hexagon}$

20. $\dfrac{\triangle}{\hexagon}$ **21.** $\dfrac{\hexagon}{\pentagon}$ **22.** $\dfrac{\triangle}{\pentagon}$

A property of the sets of points is used to find each ratio.

$$\frac{\bullet\!-\!\bullet}{\triangle} \quad \frac{1}{3} \qquad\qquad\qquad \frac{\triangle}{\bowtie} \quad \frac{3}{6}$$

Use that property to find each ratio below.

23.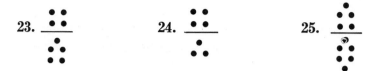

24.

25.

Gear Ratio

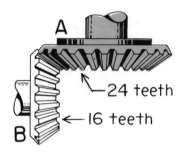

A

24 teeth

16 teeth

B

When power is applied to gear **A**, it causes gear **B** to revolve 3 times for every 2 times gear **A** revolves. Hence, the gear ratio is said to be 3 to 2. If power were applied to gear **B**, it would cause gear **A** to revolve 2 times for every 3 times gear **B** revolves. Then the gear ratio would be 2 to 3.

Find the gear ratio for each pair of gears below. (Power is applied to each gear shown in color.)

a.　　　　　　　**b.**　　　　　　　**c.**

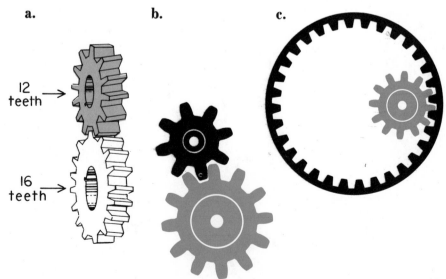

12 teeth →

16 teeth →

Three ways of comparing four ■ 's to eight △ 's are shown below.

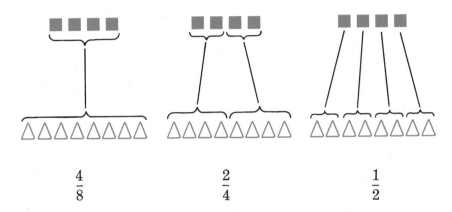

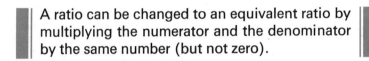

$$\frac{4}{8} \qquad\qquad \frac{2}{4} \qquad\qquad \frac{1}{2}$$

The ratios $\frac{4}{8}$, $\frac{2}{4}$, and $\frac{1}{2}$ are different ways of comparing the same sets. They are called **equivalent ratios.**

For the equivalent ratios $\frac{4}{8}$, $\frac{2}{4}$, and $\frac{1}{2}$, the ratio $\frac{1}{2}$ is in *lowest terms* because the fraction $\frac{1}{2}$ is in lowest terms.

> A ratio can be changed to an equivalent ratio by multiplying the numerator and the denominator by the same number (but not zero).

Example 1: Find two ratios equivalent to $\frac{3}{5}$.

$$\frac{3}{5} = \frac{3 \times 2}{5 \times 2} = \frac{6}{10} \qquad\qquad \frac{3}{5} = \frac{3 \times 3}{5 \times 3} = \frac{9}{15}$$

> A ratio can be changed to an equivalent ratio by dividing the numerator and the denominator by the same number (but not zero).

Example 2: Change each ratio to lowest terms.

$$\frac{6}{10} = \frac{6 \div 2}{10 \div 2} = \frac{3}{5} \qquad\qquad \frac{24}{32} = \frac{24 \div 8}{32 \div 8} = \frac{3}{4}$$

Exercises

A Answer the following.

1. What is the ratio of shaded sections to unshaded sections in each circle? Are they equivalent ratios?

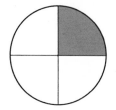 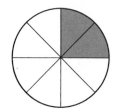 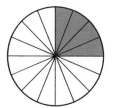

2. What is the ratio of ●'s to △'s in each comparison? Are they equivalent ratios?

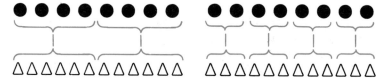

B Find two equivalent ratios for each ratio below.

Example: $\dfrac{4}{5} = \dfrac{4 \times 2}{5 \times 2} = \dfrac{8}{10}$ $\qquad$ $\dfrac{4}{5} = \dfrac{4 \times 3}{5 \times 3} = \dfrac{12}{15}$

3. $\frac{1}{4}$ $\qquad$ 4. $\frac{2}{5}$ $\qquad$ 5. $\frac{6}{7}$ $\qquad$ 6. $\frac{4}{7}$ $\qquad$ 7. $\frac{10}{13}$ $\qquad$ 8. $\frac{9}{11}$

9. $\frac{1}{5}$ $\qquad$ 10. $\frac{7}{9}$ $\qquad$ 11. $\frac{14}{17}$ $\qquad$ 12. $\frac{15}{23}$ $\qquad$ 13. $\frac{20}{31}$ $\qquad$ 14. $\frac{30}{31}$

15. $\frac{5}{8}$ $\qquad$ 16. $\frac{3}{4}$ $\qquad$ 17. $\frac{5}{9}$ $\qquad$ 18. $\frac{19}{21}$ $\qquad$ 19. $\frac{7}{12}$ $\qquad$ 20. $\frac{5}{7}$

Change each ratio to lowest terms.

Examples: $\dfrac{16}{20} = \dfrac{16 \div 4}{20 \div 4} = \dfrac{4}{5}$ $\qquad$ $\dfrac{36}{24} = \dfrac{36 \div 12}{24 \div 12} = \dfrac{3}{2}$

21. $\frac{2}{6}$ $\qquad$ 22. $\frac{8}{6}$ $\qquad$ 23. $\frac{6}{12}$ $\qquad$ 24. $\frac{18}{24}$ $\qquad$ 25. $\frac{15}{35}$

26. $\frac{14}{28}$ $\qquad$ 27. $\frac{18}{81}$ $\qquad$ 28. $\frac{20}{50}$ $\qquad$ 29. $\frac{20}{45}$ $\qquad$ 30. $\frac{30}{100}$

31. $\frac{60}{24}$ $\qquad$ 32. $\frac{8}{10}$ $\qquad$ 33. $\frac{21}{9}$ $\qquad$ 34. $\frac{150}{200}$ $\qquad$ 35. $\frac{18}{54}$

C Write each ratio in lowest terms.

Example: 2 feet to 6 inches

First express both measures with the same unit.

$$\frac{2 \text{ feet}}{6 \text{ inches}} \longrightarrow \frac{24 \text{ inches}}{6 \text{ inches}} \longrightarrow \frac{24}{6} = \frac{24 \div 6}{6 \div 6} = \frac{4}{1}$$

36. 4 yards to 3 feet

37. 3 hours to 5 seconds

38. 6 pints to 1 gallon

39. 75 centimeters to 2 meters

40. 2 pounds to 1 ton

41. 8 ounces to 3 pounds

42. 40 minutes to 2 hours

43. 450 grams to 2 kilograms

Write each comparison below as a rate.

Note: A **rate** is a comparison of unlike measurements and is usually written so the second measurement is 1 unit.

Example: 60 miles in 3 hours

$$\frac{60 \text{ miles}}{3 \text{ hours}} \longrightarrow \frac{(60 \div 3) \text{ miles}}{(3 \div 3) \text{ hours}} \longrightarrow \frac{20 \text{ miles}}{1 \text{ hour}} \text{ or 20 miles per hour}$$

44. 100 miles for every 5 gallons of gasoline

45. 200 feet in 4 minutes

46. 96¢ for 12 pencils

47. $500 for 100 hours of work

48. 8 pounds lost in 4 weeks

11.3 ◆ PROPORTIONS

Taylors sell 2 color TV sets for every 3 black-and-white sets. One month they sold 34 color sets. How many black-and-white sets did they sell that month?

Let n stand for the number of black-and-white sets. Then you can write two ratios for comparing the number of color sets to black-and-white sets.

$$\frac{2}{3} \longleftarrow \text{color sets} \longrightarrow \frac{34}{n}$$
$$\longleftarrow \text{black-and-white sets} \longrightarrow$$

Since $\frac{2}{3}$ and $\frac{34}{n}$ are two ratios for the same comparison, they are equivalent.

$$\frac{2}{3} = \frac{34}{n}$$

▌ A **proportion** is an equation that states that two ratios are equivalent. ▌

You can use the pattern of **cross products** to solve $\frac{2}{3} = \frac{34}{n}$.

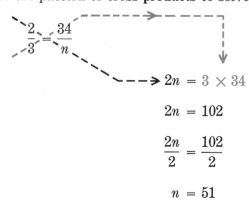

$$2n = 3 \times 34$$
$$2n = 102$$
$$\frac{2n}{2} = \frac{102}{2}$$
$$n = 51$$

Check:
$$\frac{2}{3} = \frac{34}{n}$$

$$\frac{2}{3} = \frac{34}{51}$$ Replace *n* with 51.

$$2 \times 51 = 3 \times 34$$ cross products

$$102 = 102$$

| | If $\frac{a}{b} = \frac{c}{d}$ is a proportion, then *ad = bc*. | |

Exercises

[A] Use cross products to tell whether each should be replaced by = or ≠ to make the sentence true.

Examples:

$$\frac{2}{3} \quad \frac{6}{9} \qquad\qquad \frac{4}{6} \quad \frac{9}{10}$$

$$2 \times 9 \quad 3 \times 6 \qquad 4 \times 10 \quad 6 \times 9$$

$$18 = 18 \qquad\qquad 40 \neq 54$$

Hence, $\frac{2}{3} = \frac{6}{9}$. Hence, $\frac{4}{6} \neq \frac{9}{10}$.

1. $\frac{21}{7}$ $\frac{3}{1}$ 2. $\frac{5}{2}$ $\frac{10}{4}$ 3. $\frac{6}{8}$ $\frac{2}{3}$

4. $\frac{7}{5}$ $\frac{9}{3}$ 5. $\frac{6}{9}$ $\frac{4}{6}$ 6. $\frac{4}{7}$ $\frac{8}{10}$

7. $\frac{10}{3}$ $\frac{50}{9}$ 8. $\frac{10}{18}$ $\frac{5}{9}$ 9. $\frac{5}{6}$ $\frac{10}{12}$

[B] Solve each proportion.

10. $\frac{3}{4} = \frac{n}{20}$ 11. $\frac{2}{3} = \frac{6}{n}$ 12. $\frac{6}{n} = \frac{3}{8}$

13. $\frac{1}{2} = \frac{n}{24}$ 14. $\frac{45}{90} = \frac{n}{100}$ 15. $\frac{3}{4} = \frac{n}{40}$

16. $\frac{8}{6} = \frac{32}{n}$ 17. $\frac{n}{8} = \frac{25}{40}$ 18. $\frac{24}{36} = \frac{n}{12}$

19. $\frac{4}{5} = \frac{n}{15}$ 20. $\frac{3}{8} = \frac{n}{16}$ 21. $\frac{n}{5} = \frac{10}{25}$

22. $\frac{4}{n} = \frac{3}{3}$ **23.** $\frac{2}{3} = \frac{4}{n}$ **24.** $\frac{n}{7} = \frac{9}{63}$

25. $\frac{n}{4} = \frac{18}{8}$ **26.** $\frac{6}{n} = \frac{60}{70}$ **27.** $\frac{5}{12} = \frac{75}{n}$

Use a proportion to solve each problem.

28. At 60 mph a car travels 88 feet per second. How many feet per second does a car travel at 15 mph?

29. A car used 6 gallons of gasoline in 120 miles. At this rate, how much gasoline will the car use in 360 miles?

30. Mrs. Rackow won an election by a 5 to 2 margin. Her opponent got 2800 votes. How many votes did Mrs. Rackow get?

31. If a 3-pound roast requires 60 minutes to cook, how long should a 4-pound roast be cooked?

32. A jogger runs 1 mile in 8 minutes and uses 97 calories. How many calories would he use to jog 1 mile on each of 3 mornings?

C Solve.

33. $\frac{n}{n-1} = \frac{3}{4}$ **34.** $\frac{n}{n+1} = \frac{2}{3}$ **35.** $\frac{3}{n+1} = \frac{4}{n}$

36. $\frac{5}{n-1} = \frac{8}{n}$ **37.** $\frac{n-1}{5} = \frac{n}{6}$ **38.** $\frac{n+1}{9} = \frac{n}{6}$

Answer the following.

39. Does $\frac{2}{3} = \frac{2+3}{3+3}$?

40. Does $\frac{2}{3} = \frac{2 \times 3}{3 \times 3}$?

41. Does $\frac{2}{3} = \frac{2-1}{3-1}$?

42. Does $\frac{4}{6} = \frac{4 \div 2}{6 \div 2}$?

43. Try the above patterns in other ratios. What do you conclude?

Player	Free Throws	
	made	*attempted*
Fremond	16	20
Reed	7	10
Tooms	9	15
Smith	21	25
Reynolds	12	16

To tell who was best at shooting free throws, you can change each ratio to a *per cent*.

% is a symbol for *per cent*.

n per 100.

$n\%$ means the ratio of n to 100.

$\dfrac{n}{100}$.

Example 1: What per cent of her free throws did Fremond make?

$$\text{free throws made} \longrightarrow \frac{16}{20} = \frac{n}{100} \longleftarrow \text{free throws attempted}$$

$$16 \times 100 = 20n$$

$$\frac{16 \times 100}{20} = \frac{20n}{20}$$

$$80 = n$$

$$\frac{16}{20} = \frac{80}{100} \text{ or } 80\%$$

Fremond made 80% of her free throws.

Example 2: Use per cents to compare the free-throw records.

Player		Ratio		Per cent
Smith		$\frac{21}{25} = \frac{84}{100}$	$\longrightarrow$	84%
Fremond		$\frac{16}{20} = \frac{80}{100}$	$\longrightarrow$	80%
Reynolds		$\frac{12}{16} = \frac{75}{100}$	$\longrightarrow$	75%
Reed		$\frac{7}{10} = \frac{70}{100}$	$\longrightarrow$	70%
Tooms		$\frac{9}{15} = \frac{60}{100}$	$\longrightarrow$	60%

Smith had the best free-throw record.

Exercises

A Give each of the following as a per cent.

1. 50 out of 100   **2.** 70 per 100   **3.** $\frac{9}{100}$

4. 45 to 100   **5.** 59 out of 100   **6.** 85 per 100

7. $\frac{64}{100}$ **8.** 78 to 100   **9.** $\frac{35}{100}$

B Change each fraction to a per cent.

Example: $\frac{2}{3} = \frac{n}{100}$

$2 \times 100 = 3n$

$\dfrac{2 \times 100}{3} = \dfrac{3n}{3}$

$66\frac{2}{3} = n$ so $\frac{2}{3} = 66\frac{2}{3}\%.$

10. $\frac{3}{10}$ **11.** $\frac{1}{20}$ **12.** $\frac{1}{2}$ **13.** $\frac{3}{4}$

14. $\frac{1}{5}$ **15.** $\frac{1}{6}$ **16.** $\frac{3}{8}$ **17.** $\frac{2}{5}$

18. $\frac{1}{4}$ **19.** $\frac{1}{3}$ **20.** $\frac{3}{5}$ **21.** $\frac{5}{6}$

22. $\frac{1}{8}$ **23.** $\frac{4}{5}$ **24.** $\frac{5}{8}$ **25.** $\frac{7}{10}$

26. $\frac{7}{8}$ **27.** $\frac{9}{20}$ **28.** $\frac{4}{25}$ **29.** $\frac{7}{50}$

30. $\frac{9}{10}$ **31.** $\frac{2}{25}$ **32.** $\frac{7}{20}$ **33.** $\frac{9}{25}$

Solve each problem.

34. In a contest, Wally scored 37 points out of a possible 40. Express his score as a per cent.

35. Per cent is used to compare the steepness of hills. Drawing **I** shows a road with a slope of 5%—it rises 5 feet for 100 feet of horizontal distance. What is the slope of the road shown in drawing **II**?

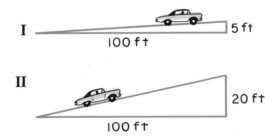

36. A 20% alcohol solution means there are 20 parts alcohol for 100 parts solution. How would you describe a solution which is 15 parts alcohol for 100 parts solution?

37. The interest for a new-car loan is stated as $6 per $100. What is the per cent of interest?

38. A hardware store advertised a discount of $1 on every $5 purchase. What is the per cent of discount?

C Replace each ⬤ with =, <, or > to make the sentence true.

39. $\frac{7}{8}$ ⬤ 80% **40.** $\frac{3}{4}$ ⬤ $83\frac{1}{3}\%$

41. $\frac{1}{3}$ ⬤ $33\frac{1}{3}\%$ **42.** 95% ⬤ $\frac{24}{25}$

43. 68% ⬤ $\frac{15}{25}$ **44.** $\frac{15}{30}$ ⬤ 50%

45. 72% ⬤ $\frac{17}{20}$ **46.** $62\frac{1}{2}\%$ ⬤ $\frac{6}{9}$

11.5 ◆ MORE PER CENT

The community blood-bank program was so successful that $1\frac{1}{2}$ times as much blood was donated as was expected.

How can this achievement be expressed in terms of per cent of the goal?

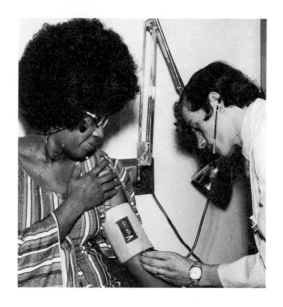

Example 1: Change $1\frac{1}{2}$ to a per cent.

$$1\frac{1}{2} = \frac{n}{100}$$

$$\frac{3}{2} = \frac{n}{100} \qquad \text{Rename } 1\frac{1}{2} \text{ as a fraction.}$$

$$300 = 2n \qquad \text{cross products}$$

$$\frac{300}{2} = \frac{2n}{2}$$

$$150 = n$$

Thus, $1\frac{1}{2} = 150\%$.

The blood-bank program achieved 150% of its goal.

Suppose the blood-bank program had collected twice as much blood as expected. How would this achievement be expressed as a per cent of the goal?

Example 2:   Change 2 to a per cent.

$$2 = \frac{n}{100}$$

$$\frac{2}{1} = \frac{n}{100}$$ Rename 2 as a fraction.

$$200 = n$$ cross products

Thus, $2 = 200\%$.

In this case, the program would have achieved 200% of its goal.

Exercises

A Express each of the following as a fraction.

1. 1   2. $2\frac{1}{4}$ 3. 3   4. $3\frac{3}{4}$

5. $1\frac{3}{4}$ 6. 4   7. $2\frac{1}{2}$ 8. $1\frac{3}{8}$

Express as a per cent.

9. $\frac{112}{100}$ 10. $\frac{300}{100}$ 11. $\frac{166\frac{2}{3}}{100}$ 12. $\frac{237\frac{1}{2}}{100}$

B Change each of the following to a per cent.

13. 1   14. $1\frac{1}{4}$ 15. $1\frac{1}{2}$ 16. $1\frac{3}{4}$

17. 2   18. $3\frac{1}{2}$ 19. $\frac{2}{2}$ 20. $1\frac{7}{8}$

21. $2\frac{1}{2}$ 22. $\frac{1}{3}$ 23. $\frac{7}{4}$ 24. $3\frac{1}{4}$

Replace each ● with $<$, $>$, or $=$ to make the sentence true.

25. $\frac{1}{3}$ ● 100%   26. $\frac{5}{4}$ ● 100%   27. $\frac{2}{2}$ ● 100%

28. 1 ● 100%   29. $2\frac{1}{4}$ ● 100%   30. 3 ● 100%

C Change each ratio to a per cent.

31. 3 to 2   32. 6:5   33. 4 to 3

34. $\frac{3}{4}$ to $\frac{1}{2}$ 35. $\frac{7}{8}:\frac{5}{8}$ 36. $1\frac{1}{2}$ to $1\frac{1}{4}$

37. 7.5 to 5.0   38. 3.2:2.4   39. 3.25 to 2.5

11.6 ◆ FRACTIONS, DECIMALS, PER CENTS

$$\frac{3}{4} = \frac{75}{100} = 0.75 = 75\%$$

Any ratio, like 3 to 4, can be named by a fraction, a decimal, or a per cent.

Example 1: Change each per cent to a fraction or mixed numeral.

$$35\% = \frac{35}{100} \qquad 166\% = \frac{166}{100} \qquad 37\frac{1}{2}\% = \frac{37\frac{1}{2}}{100}$$

$$= \frac{7}{20} \qquad\qquad = \frac{83}{50} \qquad\qquad = \frac{37\frac{1}{2} \times 2}{100 \times 2}$$

$$\qquad\qquad\qquad = 1\frac{33}{50} \qquad\qquad = \frac{75}{200}$$

$$\qquad\qquad\qquad\qquad\qquad\qquad = \frac{3}{8}$$

Example 2: Change each per cent to a decimal.

$$35\% = \frac{35}{100} \qquad 166\% = \frac{166}{100} \qquad 37\frac{1}{2}\% = \frac{37\frac{1}{2}}{100}$$

$$= 0.35 \qquad\qquad = 1.66 \qquad\qquad = \frac{37.5}{100}$$

$$\qquad\qquad\qquad\qquad\qquad\qquad = 0.375$$

Example 3: Change each decimal to a per cent.

$$0.35 = \frac{35}{100} \qquad 1.66 = \frac{166}{100} \qquad 0.375 = \frac{37.5}{100}$$

$$= 35\% \qquad\qquad = 166\% \qquad\qquad = 37.5\% \text{ or } 37\frac{1}{2}\%$$

Exercises

A What number should replace n?

1. $68\% = \frac{n}{100}$

2. $28\% = \frac{n}{100}$

3. $135\% = \frac{n}{100}$

4. $232\% = \frac{n}{100}$

B Complete the following tables.

	Fraction	Decimal	Per cent
5.	$\frac{1}{2}$	———	———
7.	———	0.3	———
9.	———	———	21%
11.	$\frac{1}{4}$	———	———
13.	———	0.31	———
15.	———	———	$12\frac{1}{2}\%$
17.	———	1.27	———
19.	———	———	168%

	Fraction	Decimal	Per cent
6.	$\frac{7}{10}$	———	———
8.	———	0.8	———
10.	———	———	6%
12.	$\frac{9}{20}$	———	———
14.	———	0.54	———
16.	———	———	143%
18.	———	2.48	———
20.	———	———	2.3%

C Change each of the following to a decimal.

Example:

$$124\% = 1.24$$

Move the decimal point two places to the left and drop the symbol %.

21. 7%

22. 61%

23. 49%

24. 125%

25. 340%

26. 250%

27. 6.5%

28. 8.75%

29. 9.25%

Change each decimal to a per cent.

Example:

$$0.37 = 37\%$$

Move the decimal point two places to the right and write the symbol %.

30. 0.53   **31.** 0.06   **32.** 0.7

33. 1.12   **34.** 2.5   **35.** 4

36. 0.125   **37.** 0.075   **38.** 1.375

Which Job Would You Take?

Suppose you were offered two jobs. The first job has a starting salary of $800 per month with a 6% increase every year.

The second job has a starting salary of $800 per month with a 3% increase every six months. Which is the better-paying job?

Per cent problems can be solved by following these steps.

a. *Decide what is asked.*

b. *Write an equation for the problem.*

c. *Solve the equation.*

d. *Write an answer for the problem.*

Example 1: A student must score at least 60% to pass an exam. There are 150 points possible. What is the minimum number of points needed to pass?

    a. 60% of 150 is what number?

    b. $0.60 \times 150 = n$

    c. $90 = n$

    d. A student must score at least 90 points to pass.

Example 2: Wes made 9 out of 15 field-goal attempts. What per cent of his field-goal attempts did he make?

    a. 9 is what per cent of 15?

    b. $9 = \dfrac{n}{100} \times 15$

    c. $60 = n$

    d. Wes made 60% of his field-goal attempts.

Example 3: At an appliance sale, each item was reduced 20%. Gretchen saved $8 by buying a radio at the sale. What was the regular price of the radio?

    a. 20% of what number is 8?

    b. $0.20 \times n = 8$

    c. $n = 40$

    d. The regular price of the radio is $40.

Exercises

A Match each question with a suitable equation.

1. 60% of 75 is what number?

2. 60 is what per cent of 75?

3. 60% of what number is 75?

4. 45% of what number is 90?

5. 45 is what per cent of 90?

6. 45% of 90 is what number?

a. $0.60n = 75$

b. $0.45 \times 90 = n$

c. $0.60 \times 75 = n$

d. $45 = \frac{n}{100} \times 90$

e. $60 = \frac{n}{100} \times 75$

f. $0.45n = 90$

B Solve.

7. 60 is 75% of what number?

8. 80 is what per cent of 120?

9. 90 is what per cent of 150?

10. 66 is what per cent of 90?

11. 40% of what number is 90?

12. 45% of what number is 18?

13. 45 is what per cent of 75?

14. 40% of 25 is what number?

15. 16% of 85 is what number?

16. 80% of what number is 88?

17. The Millers are now getting 16 miles per gallon. How much could their gas mileage increase with a tune-up?

18. After the tune-up the Millers' gas mileage increased 2 miles per gallon. What per cent did their gas mileage increase?

19. The largest mountain lion on record weighed 276 pounds. The average mountain lion weighs about 150 pounds. The record weight is what per cent of the average weight?

20. How much can be saved by buying the coat shown at the right on sale?

21. Holly answered 22 questions correctly. This was 88 per cent of the questions on the test. How many questions were on the test?

C Answer each of the following.

Example: Last year there were 5 Eagle Scouts in the district. This year there are 7. Find the per cent of increase.

a. The amount of increase is what per cent of last year's number?

b. $\qquad 7 - 5 \qquad = \qquad \dfrac{n}{100} \qquad \times \qquad 5$

c. $\qquad\qquad\qquad\qquad 40 = n$

d. The number of Eagle Scouts has increased 40%.

22. An increase from 10 to 15 is what per cent of increase?

23. An increase from 8 to 10 is what per cent of increase?

24. An increase from 3.2 to 3.6 is what per cent of increase?

25. An increase from $2\frac{1}{2}$ to $3\frac{3}{4}$ is what per cent of increase?

26. Mr. Larson's salary increased from $160 to $180. What was the per cent of increase?

27. N Enterprises, sales increased from $250,000 to $350,000. What was the per cent of increase?

28. Ms. Champrey bought a stock at $15 and sold it at $20. What was the per cent of increase?

11.8 ⬤ USING FRACTIONS OR DECIMALS

Per cent problems can be solved by using fractions or by using decimals.

Example 1: Use a fraction to find 25% of 240.

25% of 240 is what number?

$$\frac{1}{4} \times 240 = n$$

$$60 = n$$

25% of 240 is 60.

Example 2: Use a decimal to find 25% of 240.

25% of 240 is what number?

$$0.25 \times 240 = n$$

$$60 = n$$

25% of 240 is 60.

Exercises

A What equation would you use for each question?

1. $33\frac{1}{3}\%$ of 2 is what number?

    a. $0.60 \times 80 = n$

2. 8.5 is what per cent of 680?

    b. $\frac{1}{3} = \frac{n}{100} \times 2$

3. 60% of 80 is what number?

    c. $\frac{1}{3} \times 2 = n$

4. $\frac{1}{3}$ is what per cent of 2?

    d. $0.085n = 680$

5. 60% of what number is 80?

    e. $0.60n = 80$

6. 8.5% of what number is 680?

    f. $8.5 = \frac{n}{100} \times 680$

7. An engine with a supercharger can develop 125% of the power of a regular engine. If a regular engine has 180 horsepower, how much horsepower can the engine develop with a supercharger?

8. Joan can save $33\frac{1}{3}\%$ by buying her fall wardrobe at the sale. How much can she save on clothes that regularly sell for $120?

9. James borrowed $680 at 8.5% interest for one year. How much interest will he pay if he pays off the loan on time?

10. A certain cereal is 12% protein. How many ounces of protein are in a 14-ounce package?

11. The Badgers won $66\frac{2}{3}\%$ of their games. If they played 12 games, how many did they win?

12. A real estate salesman receives a commission of 3% of each sale. What would be the salesman's commission for selling a $30,000 house?

13. The carrying charge is 1.5% of the unpaid balance. What would be the carrying charge on an unpaid balance of $160?

14. There were 80 flights into the air terminal yesterday. Of these, 68 were jets. What per cent of the flights were jets?

15. Elaine needs 720 points to win a prize. She has 630 points now. What per cent of the number of points needed does she have now?

16. The Lions Club has collected $12,000 for needy children. This is 75% of their goal. What goal did they set for the drive?

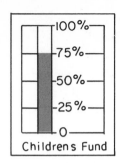

100%
75%
50%
25%
0
Childrens Fund

C Answer the following.

Example: Last year Mrs. Tomasello weighed 160 pounds. She now weighs 140 pounds. What is the per cent of decrease in her weight?

a. The amount of decrease is what per cent of last year's weight?

b. $160 - 140 = \dfrac{n}{100} \times 160$

c. $12\dfrac{1}{2} = n$

d. Her weight decreased by $12\dfrac{1}{2}\%$.

17. A decrease from 10 to 7 is what per cent of decrease?

18. A decrease from 20 to 16 is what per cent of decrease?

19. A decrease from $\frac{3}{4}$ to $\frac{1}{2}$ is what per cent of decrease?

20. A decrease from 3.2 to 2.4 is what per cent of decrease?

21. The price of a stock decreased from $12.50 to $10. What was the per cent of decrease?

22. An item which regularly sells for $25 was purchased on sale for $17.50. What was the per cent of decrease?

23. Mrs. Catalano sold 16 houses last year. This year she sold 14. What was the per cent of decrease in her number of sales?

Which example would you give for each item?

1. Ratio of 2 to 4

2. 3 ratios equivalent to $\frac{3}{4}$

3. Proportion

4. Per cent

5. 3 ways to write a ratio

a. $\frac{3}{4} = \frac{12}{16}$

b. $16\frac{2}{3}\%$

c. 2:4

d. $\frac{6}{8}, \frac{9}{12}, \frac{12}{16}$

e. $\frac{1}{2}$, 1 to 2, 1:2

CHAPTER REVIEW

Write a ratio for each of the following.   11.1

1. 3 hits to 4 times at bat   2. 3 votes to 2 votes

3. 6 baskets to 9 attempts   4. 8 baseballs to 10 bats

Write two equivalent ratios for each ratio.   11.2

5. $\frac{1}{2}$ 6. $\frac{3}{4}$ 7. $\frac{10}{16}$

8. $\frac{5}{3}$ 9. $\frac{8}{6}$ 10. $\frac{3}{3}$

Solve each proportion.   11.3

11. $\frac{1}{4} = \frac{n}{20}$ 12. $\frac{2}{3} = \frac{6}{n}$

13. $\frac{n}{8} = \frac{10}{16}$ 14. $\frac{8}{n} = \frac{16}{18}$

15. $\frac{4}{5} = \frac{n}{10}$ 16. $\frac{n}{8} = \frac{14}{16}$

Express as a per cent.   11.4

17. $\frac{7}{10}$ 18. $\frac{2}{3}$ 19. $\frac{3}{5}$

20. $\frac{3}{4}$ 21. $\frac{3}{12}$ 22. $\frac{7}{20}$

11.5   **23.** $\frac{3}{2}$ **24.** 1   **25.** 2

        26. $\frac{5}{2}$ **27.** $3\frac{1}{4}$ **28.** $3\frac{1}{2}$

11.6   Complete the tables below.

	Fraction	Decimal	Per cent
29.	$\frac{9}{10}$	_____	_____
31.	_____	0.7	_____

	Fraction	Decimal	Per cent
30.	_____	_____	2.8%
32.	_____	1.68	_____

11.7   Solve each of the following.

33. 50% of 75 is what number?   **34.** 56% of 56 is what number?

35. 20% of what number is 9?   **36.** 6% of what number is 18?

37. 12 is what per cent of 16?   **38.** 8 is what per cent of 10?

11.8   Solve.

39. Jean bought a coat marked down 35% from the regular price of $60. How much did she save?

40. Mr. Bathke sold 16 cases of merchandise last week. This was 40% of his monthly quota. What was his monthly quota?

Change each ratio to lowest terms.

1. $\frac{30}{50}$

2. $\frac{36}{48}$

3. $\frac{16}{24}$

4. $\frac{27}{81}$

5. $\frac{21}{12}$

6. $\frac{18}{54}$

Solve each proportion.

7. $\frac{2}{3} = \frac{n}{24}$

8. $\frac{5}{8} = \frac{15}{n}$

9. $\frac{5}{n} = \frac{20}{48}$

10. $\frac{n}{6} = \frac{20}{24}$

11. $\frac{7}{8} = \frac{n}{16}$

12. $\frac{3}{4} = \frac{18}{n}$

Solve.

13. 6% of 200 is what number?

14. 2.5% of 40 is what number?

15. 12 is what per cent of 25?

16. 9 is what per cent of 20?

17. 25% of what number is 8?

18. 75% of what number is 90?

Complete the following tables.

	Fraction	Decimal	Per cent
19.	$\frac{1}{5}$	_____	_____
21.	_____	0.9	_____
23.	_____	_____	63%

	Fraction	Decimal	Per cent
20.	_____	0.875	_____
22.	$\frac{3}{8}$	_____	_____
24.	_____	_____	150%

Activity 1

Ratios can be shown by lines on a grid. For example, from **A** to **B** the line rises *one* unit vertically for *three* units horizontally. The line represents the ratio $\frac{1}{3}$.

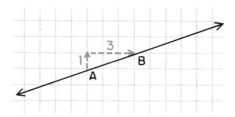

From **A** to **C** the line rises *two* units vertically for *six* units horizontally, so it also represents the ratio $\frac{2}{6}$. This is not surprising since $\frac{1}{3}$ and $\frac{2}{6}$ are equivalent ratios.

Draw lines on a grid to represent the following ratios.

1. $\frac{1}{2}$ 2. $\frac{2}{3}$ 3. $\frac{4}{6}$ 4. $\frac{4}{3}$

5. $\frac{5}{6}$ 6. $\frac{9}{4}$ 7. $\frac{3}{1}$ 8. $\frac{0}{1}$

Activity 2

From **D** to **E** the line declines *two* units vertically for every *three* units horizontally. The line represents the ratio $\frac{-2}{3}$. How could you show that the line also represents the ratios $\frac{-4}{6}$ and $\frac{-6}{9}$?

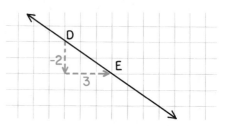

Draw lines on a grid to represent the following ratios.

1. $\frac{-1}{2}$ 2. $\frac{-2}{4}$ 3. $\frac{-5}{3}$ 4. $\frac{-10}{6}$

5. $\frac{-3}{1}$ 6. $\frac{-4}{2}$ 7. $\frac{-2}{1}$ 8. $\frac{-8}{3}$

Mathematics and Music

As shown below, there are only eight notes in an octave. When you strike the piano key for middle C, the C strings vibrate 264 times a second or have a frequency of 264. All other notes have frequencies related to middle C by designated ratios.

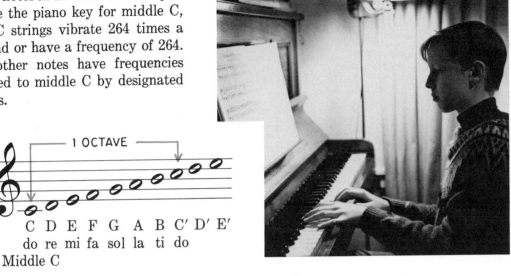

1 OCTAVE

C D E F G A B C′ D′ E′
do re mi fa sol la ti do
Middle C

Example 1: The ratio of any note to the corresponding note one octave higher is 1:2. Find the frequency of C′.

$$\frac{C}{C'} = \frac{1}{2} \longrightarrow \frac{264}{C'} = \frac{1}{2} \longrightarrow C' = 528$$

The frequency of C′ is 528.

Example 2: Find the frequencies of E and G, if C:E = 4:5 and E:G = 5:6.

$$\frac{C}{E} = \frac{4}{5} \longrightarrow \frac{264}{E} = \frac{4}{5}$$

$$E = 330$$

$$\frac{E}{G} = \frac{5}{6} \longrightarrow \frac{330}{G} = \frac{5}{6}$$

$$G = 396$$

The frequency of E is 330.　　　　The frequency of G is 396.

1. Find the frequencies of A and F, if C:A = 3:5 and A:F = 5:4.

2. Find the frequencies of B and D′, if C:B = 8:15 and B:D′ = 5:6.

3. Find the frequency of D, if D:D′ = 1:2 and D′ has a frequency of 594.

Getting Ready for Chapter 12

a. 　b. 　c. 　d.

e. 　f. 　g. 　h.

ES　Tell which figures are named by each of these words.

1. circles

2. rectangles

3. squares

4. triangles

11.2　Write two equivalent ratios for each ratio.

5. $\frac{1}{3}$　　　　**6.** $\frac{3}{4}$　　　　**7.** $\frac{2}{5}$

8. $\frac{5}{2}$　　　　**9.** $\frac{9}{4}$　　　　**10.** $\frac{3}{2}$

11. $\frac{12}{15}$　　　　**12.** $\frac{24}{20}$　　　　**13.** $\frac{18}{72}$

11.3　Solve each proportion.

14. $\frac{3}{4} = \frac{n}{20}$　　　　**15.** $\frac{n}{8} = \frac{1}{4}$

16. $\frac{6}{9} = \frac{24}{n}$　　　　**17.** $\frac{3}{n} = \frac{9}{15}$

Indirect Measurement _____ 12

You often make direct measurements by using a tape measure, ruler, or meter stick. In some jobs, such as surveying, it is impractical or impossible to make all the measurements directly. For this reason, methods of making indirect measurements have been devised.

In this chapter you will learn how to use similar figures to make indirect measurements.

The magnifying glass enlarges the letters. The size of the letters changes, but their shape remains the same. In mathematics we say that corresponding letters in the two views are *similar*.

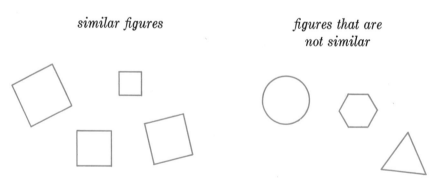

similar figures

figures that are not similar

Similar figures have the same shape, but may differ in size.

These two triangles are similar.

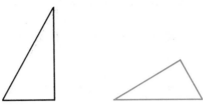

They may not look like it at first. If you rotate one of the triangles, it makes it easier to see that they have the same shape.

The two figures below are also similar.

They may not look like it at first. Rotating either figure does not help. But you can "flip" one of them to make it easier to see that they are similar.

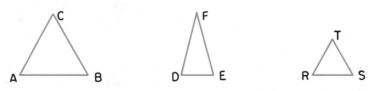

Example: Tell which triangles are similar.

△ABC (triangle ABC) is similar to △RST because they have the same shape.

△DEF is not similar to either of the other triangles. It could never be enlarged or reduced so that it would have the same shape as the other two triangles.

Exercises

A Choose the figure in each row that is similar to the colored figure.

1.

 a. *b.* *c.* *d.*

2.

 *a.* *b.* *c.* *d.*

3.

 *a.*  *b.* *c.* *d.*

Answer each question.

4. Are all squares similar?

5. Are all rectangles similar?

6. Are all circles similar?

Are the two figures similar ?

7.

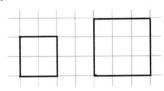

8.

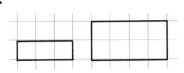

9.

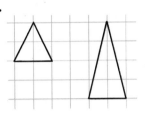

10.

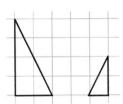

11.

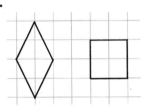

12.

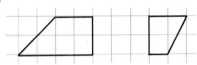

13.

14.

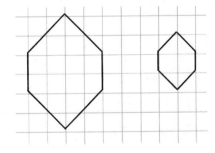

15.

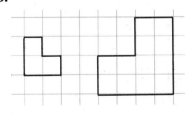

16.

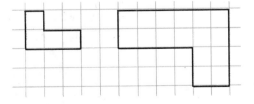

Use graph paper to do the following.

17. Draw 2 rectangles that are similar.

18. Draw 2 rectangles that are not similar.

19. Draw 2 triangles that are similar.

20. Draw 2 triangles that are not similar.

21. Using the figures below, name the triangles that are similar.

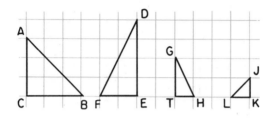

Complete the following.

22. How many similar triangles are in this figure?

23. Name all the similar triangles in this figure.

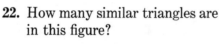

C Use the figure below to help you do the following.

24. Name 5 triangles similar to △BCD.

25. Name 7 triangles similar to △ANM.

26. Name 11 triangles similar to △PDE.

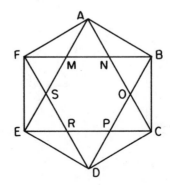

Enlarging a triangle changes the lengths of the sides, but the size or measures of the angles remain the same. The symbols ⊦, ⊬, and ⊭ are used to show which angles have the same measure.

△CDE is similar to △FGH.

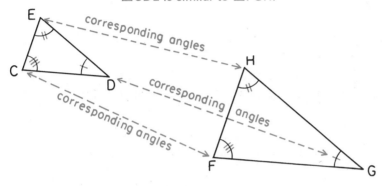

| In similar triangles, angles that have the same measure are **corresponding angles.**

Example 1:   Tell which angles are corresponding angles.

△ABC is similar to △RTS.

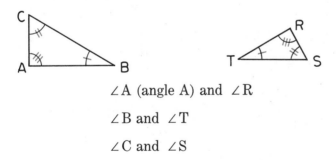

∠A (angle A) and ∠R

∠B and ∠T

∠C and ∠S

Example 2:   Tell which sides are corresponding sides.

△KLM is similar to △XZY.

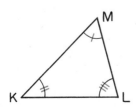 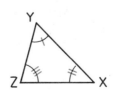

There are three pairs of corresponding sides.

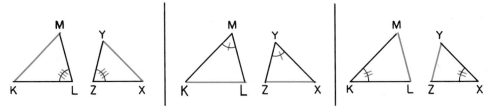

sides KM and XY   sides KL and XZ   sides LM and ZY

▌▌ In similar triangles, the sides opposite corresponding angles are **corresponding sides.** ▐▐

Exercises

A Name the corresponding angles for each pair of similar triangles.
(See Example 1.)

1.   **2.**

Name the corresponding sides for each pair of similar triangles.
(See Example 2.)

3.   **4.**

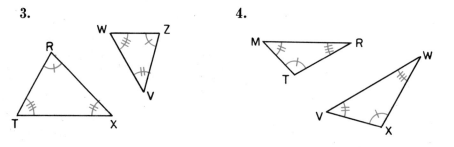

Name the corresponding angles and sides for each pair of similar triangles.

5.

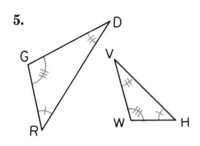

6.

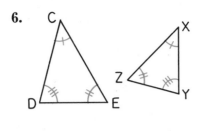

Corresponding angles of the similar triangles are listed. Name the corresponding sides.

7.

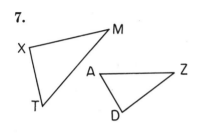

8.

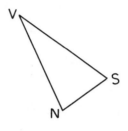

∠X and ∠D

∠M and ∠Z

∠T and ∠A

∠R and ∠V

∠B and ∠S

∠C and ∠N

Corresponding sides of the similar triangles are listed. Name the corresponding angles.

9.

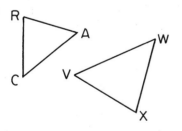

10.

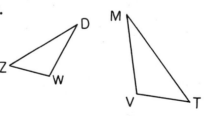

sides AC and VW

sides CR and WX

sides RA and XV

sides DW and MV

sides ZW and TV

sides ZD and TM

Example :   △ABC is similar to △DEC.

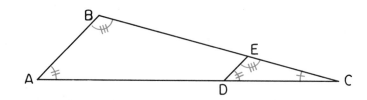

∠A and ∠D   sides BC and EC

∠B and ∠E   sides AC and DC

∠C is the same for   sides AB and DE
   both triangles.

11. △FGR is similar to △FCW.   12. △VNJ is similar to △VTW.

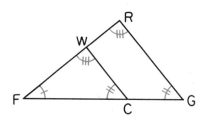

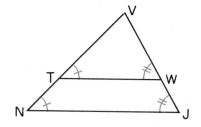

13. △KEC is similar to △LEK.   14. △TKS is similar to △TUY.

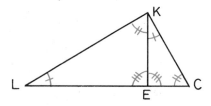

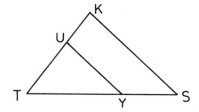

When a triangle is enlarged, the ratios of the lengths of corresponding sides are equal. Note that symbols like AB and DE represent the measures of the lengths of the sides.

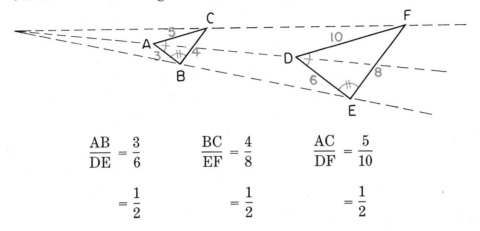

$$\frac{AB}{DE} = \frac{3}{6} \qquad \frac{BC}{EF} = \frac{4}{8} \qquad \frac{AC}{DF} = \frac{5}{10}$$

$$= \frac{1}{2} \qquad\qquad = \frac{1}{2} \qquad\qquad = \frac{1}{2}$$

Since the ratios of the lengths of corresponding sides are equal, the ratios can be expressed as proportions in many different ways.

$$\frac{AB}{DE} = \frac{BC}{EF} \qquad \frac{BC}{EF} = \frac{AC}{DF} \qquad \frac{AB}{DE} = \frac{AC}{DF} \qquad \frac{EF}{BC} = \frac{DE}{AB}$$

$$\frac{3}{6} = \frac{4}{8} \qquad\quad \frac{4}{8} = \frac{5}{10} \qquad\quad \frac{3}{6} = \frac{5}{10} \qquad\quad \frac{8}{4} = \frac{6}{3}$$

In similar triangles, corresponding sides are proportional.

Example 1: What letter should replace each question mark?

△RST is similar to △XYZ.

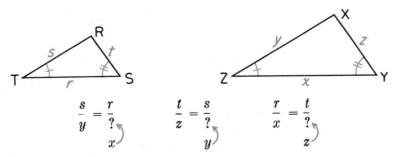

$$\frac{s}{y} = \frac{r}{?_x} \qquad \frac{t}{z} = \frac{s}{?_y} \qquad \frac{r}{x} = \frac{t}{?_z}$$

Example 2: Find the values of x and z.

△ABC is similar to △XYZ.

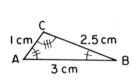

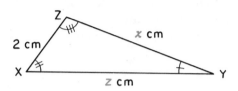

$$\frac{AC}{XZ} = \frac{AB}{XY}$$

$$\frac{1}{2} = \frac{3}{z}$$

$$z = 2 \times 3$$

$$z = 6$$

$$\frac{AC}{XZ} = \frac{BC}{YZ}$$

$$\frac{1}{2} = \frac{2.5}{x}$$

$$x = 2 \times 2.5$$

$$x = 5$$

Exercises

A What letter should replace each question mark?

△MNQ is similar to △RST.

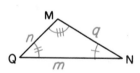

1. $\frac{n}{s} = \frac{q}{?}$

2. $\frac{n}{s} = \frac{m}{?}$

3. $\frac{s}{n} = \frac{t}{?}$

4. $\frac{r}{m} = \frac{?}{n}$

5. $\frac{q}{?} = \frac{m}{r}$

6. $\frac{?}{q} = \frac{s}{n}$

△ABC is similar to △AED.

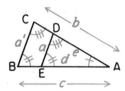

7. $\frac{e}{b} = \frac{d}{?}$

8. $\frac{a'}{?} = \frac{c}{d}$

9. $\frac{a}{a'} = \frac{?}{c}$

10. $\frac{b}{?} = \frac{c}{d}$

11. $\frac{?}{a'} = \frac{d}{c}$

12. $\frac{d}{c} = \frac{?}{b}$

B Find the values of *x* and *z*.

13. △ABC is
similar
to △DEF.

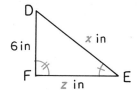

14. △GHI is
similar
to △JKL.

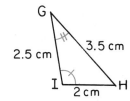

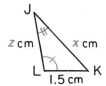

15. △MQN is
similar
to △PRT.

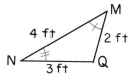

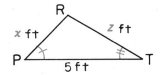

16. △STU is
similar
to △VWX.

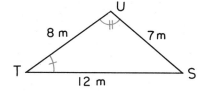

17. △YZA is
similar
to △BCD.

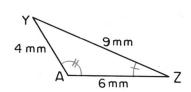

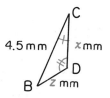

C Find the values of *x* and *z*.

18. △AED is
similar
to △CEB.

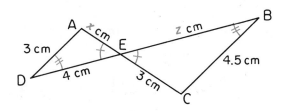

12.4 ◆ MEASURING WITH SIMILAR TRIANGLES

Similar triangles can be used to make indirect measurements.

Example 1: How high is the sign?

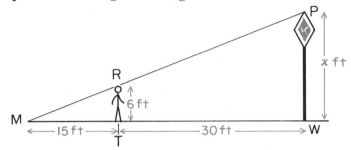

Step 1: △MRT is similar to △MPW.

Step 2: $\dfrac{MT}{MW} = \dfrac{15}{45}$ or $\dfrac{1}{3}$

Step 3: $\dfrac{MT}{MW} = \dfrac{RT}{PW} \longrightarrow \dfrac{1}{3} = \dfrac{6}{x}$

$$x = 3 \times 6$$
$$x = 18$$

The sign is 18 feet high.

Example 2: How far is it from the tee at A to the green at B?

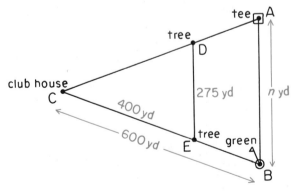

Step 1: Determine which triangles are similar.

△ABC is similar to △DEC.

Step 2: Write a proportion that includes the unknown distance.

$$\frac{CE}{CB} = \frac{DE}{AB} \quad \text{or} \quad \frac{400}{600} = \frac{275}{n}$$

Step 3: Solve the proportion. Answer the problem.

$$\frac{400}{600} = \frac{275}{n}$$

$$400n = 600 \times 275$$

$$n = \frac{600 \times 275}{400}$$

$$n = 412\frac{1}{2}$$

The distance from A to B is $412\frac{1}{2}$ yards.

Exercises

A What letter should replace each question mark ?

△CDA is similar to △BEA.

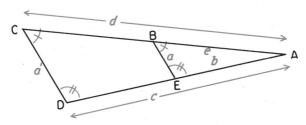

1. $\frac{e}{d} = \frac{b}{?}$ **2.** $\frac{a}{a'} = \frac{e}{?}$ **3.** $\frac{c}{b} = \frac{a'}{?}$

4. $\frac{d}{e} = \frac{?}{b}$ **5.** $\frac{b}{?} = \frac{a}{a'}$ **6.** $\frac{?}{a} = \frac{d}{e}$

The ratio of $\frac{e}{d}$ is $\frac{1}{2}$. What are the following ratios ?

7. $\frac{b}{c}$ **8.** $\frac{a}{a'}$ **9.** $\frac{d}{e}$ **10.** $\frac{c}{b}$ **11.** $\frac{a'}{a}$

12. What is true about the ratios of corresponding sides of similar triangles?

Use similar triangles to solve each problem.

13. The sign and the tree cast shadows as shown. How tall is the tree?

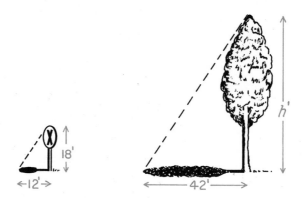

14. How high is the hotel?

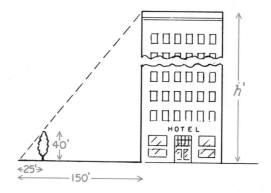

15. What is the length of the fairway?

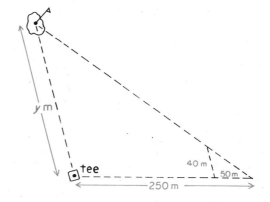

16. How far apart are the lighthouses?

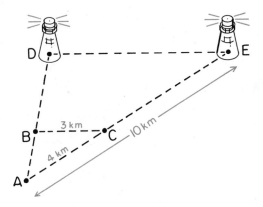

C Solve each problem.

17. By sighting as shown below, find the height of the flagpole.

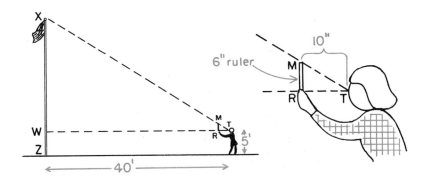

18. Triangles DCE and ABE are similar. Find the width of the river at AB.

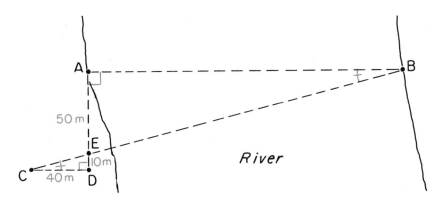

12.5  SPORTING PROBLEMS

Hockey is just one of the many games in which similar triangles are involved.

Example 1: Suppose you shoot the puck from A, it banks off at B, and scores a goal at C. For that to happen, similar triangles must be formed. Name the similar triangles.

Angles of the same size are always formed in cases like this. Thus, ∠ABD is the same size as ∠CBE.

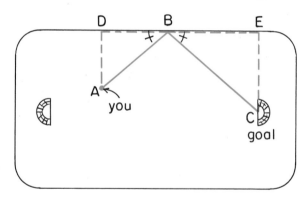

△ABD is similar to △CBE.

Example 2: In Example 1, assume AB = 20 ft, AD = 12 ft, and CE = 42 ft.

What is the distance BC?

$$\frac{AD}{AB} = \frac{CE}{BC} \qquad \frac{12}{20} = \frac{42}{x}$$

$$12x = 840$$

$$x = 70 \qquad \text{70 feet}$$

Exercises

A Answer the following.

1. Where must you bank the puck in order to make a goal?

Assume similar triangles are formed with each bank shot.

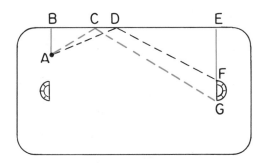

2. Name each set of similar triangles formed above.

Name the side that should replace each ?.

3. $\dfrac{AB}{?} = \dfrac{GE}{CE}$

4. $\dfrac{AD}{?} = \dfrac{DF}{FE}$

5. $\dfrac{GE}{GC} = \dfrac{AB}{?}$

6. $\dfrac{BD}{AD} = \dfrac{?}{FD}$

7. $\dfrac{?}{CA} = \dfrac{CE}{CG}$

8. $\dfrac{?}{AB} = \dfrac{DE}{FE}$

Tell how similar triangles are involved in each of the following.

9. tennis

10. basketball

11. handball

12. pool or billiards

13. golf

14. table tennis

B Solve each problem.

15. Mark wants to serve a "fast" ball so it will just clear the net. How high above the table should he hit the ball?

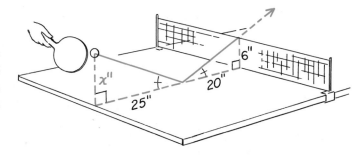

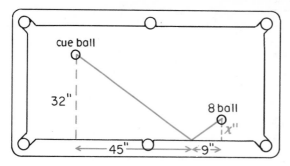

16. Sue Ann made the bank shot shown. How far from the edge of the table was the 8 ball?

17. While playing handball, Jan made the shot shown. How high above the floor did the ball strike the wall?

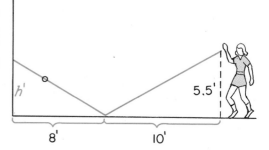

18. At the Putt-Putt Golf Course, the cup is centered between the edges of the fairway. Alice's ball traveled 9 feet from the tee, bounced, and ended up in the cup. How far did the ball travel?

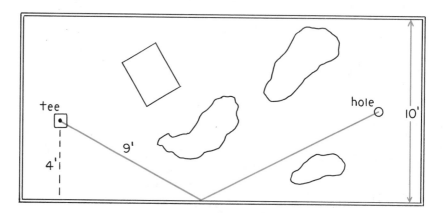

C Use a mirror and similar triangles to measure tall objects.

Example: To measure the height of the building, place a mirror a measured distance (10 meters in this case) from the base of the building. Slowly walk toward the mirror until you see the top of the building in the mirror. Measure your distance from the mirror and compute as indicated.

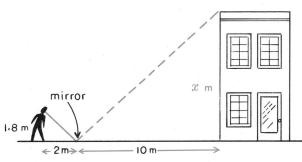

your eye-
level height   object's height
─────────── = ───────────
your distance   object's distance
from mirror   from mirror

$$\frac{1.8}{2} = \frac{x}{10}$$

$$18 = 2x$$

$$9 = x$$

The building is 9 meters high.

19. What would be the height of the flagpole if your eye-level height is 5 feet?

20. Use your eye-level height (in inches) and compute the height of the flagpole. (*Note:* It will be necessary to convert all measurements to inches.)

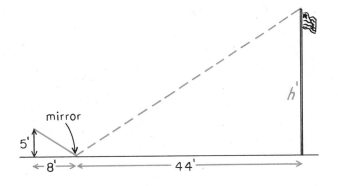

21. Use a mirror to calculate various heights. These might include the height of your classroom, your school building, a tree, and so on.

12.6 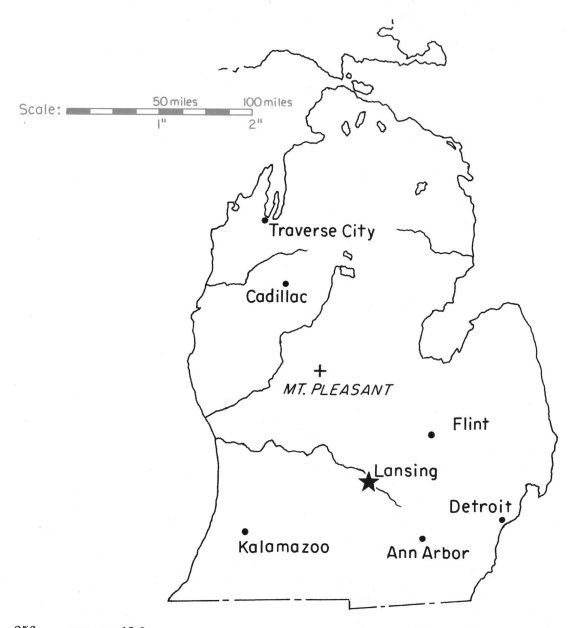 MAPS

A map is a reduction of part of the earth's surface. The amount of reduction or scale is usually given by a ratio. For example, on the following map *1 inch represents 50 miles*. That means the ratio of distances on the map to those on earth is 1 inch to 50 miles.

Scale:

50 miles   100 miles

1"   2"

Traverse City

Cadillac

+
MT. PLEASANT

Flint

Lansing

Detroit

Kalamazoo   Ann Arbor

Example 1: If you were to fly from Lansing to Traverse City, how many miles would you travel?

Step 1: Measure the distance between Lansing and Traverse City on the map.   3 inches

Step 2: Use a proportion to find the actual distance d.

$$\frac{1 \text{ in}}{50 \text{ mi}} = \frac{3 \text{ in}}{d \text{ mi}} \longrightarrow \left(\frac{1}{50} = \frac{3}{d} \right)$$

$$d = 50 \times 3$$

$$d = 150$$

Distance from Lansing to Traverse City: 150 miles

Example 2: What is the flight distance from Detroit to Kalamazoo?

Step 1: Measure the distance on the map. $2\frac{3}{4}$ inches

Step 2: Use a proportion to find the actual distance d.

$$\frac{1}{50} = \frac{2\frac{3}{4}}{d}$$

$$d = 50 \times 2\frac{3}{4}$$

$$d = 137\frac{1}{2}$$

Distance from Detroit to Kalamazoo: $137\frac{1}{2}$ miles

Exercises

A By using the map on page 356, tell how you could find the distance between each pair of cities given below.

1. Detroit and Mt. Pleasant

2. Flint and Kalamazoo

Answer each question about the actual car and the scale model.

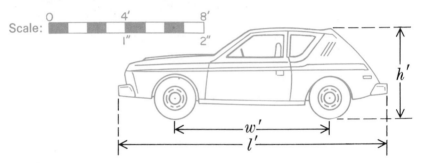

3. What scale is indicated for these cars?

4. What proportion would you use to find the height of the model?

5. What proportion would you use to find the length of the model?

6. What proportion would you use to find the distance between the centers of the front and rear wheels of the model?

B Use the map on page 356 to find the flight distance between each pair of cities given below.

7. Mt. Pleasant and Lansing

8. Ann Arbor and Traverse City

9. Ann Arbor and Detroit

10. Cadillac and Kalamazoo

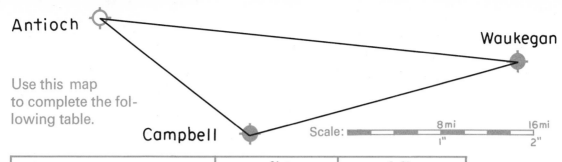

Antioch

Waukegan

Use this map
to complete the fol-
lowing table.

Campbell

Scale: 8 mi   16 mi
1"   2"

Flight between	map distance (in inches)	actual distance (in miles)
11. Campbell and Waukegan		
12. Waukegan and Antioch		
13. Antioch and Campbell		

14. What was the total distance of the trip above?

15. If the plane averaged 120 mph, how long would it take for the trip, allowing 5 minutes for the touchdown at Waukegan and 5 minutes for the touchdown at Antioch?

Complete the following table for a model car that is based on a 1 to 48 reduction from the original. Thus, the scale is 1 inch for every 4 feet.

Measurements	actual dimensions (in feet)	model dimensions (in inches)
16. length	16	
17. height	4.0	
18. distance from center of front wheels to center of rear wheels	10.5	
19. distance between headlights	5.0	
20. length of hood	3.5	
21. overall width	5.5	
22. distance between taillights	4.5	

23. The map below is a reduction of the map on page 359. The scale is missing. What should the scale be?

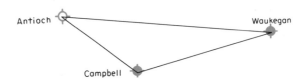

24. The map below is a reduction of the map on page 356. The scale is missing. What should the scale be?

Complete each sentence. Choose from these words.

corresponding   *indirect*   *proportional*   *ratio*   *shape*   *size*

1. Similar figures have the same _____, but may differ in _____.

2. In similar triangles, _____ angles have the same measure.

3. In similar triangles, corresponding sides are _____.

4. Similar triangles can be used to make _____ measurements.

5. The scale of a map is usually given by a _____.

CHAPTER REVIEW

Which pairs of figures are similar ?   12.1

1.   **2.**

3.   **4.**

5. 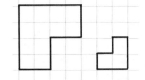   **6.**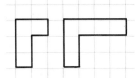

Name the corresponding angles for each pair of similar triangles.   12.2

7. 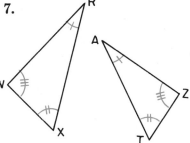   **8.**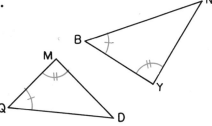

Name the corresponding sides for each pair of similar triangles.

9.

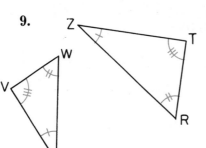

10.

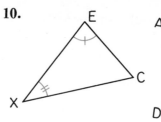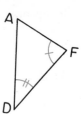

12.3   What letter should replace each question mark ?

△RPW is similar to △ZNV.

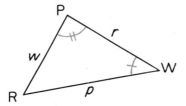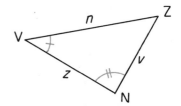

11. $\dfrac{w}{v} = \dfrac{p}{?}$

12. $\dfrac{r}{z} = \dfrac{w}{?}$

13. $\dfrac{p}{n} = \dfrac{?}{v}$

14. Find the values of x and z.

△ABC is similar to △DEF.

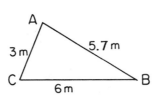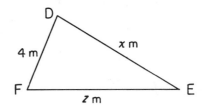

Use similar triangles to solve the problem. 12.4

15. What is the height of the tree? (The triangles are similar.)

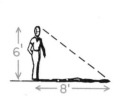
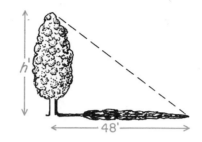

Solve the problem. 12.5

16. Herbert made the bank shot shown. What was the total distance the ball traveled?

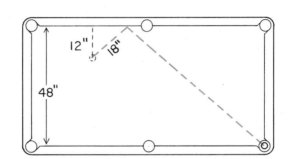

Use this map to complete the table. 12.6

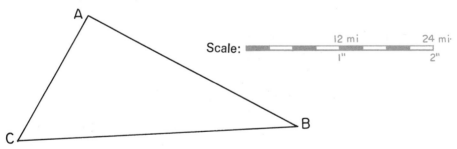

Scale: 12 mi 24 mi·
        1"   2"

Distance between	map distance (in inches)	actual distance (in miles)
17. A and B		
18. B and C		
19. C and A		

▶ CHAPTER TEST

1. Name the corresponding angles.

2. Name the corresponding sides.

△BDX is
similar
to △WAZ.

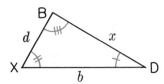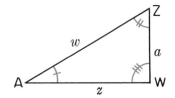

What letter should replace each question mark ?

3. $\dfrac{x}{z} = \dfrac{b}{?}$

4. $\dfrac{d}{a} = \dfrac{?}{z}$

5. $\dfrac{b}{?} = \dfrac{d}{a}$

6. What is the actual distance between A and B? Between B and C? Between C and A?

Scale:

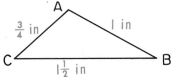

7. Find the height of the building. (The triangles are similar.)

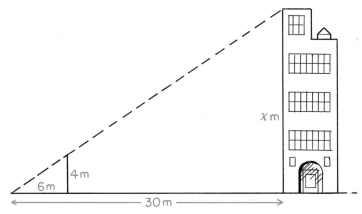

Activities for Chapter 12

Activity 1

Find the diameter of the moon by following these steps. (*CAUTION:* DO NOT try this activity with the sun. It could damage your eyes!!)

Step 1: Put two strips of tape on a window as shown.

Step 2: Make a pinhole in a card. Sight the moon through the pinhole and the two strips as shown.

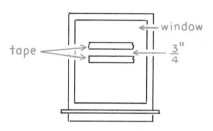

Step 3: Back away from the window until the moon just fills the space between the two strips. Measure the distance from the card to the window. Use the proportions obtained from the similar triangles to calculate the diameter of the moon.

Activity 2

Use the diameter of the moon you found in Activity 1 to find the diameter of the sun as observed on earth during an eclipse.

Mathematics and Pipelines

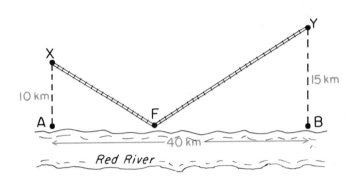

A petroleum company owns two high-producing oil fields, one located at X and the other at Y. The company wants to connect the two fields by pipeline to a single tank farm F located along the Red River. How far from A should they build the tank farm so the least amount of pipe is used?

Suppose the distances remained the same, but X and Y were on opposite sides of riverbank AB. Then the shortest distance from X to F to Y would be the line segment XY'. You could draw that line segment to locate F.

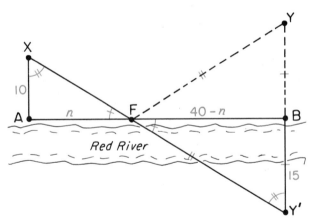

Side FY is the same length as FY'.

$\triangle XAF$ is similar to $\triangle YBF$.

$$\frac{n}{10} = \frac{40-n}{15}$$

$$15n = 400-10n$$

$$25n = 400$$

$$n = 16$$

Locate the tank farm 16 km from A.

1. Assume the distance from A to B is 60 km. How far from A should the tank farm be built?

2. Assume the following distances: AX = 20 km, BY = 30 km, and AB = 40 km. How far from A should the tank farm be built?

Find each sum or difference.

1. $\frac{1}{7} + \frac{3}{7}$	**2.** $\frac{5}{9} - \frac{4}{9}$	**3.** $\frac{3}{4} + \frac{2}{4}$	6.7
4. $\frac{1}{2} - \frac{2}{5}$	**5.** $\frac{2}{3} + \frac{1}{6}$	**6.** $\frac{5}{8} - \frac{1}{6}$	6.8
7. $1\frac{5}{6} - 1\frac{3}{4}$	**8.** $2\frac{1}{2} + 1\frac{7}{8}$	**9.** $3\frac{1}{2} - 2\frac{2}{3}$	6.9
10. $0.47 + 0.23$	**11.** $6.73 - 2.41$	**12.** $2.537 - 1.72$	7.2
13. $^-7 + 6$	**14.** $7 + {}^-5$	**15.** $^-8 + {}^-18$	8.3
16. $6 - 13$	**17.** $^-7 - 13$	**18.** $8 - {}^-26$	8.4

Find each product or quotient.

19. $\frac{1}{8} \times \frac{3}{2}$	**20.** $\frac{3}{4} \times \frac{5}{12}$	**21.** $\frac{2}{3} \times \frac{9}{16}$	6.2
22. $4\frac{1}{2} \times 3$	**23.** $3 \times 2\frac{2}{3}$	**24.** $2\frac{1}{2} \times 1\frac{2}{3}$	6.5
25. $\frac{1}{8} \div \frac{2}{3}$	**26.** $\frac{3}{5} \div \frac{9}{16}$	**27.** $1\frac{1}{2} \div 2\frac{3}{8}$	6.6
28. 4.3×2.1	**29.** 3×3.782	**30.** 3.14×65	7.3
31. $0.196 \div 14$	**32.** $9 \div 2.25$	**33.** $10.24 \div 3.2$	7.5
34. $8 \times {}^-7$	**35.** $^-7 \times 8$	**36.** $^-14 \times 9$	8.5
37. $^-21 \div 7$	**38.** $^-42 \div {}^-6$	**39.** $84 \div {}^-12$	8.7

Solve each equation.

40. $n + 8 = 24$	**41.** $n + 7 = 5$	1.5
42. $2n = 10$	**43.** $5k = 35$	2.1
44. $n - 3 = 6$	**45.** $n - 15 = 37$	2.2
46. $\frac{n}{4} = 8$	**47.** $\frac{x}{9} = 17$	
48. $2x - 3 = 17$	**49.** $\frac{z}{6} + 5 = 12$	2.8

Rational Numbers ———————— 13

Most artisans start with a small set of tools. As needs arise, artisans gradually expand their set of tools to meet those needs.

By the same token, you started your study of mathematics with the set of whole numbers. As the need to solve particular problems arose, the set of numbers was expanded to include integers and numbers named by positive fractions and decimals. In this chapter the set of numbers will be expanded to include all rational numbers.

In an earlier lesson, the number line was extended to show negative integers. Similarly, the number line can be used to show negative numbers named by fractions.

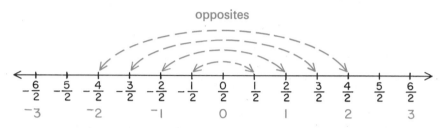

You could also construct number lines for thirds, fourths, fifths, and so on. The set of numbers shown on all such number lines is called the set of **rational numbers.**

> Rational numbers can be named by fractions, decimals, or mixed numerals.

$$\frac{1}{2} = 0.5 \qquad 1 = \frac{10}{10} \qquad -1\frac{1}{2} = {}^-1.5 = -\frac{3}{2}$$

$$-\frac{1}{4} = {}^-0.25 \qquad {}^-2 = -\frac{200}{100}$$

Example 1: How do you read $-\frac{1}{2}$ and $^-1.5$?

$-\frac{1}{2}$ is read *negative one-half.*

$^-1.5$ is read *negative one and five-tenths.*

Example 2: What number is the opposite of $\frac{2}{3}$? Of $^-1.5$?

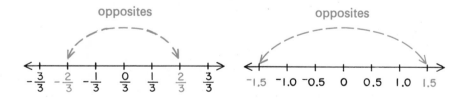

You can use a number line to compare two rational numbers like $\frac{4}{5}$ and $\frac{2}{3}$.

Since $\frac{4}{5}$ is to the right of $\frac{2}{3}$, $\frac{4}{5} > \frac{2}{3}$ or $\frac{2}{3} < \frac{4}{5}$.

An easier way to compare two rational numbers is to rename them so they have the same denominator. Then compare the numerators.

Example 3: Compare $\frac{4}{5}$ and $\frac{2}{3}$.

$$\frac{4}{5} = \frac{4 \times 3}{5 \times 3} = \frac{12}{15}$$

$$12 > 10, \quad \text{so} \quad \frac{12}{15} > \frac{10}{15}$$

$$\frac{2}{3} = \frac{2 \times 5}{3 \times 5} = \frac{10}{15} \qquad \text{and} \quad \frac{4}{5} > \frac{2}{3}.$$

Example 4: Compare $-\frac{5}{6}$ and $-\frac{7}{8}$.

$$-\frac{5}{6} = -\frac{5 \times 4}{6 \times 4} = -\frac{20}{24} \quad \text{or} \quad \frac{-20}{24}$$

$$-20 > {-21}, \quad \text{so} \quad \frac{-20}{24} > \frac{-21}{24}$$

$$-\frac{7}{8} = -\frac{7 \times 3}{8 \times 3} = -\frac{21}{24} \quad \text{or} \quad \frac{-21}{24} \qquad \text{and} \quad -\frac{5}{6} > -\frac{7}{8}.$$

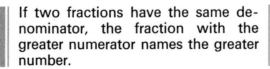

If two fractions have the same denominator, the fraction with the greater numerator names the greater number.

Exercises

A Name the opposite of each number.

1. $\frac{3}{4}$ 2. $-\frac{1}{2}$ 3. 0.34 4. $^-0.57$

5. $\frac{5}{3}$ 6. $^-1\frac{2}{3}$ 7. $3\frac{1}{2}$ 8. $^-4.795$

Tell which fraction in each pair names the greater number.

9. $\frac{5}{12}$ or $\frac{7}{12}$ 10. $\frac{9}{16}$ or $\frac{3}{16}$ 11. $-\frac{1}{2}$ or $\frac{1}{2}$

12. $-\frac{7}{12}$ or $-\frac{5}{12}$ 13. $-\frac{11}{20}$ or $-\frac{9}{20}$ 14. $-\frac{2}{3}$ or $\frac{3}{4}$

B Should $>$, $<$, or $=$ replace ⬤ to make the sentence true ?

15. $\frac{4}{9}$ ⬤ $\frac{7}{9}$ 16. $-\frac{5}{7}$ ⬤ $-\frac{3}{7}$ 17. $\frac{3}{4}$ ⬤ $-\frac{2}{3}$

18. $\frac{1}{3}$ ⬤ $\frac{1}{2}$ 19. $\frac{3}{4}$ ⬤ $\frac{5}{2}$ 20. $-\frac{7}{8}$ ⬤ $-\frac{8}{9}$

21. $-\frac{7}{24}$ ⬤ $-\frac{3}{8}$ 22. $\frac{5}{16}$ ⬤ $-\frac{1}{4}$ 23. $\frac{5}{8}$ ⬤ $\frac{10}{16}$

24. $-\frac{10}{12}$ ⬤ $\frac{5}{6}$ 25. $\frac{9}{16}$ ⬤ $\frac{11}{24}$ 26. $\frac{3}{4}$ ⬤ $-\frac{9}{12}$

27. $\frac{7}{4}$ ⬤ $-\frac{5}{3}$ 28. $\frac{6}{5}$ ⬤ $\frac{5}{4}$ 29. $-\frac{8}{5}$ ⬤ $\frac{4}{3}$

C Determine which fraction in each pair names the greater number.

Examples : $\frac{3}{4}$ ⤫ $\frac{1}{2}$ → $4 \times 1 = 4$ ⟶ $6 > 4$, so $\frac{3}{4} > \frac{1}{2}$.
→ $3 \times 2 = 6$

$\frac{^-2}{3}$ ⤫ $\frac{^-5}{8}$ → $3 \times {}^-5 = {}^-15$ ⟶ $^-16 < {}^-15$ so $\frac{^-2}{3} < \frac{^-5}{8}$.
→ $^-2 \times 8 = {}^-16$

Note: The above method can only be used when both denominators are positive.

30. $\frac{2}{3}$ or $\frac{1}{2}$ 31. $\frac{9}{10}$ or $\frac{7}{12}$ 32. $\frac{3}{4}$ or $\frac{4}{5}$

33. $\frac{^-2}{3}$ or $\frac{^-3}{4}$ 34. $\frac{^-5}{12}$ or $\frac{^-1}{3}$ 35. $\frac{^-7}{8}$ or $\frac{^-3}{4}$

36. $\frac{4}{5}$, or $\frac{^-3}{4}$ 37. $\frac{^-3}{8}$, or $\frac{2}{5}$ 38. $\frac{5}{6}$, or $\frac{^-13}{16}$

⬙ **ADDITION AND SUBTRACTION WITH DECIMALS**

Hourly Barometric Changes	
Time	Change
7 P.M.	
	−0.25
8 P.M.	
	−0.18
9 P.M.	
	+0.35
10 P.M.	
	+0.12
11 P.M.	

You add and subtract with decimals the same way you add and subtract integers.

Example 1: What was the change between 7 and 9 P.M.? Between 8 and 10 P.M.?

7 P.M. to 9 P.M.	8 P.M. to 10 P.M.
Both addends have the same sign.	The addends have different signs.

	−0.25 + −0.18		−0.18 + 0.35	
	↓ ↓		↓ ↓	
Add their absolute values.	0.25 + 0.18		0.35 − 0.18	Subtract their absolute values.
Use the sign of the addends.	↗ −0.43		+0.17 ↙	Use the sign of the addend with the greater absolute value.

$$-0.25 + {}^-0.18 = {}^-0.43 \qquad {}^-0.18 + 0.35 = 0.17$$

Example 2: If the 9 P.M. barometer reading was 29.72, what was the 8 P.M. reading?

$$29.72 - {}^-0.18 = 29.72 + 0.18 \qquad \text{To subtract } {}^-0.18,$$
$$\text{add its opposite.}$$

$$= 29.90$$

Exercises

A Tell whether each sum is positive or negative.

1. $1.8 + 4.7$ **2.** ${}^-0.73 + {}^-0.69$ **3.** $1.217 + {}^-1.952$

4. ${}^-27.22 + 14.96$ **5.** $6.251 + {}^-4.213$ **6.** ${}^-8.3 + 14.9$

Give an addition phrase for each of the following.

7. $1.6 - 1.9$ **8.** ${}^-4.3 - {}^-5.6$ **9.** $8.27 - {}^-6.28$

10. ${}^-7.234 - 1.732$ **11.** $0.632 - {}^-9.568$ **12.** ${}^-7.35 - 17.58$

B Find each sum or difference.

13. $1.9 + 3.8$ **14.** ${}^-1.6 + {}^-5.9$ **15.** $0.834 + {}^-4.675$

16. ${}^-1.732 + 1.414$ **17.** $6.38 + 4.35$ **18.** ${}^-4.7 + {}^-3.2$

19. $4.9 - 1.6$ **20.** $8.3 - 9.7$ **21.** ${}^-4.65 - 3.78$

22. ${}^-1.752 - 2.869$ **23.** $6.5 - {}^-4.8$ **24.** $7.65 - {}^-10.87$

25. $2.366 + {}^-1.021$ **26.** ${}^-4.1 - {}^-2.3$ **27.** ${}^-8.65 + 9.52$

28. ${}^-8.751 - {}^-9.914$ **29.** $0.35 + 0.75$ **30.** $0.125 - 0.876$

31. ${}^-0.165 + {}^-0.425$ **32.** ${}^-17.3 - 21.4$ **33.** $0.438 + {}^-5.764$

34. $8.6 - {}^-2.9$ **35.** ${}^-2.371 + 4.141$ **36.** ${}^-1.4 - {}^-6.7$

37. ${}^-7.4 + {}^-6.9$ **38.** ${}^-1.234 - {}^-0.879$ **39.** $66.23 + {}^-21.10$

40. ${}^-13.75 - 11.98$ **41.** ${}^-5.68 + 2.59$ **42.** $6.28 - {}^-29.52$

43. The profits of Ace Distributors for January through March are shown at the right. Find the total profit for the three months.

Month	Profit (Loss)
Jan.	(−$795.48)
Feb.	$367.42
Mar.	$969.67

44. Floyd Hemphill wrote checks for $20.95 and $16.49. Then he made a deposit of $30.00. What was the change in his bank balance due to these transactions?

45. The changes in the Dow Jones stock average for one week are given at the right. Find the change for the week.

Day	Change
Mon.	+1.76
Tues.	+4.38
Wed.	−2.69
Thur.	−5.99
Fri.	−2.78

46. The level of Oxbow Lake was 3.75 feet above normal in the spring. By late fall, it was 2.38 feet below normal. How much had the level of the lake changed during this period?

ADDITION AND SUBTRACTION WITH FRACTIONS ◆ 13.3

Price Changes in DATA Stock	
Day	Change
Monday	$-\dfrac{1}{4}$
Tuesday	$-\dfrac{1}{8}$
Wednesday	$+\dfrac{3}{4}$
Thursday	$-\dfrac{1}{2}$
Friday	$-\dfrac{3}{8}$

The techniques you use with fractions and integers are now used to add and subtract rational numbers.

Example 1: What was the change in the price of DATA stock on Monday and Tuesday? On Wednesday and Thursday?

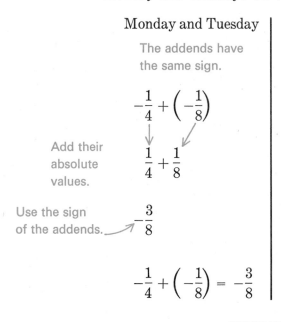

Monday and Tuesday

The addends have the same sign.

$$-\frac{1}{4}+\left(-\frac{1}{8}\right)$$

Add their absolute values.

$$\frac{1}{4}+\frac{1}{8}$$

Use the sign of the addends. $-\dfrac{3}{8}$

$$-\frac{1}{4}+\left(-\frac{1}{8}\right)=-\frac{3}{8}$$

Wednesday and Thursday

The addends have different signs.

$$\frac{3}{4}+\left(-\frac{1}{2}\right)$$

$$\frac{3}{4}-\frac{1}{2}$$

Subtract their absolute values.

$$+\frac{1}{4}$$

Use the sign of the addend with the greater absolute value.

$$\frac{3}{4}+\left(-\frac{1}{2}\right)=\frac{1}{4}$$

Example 2: If the closing price on Friday was $17\frac{1}{4}$, what was the opening price?

$$17\frac{1}{4} - \left(-\frac{3}{8}\right) = 17\frac{1}{4} + \frac{3}{8}$$

To subtract $-\frac{3}{8}$, add its opposite.

$$= 17\frac{5}{8}$$

Exercises

A Tell whether each sum is positive or negative.

1. $\frac{3}{4} + \frac{2}{3}$

2. $\frac{1}{2} + \left(-\frac{7}{8}\right)$

3. $-\frac{1}{4} + \left(-\frac{3}{8}\right)$

4. $-\frac{5}{6} + \frac{1}{3}$

5. $-\frac{1}{8} + 1\frac{3}{4}$

6. $2\frac{9}{16} + {}^-1\frac{1}{10}$

Give an addition phrase for each of the following.

7. $\frac{1}{8} - \frac{7}{8}$

8. $-\frac{1}{4} - \left(-\frac{1}{2}\right)$

9. $\frac{1}{2} - \left(-\frac{7}{8}\right)$

10. $-\frac{5}{6} - \frac{1}{2}$

11. ${}^-1\frac{2}{3} - 2\frac{1}{2}$

12. $6\frac{7}{8} - {}^-4\frac{2}{3}$

B Find each sum.

13. $\frac{1}{3} + \frac{1}{2}$

14. $\frac{1}{4} + \left(-\frac{3}{4}\right)$

15. $-\frac{7}{10} + \frac{1}{10}$

16. $-\frac{1}{5} + \left(-\frac{2}{5}\right)$

17. $1\frac{3}{4} + {}^-1\frac{1}{4}$

18. ${}^-2\frac{1}{2} + 1\frac{7}{8}$

19. ${}^-2\frac{1}{3} + {}^-1\frac{7}{8}$

20. $\frac{1}{4} + \left(-\frac{7}{8}\right)$

21. ${}^-1\frac{1}{4} + \left(-\frac{5}{8}\right)$

22. $1\frac{7}{8} + \left(-\frac{3}{4}\right)$

23. ${}^-17\frac{1}{2} + 3\frac{1}{4}$

24. $8\frac{3}{4} + {}^-7\frac{1}{2}$

Find each difference.

25. $\frac{7}{8} - \frac{3}{8}$

26. $\frac{1}{2} - \frac{2}{3}$

27. $-\frac{5}{6} - \frac{1}{2}$

28. $\frac{7}{8} - \left(-\frac{1}{4}\right)$

29. $-\frac{3}{5} - \left(-\frac{1}{5}\right)$

30. ${}^-1\frac{3}{4} - 1\frac{1}{2}$

31. $2\frac{1}{2} - {}^-1\frac{7}{8}$

32. $-\frac{2}{3} - \frac{3}{4}$

33. $3\frac{1}{2} - 4\frac{9}{10}$

34. $8\frac{1}{2} - {}^-3\frac{1}{4}$

35. ${}^-2\frac{7}{8} - {}^-1\frac{1}{2}$

36. ${}^-3\frac{1}{4} - \left(-\frac{2}{3}\right)$

Solve each problem.

37. The level of the city reservoir was up $3\frac{1}{2}$ inches in January. In February, it went down $5\frac{1}{4}$ inches. What was the change in the level of the reservoir during these two months?

38. In boxing, a lightweight can weigh as much as 135 pounds. Pete weighs $4\frac{3}{4}$ pounds less than the limit. What is Pete's weight?

39. A weight watcher lost $3\frac{1}{2}$ pounds one week and gained $1\frac{1}{4}$ pounds the next. What was the change in weight for the two weeks?

40. Last year the wheat yield on Jones's farm was $27\frac{1}{2}$ bushels per acre. Due to the lack of rain, the yield is expected to change by $^{-}3\frac{3}{4}$ bushels per acre this year. What yield per acre is expected this year?

C Determine if the following are true.

41. $\frac{3}{4} + \frac{1}{2} = \frac{1}{2} + \frac{3}{4}$

42. $-\frac{2}{3} + 1\frac{1}{4} = 1\frac{1}{4} + (-\frac{2}{3})$

43. $(\frac{1}{2}+\frac{2}{3}) +\frac{3}{4} = \frac{1}{2}+(\frac{2}{3}+\frac{3}{4})$

44. $(-1\frac{1}{4}+\frac{2}{3}) +(-\frac{7}{8}) = -1\frac{1}{4}+[\frac{2}{3}+(-\frac{7}{8})]$

45. $\frac{3}{4} + 0 = \frac{3}{4}$

46. $0 + {}^{-}6\frac{7}{8} = {}^{-}6\frac{7}{8}$

Use your answers for exercises **41–46** to answer the following.

47. Do you think addition of rational numbers is commutative?

48. Do you think addition of rational numbers is associative?

49. What number do you think is the identity number for addition of rational numbers?

13.4 ◆ SOLVING EQUATIONS

You already know the techniques for solving equations with rational numbers.

Example 1: Solve and check $x - 2.4 = 8.7$.

$$x - 2.4 = 8.7$$

$$x - 2.4 + 2.4 = 8.7 + 2.4 \qquad \text{Add 2.4 to each side.}$$

$$x + 0 = 11.1$$

$$x = 11.1$$

$$\textit{Check:} \quad x - 2.4 = 8.7$$

$$11.1 - 2.4 = 8.7 \qquad \text{Replace } x \text{ with 11.1.}$$

$$8.7 = 8.7$$

Example 2: Solve and check $y + 1\frac{3}{4} = {}^-5\frac{1}{2}$.

$$y + 1\frac{3}{4} = {}^-5\frac{1}{2}$$

$$y + 1\frac{3}{4} - 1\frac{3}{4} = {}^-5\frac{1}{2} - 1\frac{3}{4} \qquad \text{Subtract } 1\frac{3}{4} \text{ from both sides.}$$

$$y + 0 = {}^-7\frac{1}{4}$$

$$y = {}^-7\frac{1}{4}$$

$$\textit{Check:} \quad y + 1\frac{3}{4} = {}^-5\frac{1}{2}$$

$${}^-7\frac{1}{4} + 1\frac{3}{4} = {}^-5\frac{1}{2} \qquad \text{Replace } y \text{ with } {}^-7\frac{1}{4}.$$

$${}^-5\frac{1}{2} = {}^-5\frac{1}{2}$$

Exercises

A Explain what is done in each step.

1. $x - {}^-6.3 = 9.7$

$x - {}^-6.3 + {}^-6.3 = 9.7 + {}^-6.3$

$x + 0 = 3.4$

$x = 3.4$

2. $y + {}^-1\frac{1}{3} = 5\frac{1}{2}$

$y + {}^-1\frac{1}{3} - {}^-1\frac{1}{3} = 5\frac{1}{2} - {}^-1\frac{1}{3}$

$y + 0 = 6\frac{5}{6}$

$y = 6\frac{5}{6}$

Tell how you would solve each equation.

3. $n - \frac{3}{4} = {}^-1\frac{2}{3}$ **4.** $m + 6.7 = 9.4$ **5.** $k - {}^-1\frac{1}{2} = {}^-1\frac{2}{3}$

6. $t + {}^-3.7 = {}^-2.4$ **7.** $x - 5.7 = 0$ **8.** $y + 1\frac{7}{8} = 0$

B Solve and check.

9. $n - 6.3 = 9.5$ **10.** $k + {}^-4.6 = 4.7$ **11.** $n - 7.62 = {}^-6.25$

12. $t + {}^-1\frac{3}{4} = 2\frac{1}{2}$ **13.** $n - \frac{3}{4} = {}^-1\frac{2}{3}$ **14.** $b + 7\frac{1}{2} = \frac{3}{4}$

15. $x - 4.2 = {}^-6.3$ **16.** $x + 7.5 = {}^-2.5$ **17.** $y - \frac{3}{4} = {}^-\frac{7}{8}$

18. $m + (-\frac{3}{4}) = \frac{1}{3}$ **19.** $y - {}^-4.7 = 9.7$ **20.** $n + 0.75 = {}^-0.26$

21. $t - {}^-1\frac{3}{4} = {}^-2\frac{1}{2}$ **22.** $t + {}^-1\frac{3}{4} = {}^-1\frac{1}{2}$ **23.** $b - 4.5 = 2.3$

Solve each problem.

24. The opening price of a stock was $17\frac{1}{2}$. The change for the day was $-1\frac{1}{4}$. What was the closing price of the stock?

25. The barometric pressure this morning was 30.36 inches. It is now 29.52 inches. What was the change in barometric pressure during this period?

26. Last year Sandy had an earned–run average of 2.96. This was 0.52 more than this year's average. What was his earned–run average this year?

27. Mrs. James had a weight loss of $1\frac{1}{2}$ pounds this week. She now weighs $105\frac{3}{4}$. What was her weight last week?

28. This year's sales for 4N Company were down $1.7 million from last year's sales. If this year's sales were $30.5 million, what were last year's sales?

C Solve each equation.

Examples: $7.1 + x = 4$

$$x + 7.1 = 4$$

$$x + 7.1 - 7.1 = 4 - 7.1$$

$$x + 0 = {}^{-}3.1$$

$$x = {}^{-}3.1$$

$$\frac{3}{4}x + \frac{1}{4}x = 2\frac{1}{2}$$

$$\left(\frac{3}{4} + \frac{1}{4}\right)x = 2\frac{1}{2}$$

$$1x = 2\frac{1}{2}$$

$$x = 2\frac{1}{2}$$

29. $1\frac{3}{4} + x = 2\frac{1}{2}$

30. ${}^{-}2.5 + x = 1.2$

31. $0.7x + 0.3x = {}^{-}4.2$

32. $1\frac{3}{4}x + \left(-\frac{3}{4}x\right) = 2$

33. ${}^{-}4\frac{1}{2} + x = {}^{-}6\frac{1}{2}$

34. $\frac{2}{3}x + \frac{1}{3}x = 8.7$

35. $7.5x - 6.5x = 4.7$

36. $-\frac{3}{4}x + 1\frac{3}{4}x = 3\frac{1}{4}$

37. ${}^{-}6\frac{1}{2} + x = {}^{-}1\frac{1}{4}$

38. $6.5 + x = {}^{-}4.3$

39. $1.4x - 2.4x = 3$

40. $9.5x + {}^{-}8.5x = 3\frac{3}{4}$

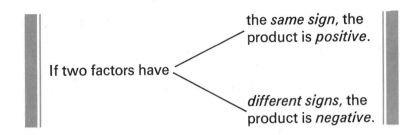

Example 1: Find each product.

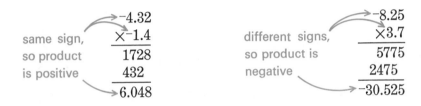

same sign,
so product
is positive

$$\begin{array}{r} {}^{-}4.32 \\ \times {}^{-}1.4 \\ \hline 1728 \\ 432 \\ \hline 6.048 \end{array}$$

different signs,
so product is
negative

$$\begin{array}{r} {}^{-}8.25 \\ \times 3.7 \\ \hline 5775 \\ 2475 \\ \hline {}^{-}30.525 \end{array}$$

A similar pattern exists for division.

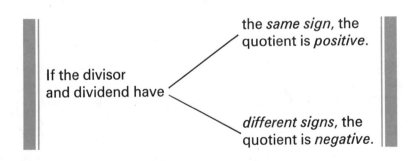

Example 2: Find each quotient.

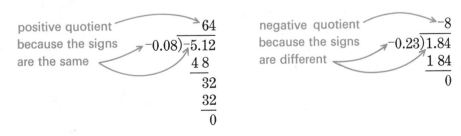

positive quotient
because the signs
are the same

$$\begin{array}{r} 64 \\ {}^{-}0.08\overline{)^{-}5.12} \\ 48 \\ \hline 32 \\ 32 \\ \hline 0 \end{array}$$

negative quotient
because the signs
are different

$$\begin{array}{r} {}^{-}8 \\ {}^{-}0.23\overline{)1.84} \\ 184 \\ \hline 0 \end{array}$$

Exercises

A Tell whether each product is positive or negative.

1. 123×4.7

2. $^-4.3 \times 7.2$

3. $8.6 \times ^-4.9$

4. $^-2.37 \times ^-6.67$

5. $6 \times ^-1.672$

6. $^-9.125 \times ^-8$

Tell whether each quotient is positive or negative.

7. $927 \div 7.8$

8. $628 \div ^-4.8$

9. $^-9.63 \div 0.037$

10. $^-0.69 \div ^-0.03$

11. $^-8.84 \div 1.25$

12. $^-1.98 \div ^-9$

B Find each product.

13. 1.7×4.6

14. $^-1.65 \times 46.9$

15. $0.125 \times ^-48.9$

16. $^-8.6 \times ^-9.2$

17. $0.25 \times ^-1.95$

18. $^-6.75 \times 2.57$

19. $^-2.95 \times ^-4.2$

20. $1.732 \times ^-5$

21. $^-1.414 \times 6$

22. 6.2×4.7

23. $8.8 \times ^-6.75$

24. $^-9.99 \times ^-0.55$

Find each quotient.

25. $3.19 \div 2.9$

26. $^-0.498 \div 8.3$

27. $9.99 \div ^-2.7$

28. $^-13.69 \div ^-0.37$

29. $19.69 \div 0.11$

30. $^-0.1794 \div 0.26$

31. $855 \div ^-9.5$

32. $^-9.90 \div ^-2.2$

33. $184.8 \div ^-0.77$

34. $158.1 \div 9.3$

35. $0.304 \div ^-0.16$

36. $^-23.8 \div ^-1.4$

37. A weather balloon is descending at a rate of 4.5 feet per second. What will be the change in the altitude of the balloon in 15 seconds?

38. The temperature of a gas is to be lowered from 0°C. to ⁻37.5°C. in three stages. If the degree drop is the same in each stage, what will be the temperature of the gas after the first stage?

39. The level of the city reservoir is changing ⁻1.75 feet per day, At this rate, what will be the change for a 5-day period?

40. The depth of an oil well is to be 3680 feet. The drilling is now 68% complete. At what depth are they now drilling?

C Find the number named by each phrase.

41. $1.7 \times (^-2.8 \times 8.3)$

42. $(1.26 \div 0.3) \div {^-0.3}$

43. $(6.5 \div {^-1.3}) \times 4.6$

44. $(8.7 \div {^-2.9}) \times {^-9.7}$

45. $(1.4 \times {^-1.6}) \div 0.56$

46. $1.96 \div (^-0.2 \times 0.7)$

47. $1.44 \div (^-0.9 \times {^-1.6})$

48. $(^-1.728 \div {^-1.44}) \div {^-12}$

Matchless Problems

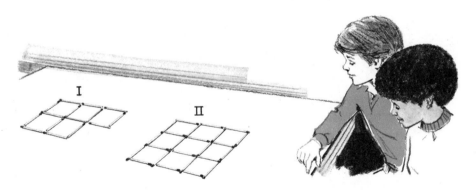

Arrange matchsticks to form arrays as shown above.

1. Remove 3 matchsticks from **I** so that only 3 squares are left.

2. Remove 4 matchsticks from **I** so that only 2 squares are left.

3. Remove 8 matchsticks from **II** so that only 2 squares are left.

13.6 ◆ MULTIPLICATION AND DIVISION WITH FRACTIONS

You already know how to multiply and divide with fractions. You also know how to tell when a product or quotient is positive or negative. These two things are all you need to know to multiply or divide rational numbers.

Example 1: Find each product.

same sign → positive product

$$-\frac{3}{8} \times {}^-\frac{3}{4} = +\left(\frac{3}{8} \times \frac{3}{4}\right)$$

$$= \frac{3 \times 3}{8 \times 4}$$

$$= \frac{9}{32}$$

different signs → negative product

$$-1\frac{1}{4} \times \frac{2}{3} = {}^-\left(1\frac{1}{4} \times \frac{2}{3}\right)$$

$$= {}^-\left(\frac{5}{4} \times \frac{2}{3}\right)$$

$$= -\frac{5 \times 1}{2 \times 3}$$

$$= -\frac{5}{6}$$

Example 2: Find each quotient.

same sign → positive quotient

$$-\frac{3}{4} \div {}^-\frac{1}{2} = +\left(\frac{3}{4} \div \frac{1}{2}\right)$$

$$= \frac{3}{4} \times \frac{2}{1}$$

$$= \frac{3}{4} \times \frac{2}{1}$$

$$= \frac{3}{2} \text{ or } 1\frac{1}{2}$$

different signs → negative quotient

$$1\frac{1}{4} \div {}^-2\frac{2}{3} = {}^-\left(1\frac{1}{4} \div 2\frac{2}{3}\right)$$

$$= {}^-\left(\frac{5}{4} \div \frac{8}{3}\right)$$

$${}^-\left(\frac{5}{4} \times \frac{3}{8}\right)$$

$$= -\frac{15}{32}$$

Exercises

A Tell whether each product is positive or negative.

1. $\frac{3}{4} \times \frac{1}{2}$

2. $\frac{3}{8}(-\frac{1}{6})$

3. $-\frac{3}{8} \times \frac{6}{7}$

4. $-\frac{2}{3}(-\frac{2}{5})$

5. $-1\frac{1}{2} \times 3\frac{3}{4}$

6. $-\frac{3}{4} \times -1\frac{7}{8}$

Tell whether each quotient is positive or negative.

7. $\frac{2}{3} \div \frac{1}{2}$

8. $1\frac{1}{4} \div -\frac{2}{3}$

9. $-\frac{3}{8} \div \frac{1}{2}$

10. $-\frac{5}{8} \div -\frac{2}{3}$

11. $-\frac{3}{8} \div 4\frac{1}{2}$

12. $-2\frac{1}{2} \div -1\frac{1}{4}$

B Find each product.

13. $\frac{2}{3} \times \frac{1}{5}$

14. $-\frac{2}{3} \times \frac{7}{8}$

15. $\frac{3}{5}(-\frac{7}{9})$

16. $-\frac{5}{6}(-\frac{3}{4})$

17. $4\frac{1}{2} \times \frac{2}{3}$

18. $-3\frac{1}{8} \times \frac{3}{4}$

19. $\frac{7}{8}(-3\frac{1}{7})$

20. $2\frac{1}{4}(-\frac{4}{5})$

21. $-3\frac{1}{2}(-\frac{2}{3})$

22. $4\frac{1}{2} \times -1\frac{1}{2}$

23. $-3\frac{1}{4} \times 2\frac{1}{2}$

24. $-5\frac{1}{2} \times -2\frac{1}{4}$

Find each quotient.

25. $\frac{3}{4} \div \frac{1}{2}$

26. $-\frac{7}{8} \div \frac{2}{3}$

27. $\frac{4}{5} \div -\frac{3}{4}$

28. $-\frac{1}{2} \div -\frac{2}{3}$

29. $3\frac{1}{7} \div 2$

30. $4\frac{1}{2} \div -\frac{1}{2}$

31. $-6\frac{3}{4} \div \frac{7}{16}$

32. $-\frac{7}{8} \div 2\frac{1}{4}$

33. $-4\frac{1}{4} \div \frac{2}{3}$

34. $3\frac{1}{2} \div -2\frac{1}{4}$

35. $-5\frac{1}{2} \div 3\frac{2}{3}$

36. $-4\frac{1}{2} \div -3\frac{1}{4}$

Solve each problem.

37. Mrs. Wilson lost $18\frac{3}{4}$ pounds over a six-week period. What was her average weekly weight loss?

38. Steel production was down an average of $\frac{3}{4}$ ton a day for 5 days. What was the total amount that production was down for this period?

39. A diving sphere can descend at a rate of $4\frac{1}{2}$ feet per second. At that rate, how long will it take to descend from the surface to a depth of 300 feet?

40. Suppose the diving sphere in Exercise **39** can rise at a rate of $4\frac{1}{2}$ feet per second and is at a depth of 400 feet. How long would it take the sphere to surface?

C Determine if the following are true.

41. $\frac{3}{4} \times -\frac{2}{3} = -\frac{2}{3} \times \frac{3}{4}$

42. $^-1.2 \times 4.3 = 4.3 \times {}^-1.2$

43. $\frac{3}{4}(\frac{2}{3} \times \frac{5}{6}) = (\frac{3}{4} \times \frac{2}{3}) \times \frac{5}{6}$

44. $(1.2 \times 2.3) \times 3.4 = 1.2(2.3 \times 3.4)$

45. $-\frac{3}{8} \times 1 = -\frac{3}{8}$

46. $1 \times {}^-7.5 = {}^-7.5$

Use your answers for exercises **41–46** to answer the following.

47. Do you think multiplication of rational numbers is commutative?

48. Do you think multiplication of rational numbers is associative?

49. What number do you think is the identity number for multiplication of rational numbers?

There are 4 runners on the school cross-country team. There was a 13.4-second difference in this week's team time and the season's average. What was the average difference per person?

The following equation can be used to solve this problem.

$$4n = 13.4$$

You already have the skills needed to solve such equations.

Example 1: Solve and check $4n = 13.4$.

$$4n = 13.4$$

$$\frac{4n}{4} = \frac{13.4}{4}$$ Divide each side by 4.

$$n = 3.35$$ The average difference per person is 3.35 seconds.

Check: $4n = 13.4$

$$4 \times 3.35 = 13.4$$ Replace n with 3.35.

$$13.4 = 13.4$$

Example 2: Solve and check $\frac{n}{5} = {}^-3\frac{1}{3}$.

$$\frac{n}{5} = {}^-3\frac{1}{3}$$

$$\frac{n}{5} \times 5 = {}^-3\frac{1}{3} \times 5$$ Multiply each side by 5.

$$n = {}^-16\frac{2}{3}$$

$$\textit{Check:} \quad \frac{n}{5} = -3\frac{1}{3}$$

$$\frac{-16\frac{2}{3}}{5} = -3\frac{1}{3} \qquad \text{Replace } n \text{ with } -16\frac{2}{3}.$$

$$-3\frac{1}{3} = -3\frac{1}{3}$$

Exercises

A Explain what is done in each step of the following examples.

1. $\dfrac{m}{-3.6} = 4$

$\dfrac{m}{-3.6} \times {}^-3.6 = 4 \times {}^-3.6$

$m = {}^-14.4$

2. $-2k = 3\frac{1}{3}$

$\dfrac{-2k}{-2} = \dfrac{3\frac{1}{3}}{-2}$

$k = {}^-1\frac{2}{3}$

Tell how you would solve each equation.

3. $\frac{x}{6} = 3\frac{1}{4}$ **4.** $4m = {}^-6\frac{1}{3}$ **5.** $\frac{t}{-3.7} = {}^-8.3$

6. $-3x = 7\frac{1}{2}$ **7.** $\frac{m}{-4} = 8.7$ **8.** $7.3m = 6.7$

B Solve and check.

9. $\frac{x}{6.3} = 5$ **10.** $3.9x = 1.95$ **11.** $\frac{m}{7.2} = {}^-8$

12. $6m = 3\frac{1}{2}$ **13.** $\frac{x}{4} = 3\frac{4}{5}$ **14.** $-2x = 27\frac{1}{2}$

15. $-1.7x = 6.8$ **16.** $\frac{x}{9} = {}^-3\frac{2}{3}$ **17.** $\frac{m}{-6.7} = 4.2$

18. $\frac{x}{-5} = 4\frac{1}{2}$ **19.** $2.7x = {}^-7.29$ **20.** $-3b = {}^-3\frac{2}{3}$

21. $\frac{t}{-4.3} = {}^-4.7$ **22.** $-5t = {}^-5\frac{1}{3}$ **23.** $-0.16x = {}^-1.44$

Solve each problem.

24. The Royster Corporation wants to increase sales $3\frac{3}{4}$ million. How long will it take to do this if sales increase $1\frac{1}{4}$ million per year?

25. The total weight of the capsules in a bottle is 64.8 grams. If each capsule weighs 0.9 grams, how many capsules are in the bottle?

26. What would be the weight of 36 of the capsules in Exercise **25**?

27. The perimeter of a square is $10\frac{1}{2}$ inches. What is the length of each side of the square? (Hint: $p = 4s$.)

28. How long will it take to inflate a balloon to a pressure of 67.5 pounds at a rate of 2.5 pounds per second?

29. How long would it take to deflate the balloon in Exercise **28** at a rate of 12.5 pounds per second?

30. The 440-yard relay team won the race with a time of 44.8 seconds. What is the average time for each of the four members of the team?

C Find the diameter of each circle whose circumference is given below. Use 3.14 for π.

Example: *Circumference:* 12.56 cm

$$C = \pi d$$
$$12.56 = 3.14d$$
$$\frac{12.56}{3.14} = \frac{3.14d}{3.14}$$

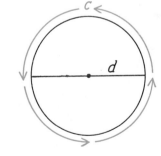

The diameter is 4 cm.

$$4 = d$$

31. 9.42 in   **32.** 4.71 m   **33.** 28.26 ft

34. 15.7 in   **35.** 56.52 cm   **36.** 23.864 yd

13.8 ◆ EQUATION REVIEW

Earlier you had a "phase check" for equations with whole numbers. This lesson is your "phase check" for equations with rational numbers.

Example 1: Solve $x - 1\frac{1}{2} = {}^-2\frac{1}{4}$.

$$x - 1\frac{1}{2} = {}^-2\frac{1}{4}$$

$$x - 1\frac{1}{2} + 1\frac{1}{2} = {}^-2\frac{1}{4} + 1\frac{1}{2}$$

$$x = -\frac{3}{4}$$

Check: $\quad x - 1\frac{1}{2} = {}^-2\frac{1}{4}$

$$-\frac{3}{4} - 1\frac{1}{2} = {}^-2\frac{1}{4}$$

$$-2\frac{1}{4} = {}^-2\frac{1}{4}$$

Example 2: Solve $x + {}^-1.4 = 3.7$.

$$x + {}^-1.4 = 3.7$$

$$x + {}^-1.4 - {}^-1.4 = 3.7 - {}^-1.4$$

$$x = 5.1$$

Check: $\quad x + {}^-1.4 = 3.7$

$$5.1 + {}^-1.4 = 3.7$$

$$3.7 = 3.7$$

Example 3: Solve $\frac{n}{8} = {}^-1\frac{3}{4}$.

$$\frac{n}{8} = {}^-1\frac{3}{4}$$

$$\frac{n}{8} \times 8 = {}^-1\frac{3}{4} \times 8$$

$$n = {}^-14$$

Check: $\quad \frac{n}{8} = {}^-1\frac{3}{4}$

$$\frac{{}^-14}{8} = {}^-1\frac{3}{4}$$

$$-1\frac{3}{4} = {}^-1\frac{3}{4}$$

Example 4: Solve $3.5x = {}^-13.65$

$$3.5x = {}^-13.65$$

$$\frac{3.5x}{3.5} = \frac{{}^-13.65}{3.5}$$

$$x = {}^-3.9$$

Check: $\quad 3.5x = {}^-13.65$

$$3.5 \times {}^-3.9 = {}^-13.65$$

$$-13.65 = {}^-13.65$$

Exercises

A Tell what you would do to solve each equation.

1. $x - {}^-2\frac{1}{2} = 1\frac{1}{4}$ 2. $\frac{n}{2.7} = {}^-3.6$ 3. ${}^-2\frac{1}{2}n = {}^-22\frac{1}{2}$

4. $x + 3.7 = {}^-2.6$ 5. $4\frac{1}{4}t = 17$ 6. ${}^-3.7m = 1.85$

B Solve each equation.

7. $b - 2\frac{1}{4} = 3\frac{3}{4}$ 8. $\frac{n}{2.3} = 5$ 9. $y + 1\frac{1}{2} = {}^-5\frac{1}{3}$

10. $2\frac{1}{2}t = {}^-12\frac{1}{2}$ 11. $d - 7.6 = {}^-3.7$ 12. $\frac{k}{2} = {}^-3\frac{1}{2}$

13. $y + {}^-1.7 = 1.5$ 14. ${}^-2.3x = 11.5$ 15. $f - {}^-1\frac{1}{4} = 6\frac{7}{8}$

16. $\frac{m}{{}^-3.2} = 5.9$ 17. $y + 2\frac{1}{3} = {}^-3\frac{1}{4}$ 18. ${}^-3\frac{1}{3}x = 16\frac{2}{3}$

19. $h - {}^-1.6 = {}^-7.5$ 20. $\frac{t}{{}^-6} = {}^-4\frac{1}{5}$ 21. $n + {}^-7.3 = {}^-4.6$

22. $0.24x = {}^-1.44$ 23. $j - {}^-1\frac{3}{4} = {}^-1\frac{1}{3}$ 24. $\frac{n}{{}^-4.7} = 5.2$

C Solve each inequality.

Examples:

$$x - 4\frac{1}{2} < {}^-3\frac{1}{3}$$

$$x - 4\frac{1}{2} + 4\frac{1}{2} < {}^-3\frac{1}{3} + 4\frac{1}{2}$$

$$x + 0 < 1\frac{1}{6}$$

$$x < 1\frac{1}{6}$$

$${}^-2.5x > {}^-4.75$$

$$\frac{{}^-2.5x}{{}^-2.5} < \frac{{}^-4.75}{{}^-2.5}$$

$$x < 1.9$$

25. $x - 1\frac{1}{3} > 1\frac{1}{2}$ 26. $x + \frac{3}{4} < {}^-\frac{2}{3}$ 27. $\frac{x}{2.5} > 4.3$

28. $2.6x < 0.78$ 29. $x - \frac{7}{8} < {}^-1\frac{1}{2}$ 30. $x + {}^-1\frac{2}{3} > 1\frac{5}{8}$

31. $\frac{x}{{}^-2.3} < 1.7$ 32. ${}^-1\frac{3}{4}x > 5\frac{1}{4}$ 33. $x - {}^-1\frac{1}{4} > 3\frac{1}{4}$

34. $x + {}^-1\frac{1}{2} < {}^-1\frac{7}{8}$ 35. $\frac{x}{{}^-2} > 1\frac{3}{4}$ 36. ${}^-1.6x < 0.96$

13.9 ◆ TWO–STEP EQUATIONS

The George Washington Bridge has two end spans of equal length and a center span that is 0.68 mile long. The overall length of the bridge is 0.9 mile. How long is each span?

The following equation can be given for the problem.

$$2n + 0.68 = 0.9$$

The techniques you use to solve two-step equations with integers can be used to solve two-step equations with rational numbers.

Example 1: Solve $2n + 0.68 = 0.9$.

$$2n + 0.68 = 0.9$$

$$2n + 0.68 - 0.68 = 0.9 - 0.68$$

$$2n = 0.22$$

$$\frac{2n}{2} = \frac{0.22}{2}$$

$$n = 0.11$$

Check: $2n + 0.68 = 0.9$

$$(2 \times 0.11) + 0.68 = 0.9$$

$$0.22 + 0.68 = 0.9$$

$$0.9 = 0.9$$

Example 2: Solve $\frac{n}{2} - \frac{2}{3} = -\frac{1}{6}$.

$$\frac{n}{2} - \frac{2}{3} = -\frac{1}{6}$$

$$\frac{n}{2} - \frac{2}{3} + \frac{2}{3} = -\frac{1}{6} + \frac{2}{3}$$

$$\frac{n}{2} = \frac{1}{2}$$

$$\frac{n}{2} \times 2 = \frac{1}{2} \times 2$$

$$n = 1$$

Check: $\frac{n}{2} - \frac{2}{3} = -\frac{1}{6}$

$$\frac{1}{2} - \frac{2}{3} = -\frac{1}{6}$$

$$-\frac{1}{6} = -\frac{1}{6}$$

Example 3: Solve $\frac{k-6}{3} = 1\frac{2}{3}$.

$$\frac{k-6}{3} = 1\frac{2}{3}$$

$$\frac{k-6}{3} \times 3 = 1\frac{2}{3} \times 3$$

$$k - 6 = 5$$

$$k - 6 + 6 = 5 + 6$$

$$k = 11$$

Check:
$$\frac{k-6}{3} = 1\frac{2}{3}$$

$$\frac{11-6}{3} = 1\frac{2}{3}$$

$$\frac{5}{3} = 1\frac{2}{3}$$

$$1\frac{2}{3} = 1\frac{2}{3}$$

Exercises

A Tell how you would solve each equation.

1. $2.4m + 0.4 = {}^{-}1.6$ 2. $\frac{4x}{3} = -\frac{7}{8}$ 3. $^{-}3.7t - 2.4 = 6.9$

4. $\frac{m}{3} + 1\frac{7}{8} = 5\frac{1}{3}$ 5. $\frac{y}{2} - 2.3 = {}^{-}4.7$ 6. $\frac{x - {}^{-}3.7}{4.6} = 3.6$

B Solve and check each equation.

7. $2.7m + 0.4 = 5.8$ 8. $3.2k - 4.7 = 4.9$ 9. $3x + 1\frac{3}{4} = {}^{-}5\frac{1}{4}$

10. $2k - 1\frac{1}{2} = 4\frac{1}{3}$ 11. $\frac{3x}{4} = 1.8$ 12. $\frac{m}{3} + \frac{3}{8} = 4\frac{1}{2}$

13. $\frac{x-3}{4} = {}^{-}1\frac{2}{3}$ 14. $3x - (-\frac{2}{3}) = 4\frac{1}{2}$ 15. $\frac{2x}{3} = {}^{-}1\frac{2}{3}$

16. $\frac{2x}{{}^{-}7} = 6.4$ 17. $\frac{k}{4} + 1.5 = {}^{-}2.7$ 18. $\frac{x - {}^{-}2.6}{5.2} = 7.3$

19. $\frac{y}{6} - 1.5 = {}^{-}7.2$ 20. $\frac{t+4}{{}^{-}7} = 1\frac{2}{3}$ 21. $\frac{5x}{4.1} = {}^{-}7.6$

22. $3.4k - {}^{-}4.7 = {}^{-}8.9$ 23. $\frac{y}{3} - 1\frac{2}{3} = {}^{-}5\frac{1}{3}$ 24. $5x - 1\frac{1}{3} = {}^{-}7\frac{1}{2}$

25. $5m + {}^{-}2.6 = 3.7$ 26. $\frac{t}{1.9} + 2 = {}^{-}1.3$ 27. $3x + 1\frac{2}{3} = {}^{-}2\frac{1}{2}$

28. $\frac{4x}{3} = {}^{-}6.9$ 29. $\frac{{}^{-}4x}{3} = {}^{-}1\frac{2}{3}$ 30. $\frac{x + 4.5}{3.2} = {}^{-}7.3$

31. $2k - 1\frac{2}{3} = {}^{-}5\frac{1}{2}$ 32. $\frac{t}{4} - 1.5 = 2.7$ 33. $\frac{m}{3} + 3\frac{1}{8} = 2\frac{1}{4}$

Solve each inequality.

Examples: $\dfrac{3x}{4} > -\dfrac{5}{8}$ $\qquad\qquad\qquad\qquad$ $^-1.2x + 1.7 < -5.8$

$\qquad\qquad \dfrac{3x}{4} \times 4 > -\dfrac{5}{8} \times 4$ $\qquad\qquad$ $^-1.2x + 1.7 - 1.7 < ^-5.8 - 1.7$

$\qquad\qquad\qquad 3x > -\dfrac{5}{2}$ $\qquad\qquad\qquad\qquad$ $^-1.2x < ^-7.5$

$\qquad\qquad\qquad \dfrac{3x}{3} > \dfrac{-\frac{5}{2}}{3}$ $\qquad\qquad\qquad\qquad$ $\dfrac{^-1.2x}{^-1.2} > \dfrac{^-7.5}{^-1.2}$

$\qquad\qquad\qquad\quad x > -\dfrac{5}{6}$ $\qquad\qquad\qquad\qquad$ $x > 6.25$

34. $\dfrac{4x}{3} < 1\dfrac{3}{4}$ $\qquad$ **35.** $^-3x + 1.7 > 6.2$ $\qquad$ **36.** $\dfrac{x}{2} - 3.2 < ^-4.9$

37. $7.5x - 4.3 > 18.2$ $\qquad$ **38.** $\dfrac{x}{^-2} - \dfrac{5}{8} > \dfrac{2}{3}$ $\qquad$ **39.** $\dfrac{x}{4} + \dfrac{3}{4} < -\dfrac{2}{3}$

40. $\dfrac{^-3x}{5} > ^-1\dfrac{2}{3}$ $\qquad$ **41.** $\dfrac{x - 2.4}{5.7} < 1.5$ $\qquad$ **42.** $\dfrac{x + 5}{^-3} > ^-4\dfrac{1}{2}$

A Weighty Problem

A fruit peddler has a 1-lb, a 3-lb, and a 9-lb weight. How can he use these weights to weigh any whole number of pounds from 1 lb through 13 lb?

Match each item with the best description.

1. $1\frac{1}{2}$, $\frac{3}{2}$, or 1.5

a. positive sum

2. $-\frac{1}{4}$

b. 3 ways to write the rational number $3 \div 2$

3. $\frac{3}{4} + -1\frac{1}{2}$

c. positive product

4. $7.5 + -1.6$

d. negative quotient

5. $-1\frac{3}{4} \times \frac{3}{4}$

e. negative sum

6. -1.7×-2.3

f. positive quotient

7. $-2\frac{3}{4} \div -1\frac{2}{3}$

g. opposite of $\frac{1}{4}$

8. $8.96 \div -2.4$

h. negative product

CHAPTER REVIEW

Should $>$, $<$, or $=$ replace ⬤ to make the sentence true ?   13.1

1. $\frac{3}{7}$ ⬤ $\frac{5}{7}$ **2.** $\frac{3}{4}$ ⬤ $\frac{7}{8}$ **3.** $\frac{3}{4}$ ⬤ $-\frac{2}{3}$

4. $-\frac{5}{6}$ ⬤ $\frac{2}{3}$ **5.** $-\frac{5}{8}$ ⬤ $-\frac{1}{2}$ **6.** $-\frac{7}{8}$ ⬤ $\frac{14}{16}$

Find each sum or difference.   13.2

7. $-5.9 + 3.7$ **8.** $-4.2 + -1.9$ **9.** $6.38 + -2.69$

10. $-1.732 - 4.12$ **11.** $-5.7 - -5.2$ **12.** $8.3 - -9.6$

13. $-\frac{1}{8} + \frac{3}{8}$ **14.** $\frac{3}{4} + \left(-\frac{1}{8}\right)$ **15.** $-2\frac{1}{2} + -3\frac{1}{3}$ 13.3

16. $\frac{1}{4} - \frac{2}{3}$ **17.** $-7\frac{1}{2} - 3\frac{3}{4}$ **18.** $-8\frac{3}{4} - -7\frac{3}{4}$

13.4   Solve each equation.

19. $n - \frac{1}{2} = 1\frac{1}{4}$ **20.** $m + 6.9 = 6.7$ **21.** $k - {}^-1\frac{1}{2} = {}^-2\frac{1}{3}$

22. $x - 6.9 = 8.3$ **23.** $x + 3\frac{1}{8} = 0$ **24.** $d + {}^-7.3 = {}^-4.2$

13.5   Find each product or quotient.

25. ${}^-1.56 \times 45.3$ **26.** $0.42 \times {}^-34.2$ **27.** ${}^-4.43 \times {}^-5.42$

28. ${}^-0.996 \div 8.3$ **29.** ${}^-0.1794 \div 1.3$ **30.** ${}^-18.48 \div {}^-1.54$

13.6   **31.** $\frac{7}{8} \times \left(-\frac{2}{3}\right)$ **32.** $-\frac{5}{9} \times \frac{3}{5}$ **33.** ${}^-3\frac{1}{7} \times \left(-\frac{3}{4}\right)$

34. $-\frac{2}{3} \div \frac{7}{8}$ **35.** $3\frac{1}{2} \div {}^-2$ **36.** ${}^-4\frac{1}{3} \div {}^-3\frac{1}{4}$

13.7   Solve each equation.

37. $7n = {}^-12\frac{1}{2}$ **38.** $\frac{m}{{}^-6} = 8.7$ **39.** ${}^-2.7m = 1.62$

13.8   **40.** $\frac{k}{4} = 3\frac{1}{3}$ **41.** ${}^-5k = 16$ **42.** $\frac{t}{4.2} = {}^-5.7$

43. $x - 1\frac{1}{2} = {}^-3\frac{3}{4}$ **44.** $z + 2.3 = 5.9$ **45.** $k + {}^-5.9 = {}^-3.75$

13.9   **46.** $\frac{t-3}{6} = {}^-1\frac{1}{3}$ **47.** $\frac{n}{3} - \frac{1}{2} = -\frac{5}{6}$ **48.** $0.6x + 8.1 = 5.1$

49. $\frac{3x}{4} = -\frac{5}{8}$ **50.** ${}^-3.6t - 2.4 = 1.02$ **51.** $\frac{x - {}^-5.2}{3.7} = {}^-3.6$

Find each sum or difference.

1. $-\frac{3}{4} + \frac{1}{8}$ **2.** $\frac{7}{8} + (-\frac{1}{2})$ **3.** $1\frac{1}{2} + (-\frac{5}{8})$

4. $^-3\frac{1}{2} + {^-4\frac{1}{2}}$ **5.** $^-3.75 + 4.29$ **6.** $^-8.79 + {^-6.75}$

7. $-\frac{4}{5} - \frac{1}{10}$ **8.** $\frac{1}{4} - (-\frac{5}{8})$ **9.** $^-1\frac{2}{5} - {^-2\frac{1}{3}}$

10. $6.7 - 9.6$ **11.** $^-8.9 - 5.2$ **12.** $1.42 - {^-6.75}$

Find each product or quotient.

13. $\frac{3}{4}(-\frac{2}{3})$ **14.** $-\frac{3}{8} \times \frac{7}{8}$ **15.** $1\frac{1}{4} \times {^-2\frac{1}{2}}$

16. $^-2\frac{3}{4} \times {^-1\frac{7}{8}}$ **17.** 8.13×4.5 **18.** $^-8.2 \times {^-7.3}$

19. $\frac{2}{3} \div \frac{7}{8}$ **20.** $\frac{1}{4} \div (-\frac{9}{10})$ **21.** $-\frac{1}{2} \div 1\frac{5}{8}$

22. $^-1\frac{1}{2} \div {^-2\frac{5}{6}}$ **23.** $9.57 \div {^-2.9}$ **24.** $^-19.46 \div {^-1.39}$

Solve each equation.

25. $x + 1\frac{3}{4} = {^-5\frac{1}{4}}$ **26.** $x + {^-7.2} = 5.3$

27. $x - 3.2 = {^-5.7}$ **28.** $x - 2\frac{2}{3} = 5\frac{1}{4}$

29. $9x = 16\frac{2}{3}$ **30.** $5.2x = {^-7.8}$

31. $\frac{x}{6.2} = {^-7.3}$ **32.** $\frac{x}{8} = {^-9\frac{2}{3}}$

33. $3x + 1\frac{2}{3} = 5\frac{1}{2}$ **34.** $\frac{3x}{4} = {^-1\frac{2}{3}}$

35. $\frac{x + {^-3.2}}{5.7} = {^-6.5}$ **36.** $3.14x - 5.7 = 10.942$

Solve each problem.

37. The average score of the golf team has changed by $^-14$ strokes since fall. If there are 4 members on the team, what is the average change per member?

38. An oil rig is drilling at the rate of $13\frac{1}{2}$ feet per hour. At that rate, how long will it take to drill 100 feet?

Activity 1

Name each of the whole numbers from 1 through 20 using the following rules.

    a. You must use four 4's.

    b. You can use $+$, $-$, $\times$, $\div$, ( ), and the decimal point as often as needed.

Examples:

$$7 = \frac{44}{4} - 4 \qquad\qquad 13 = \frac{4 - .4}{.4} + 4$$

$$= 11 - 4 \qquad\qquad\qquad = \frac{3.6}{.4} + 4$$

$$= 7 \qquad\qquad\qquad\qquad = 13$$

Activity 2

Arrange each set of numbers in the squares below so that they form magic squares. That is, the sum in each row, each column, and along each diagonal is the same. The sum for the fraction square should be $\frac{3}{2}$. The sum for the decimal square should be 1.2.

$$-\frac{7}{2}, \ -\frac{5}{2}, \ -\frac{3}{2}, \ -\frac{1}{2}, \qquad\qquad -5.2, -3.8, -2.4, -1,$$

$$\frac{1}{2}, \ \frac{3}{2}, \ \frac{5}{2}, \ \frac{7}{2}, \ \frac{9}{2} \qquad\qquad 0.4, 1.8, 3.2, 4.6, 6$$

Mathematics and Plumbing

To ensure proper flowage, drainage pipes should slope about $\frac{1}{4}$ inch per foot.

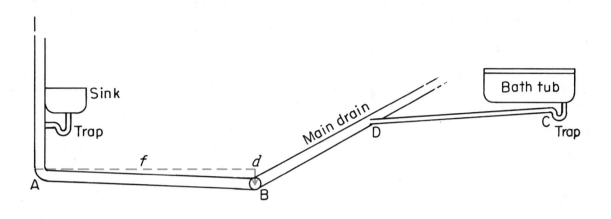

$$d = \frac{1}{4}f$$

d = number of inches of drop

f = number of feet of pipe

Example: It is 8 feet from point A to point B. How much lower should the main drain be at point B than the bottom of the sink drain at point A?

$$d = \frac{1}{4}f$$

$$= \frac{1}{4}(8) \qquad \text{Replace } f \text{ with 8.}$$

$$= 2 \qquad \text{At point B, set the main drain}$$
$$\text{2 inches lower than at point A.}$$

1. It is 6 feet from the end of the bathtub trap (point C) to the main drain (point D). How much lower should the main drain be at point D than at the end of the bathtub trap?

2. How much drop should there be in the main drain if this pipe is 24 feet long?

Getting Ready for Chapter 14

7.3   Multiply.

    1. 6×0.32 **2.** 1.48×1.1

    3. 3.4×3.4 **4.** 0.0525×0.25

7.5   Divide.

    5. $28 \div 0.07$ **6.** $12.5 \div 2.5$

    7. $0.08 \div 0.2$ **8.** $13.8 \div 0.23$

11.3   Solve each proportion.

    9. $\frac{3}{4} = \frac{x}{28}$ **10.** $\frac{2}{x} = \frac{22}{33}$ **11.** $\frac{12}{21} = \frac{x}{7}$

    12. $\frac{0.5}{0.8} = \frac{x}{16}$ **13.** $\frac{6}{30} = \frac{0.1}{x}$ **14.** $\frac{1.2}{1.8} = \frac{x}{0.6}$

Solve each equation.

13.7   **15.** $7x = 112$ **16.** $0.5x = 65$

13.8   **17.** $\frac{x}{21} = 8$ **18.** $\frac{x}{0.1} = 17$

2.8   **19.** $10 = \frac{x}{2} + 5$ **20.** $29 = \frac{x}{4} + 18$

11.6   Express as a decimal.

    21. 15% **22.** 2% **23.** $4\frac{1}{2}\%$ **24.** 8.75%

6.4   Express as a fraction.

    25. $1\frac{2}{3}$ **26.** $4\frac{1}{4}$ **27.** $2\frac{1}{2}$ **28.** $1\frac{3}{8}$

11.7   Solve each problem.

    29. 80% of a number is 12. What is the number?

    30. 15% of a number is 3.9. What is the number?

Using Algebra _____ 14

Steel has many uses—sewing needles, automobile parts, frying pans, construction beams, and hoist cables.

Likewise, algebra has many uses. In this chapter, you will use proportions, formulas, and equations in a wide variety of problem settings.

14.1 ◆ PROPORTIONS

You have learned to use proportions to solve problems.

Example 1 : There are 150 calories in 12 ounces of cola. How many calories are in 8 ounces?

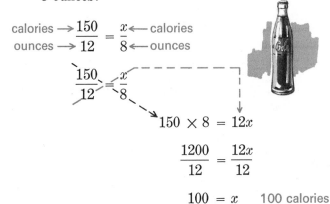

$$\text{calories} \rightarrow \frac{150}{12} = \frac{x}{8} \leftarrow \text{calories}$$
$$\text{ounces} \rightarrow 12 \quad 8 \leftarrow \text{ounces}$$

$$\frac{150}{12} = \frac{x}{8}$$

$$150 \times 8 = 12x$$

$$\frac{1200}{12} = \frac{12x}{12}$$

$$100 = x \quad \text{100 calories}$$

Diagrams can help you write proportions for problems.

Example 2 : In making plate glass, 18 kilograms of sand are used for every 7 kilograms of other ingredients. How many kilograms of sand are needed to make 125 kilograms of glass?

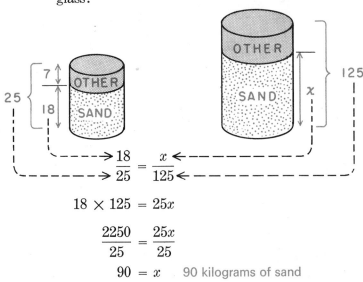

$$\frac{18}{25} = \frac{x}{125}$$

$$18 \times 125 = 25x$$

$$\frac{2250}{25} = \frac{25x}{25}$$

$$90 = x \quad \text{90 kilograms of sand}$$

Exercises

A Find the cross products for each proportion.

1. $\frac{1}{5} = \frac{3}{x}$

2. $\frac{x}{7} = \frac{2}{3.5}$

3. $\frac{6}{x} = \frac{0.3}{2}$

4. $\frac{x}{0.5} = \frac{1}{10}$

5. $\frac{1.8}{36} = \frac{1}{x}$

6. $\frac{2}{9} = \frac{x}{0.3}$

B Use a proportion to solve each problem.

7. There are 180 calories in 3 ounces of veal. How many calories are there in 4 ounces?

8. A cubic foot of water weighs 62.4 pounds and is about 7.5 gallons. How much does one gallon of water weigh? Give your answer to the nearest tenth of a pound.

9. A 5-ounce bottle of shampoo costs $0.85. Find the cost per ounce.

10. An 8-ounce bottle of another shampoo costs $1.20. Find the cost per ounce.

11. Which shampoo is a better bargain—the one in Exercise **9** or the one in Exercise **10**?

12. To make violet food coloring, you mix 3 drops of red for every 5 drops of blue. How much of each color should you mix to make 16 drops of violet food coloring?

13. Brass is an alloy made by adding 1 kilogram of zinc for every 4 kilograms of copper. How much copper is needed to make 500 kilograms of brass?

14. The alloy for 18-karat gold is made by adding 6 grams of gold for every 2 grams of other ingredients (silver and copper). How much gold is in an 18-karat bracelet that weighs 24 grams?

15. Bronze is an alloy made by adding 1 kilogram of tin for every 19 kilograms of copper. How much tin is needed to make 300 kilograms of bronze?

16. A quarter weighs 0.20 ounce. Silver quarters were made by adding 1 ounce of copper for every 9 ounces of silver. How much silver is in a silver quarter?

17. A roll of copper pennies weighs 0.35 pound. Copper pennies are made by adding 1 pound of zinc for every 19 pounds of copper. How much zinc is in a roll of copper pennies?

18. A nickel weighs 5 grams. A nickel is made by adding 3 grams of copper for every 1 gram of nickel. How much nickel is in a nickel?

19. A five-dollar roll of dimes weighs 0.25 pound. Silver dimes were made by adding 1 pound of copper for every 9 pounds of silver. How much silver is in a roll of silver dimes?

20. To make the alloy for solid-silver tableware, you add 1 pound of copper for every 9 pounds of silver. How much silver is in a 50-piece service that weighs 8 pounds?

C Use these methods to obtain two new proportions from each proportion given below.

Examples:

$$\frac{2}{5} = \frac{6}{15} \qquad\qquad \frac{2}{5} = \frac{6}{15}$$

$$\frac{2+5}{5} = \frac{6+15}{15} \qquad \frac{2}{5+2} = \frac{6}{15+6}$$

$$\frac{7}{5} = \frac{21}{15} \qquad\qquad \frac{2}{7} = \frac{6}{21}$$

Check: $\qquad\qquad$ *Check:*

$$7 \times 15 = 5 \times 21 \qquad 2 \times 21 = 7 \times 6$$

$$105 = 105 \qquad\qquad 42 = 42$$

21. $\frac{3}{4} = \frac{12}{16}$ $\qquad$ **22.** $\frac{6}{5} = \frac{30}{25}$ $\qquad$ **23.** $\frac{6}{18} = \frac{1}{3}$

24. $\frac{5}{1} = \frac{10}{2}$ $\qquad$ **25.** $\frac{1.2}{20} = \frac{0.3}{5}$ $\qquad$ **26.** $\frac{0.3}{0.2} = \frac{2.1}{1.4}$

The number of kilowatt-hours you use determines what you pay for electricity.

kilowatt-hours → k

time in hours, watts → $= \dfrac{tw}{1000}$

100 watts   400 watts

Example 1: How many kilowatt-hours are used to run the TV for 28 hours?

$$k = \dfrac{tw}{1000}$$

$$= \dfrac{28 \times 200}{1000}$$

$$= 5.6 \qquad \text{5.6 kilowatt-hours are used.}$$

200 watts

The approximate horsepower rating of an electric motor is determined by this formula.

horsepower   watts

$$h = \dfrac{w}{750}$$

Example 2: Find the number of watts for the lawn mower.

$$h = \dfrac{w}{750}$$

$$1\dfrac{1}{2} = \dfrac{w}{750}$$

$$\dfrac{3}{2} = \dfrac{w}{750}$$

$$3 \times 750 = 2w$$

$$\dfrac{3 \times 750}{2} = \dfrac{2w}{2}$$

1½ horsepower

$$1125 = w \qquad \text{The number of watts is 1125.}$$

There are many different ways to find the horsepower rating for an automobile. This formula gives the nominal horsepower.

number of cylinders   diameter of piston *(inches)*

horsepower

$$h = 0.4 \times n \times d^2$$

Example 3: Find the horsepower of a 6-cylinder engine that has a 3.5-inch piston diameter.

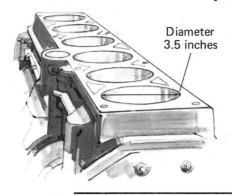

Diameter 3.5 inches

$h = 0.4 \times n \times d^2$

$= 0.4 \times 6 \times (3.5)^2 \longleftarrow 3.5 \times 3.5$

$= 0.4 \times 6 \times 12.25$

$= 29.4$ The horsepower is 29.4.

Exercises

A Use a formula to answer each question.

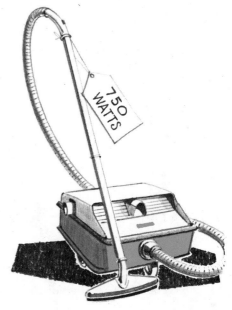

750 WATTS

1. How many kilowatt-hours are used when a 100-watt light bulb is on for 10 hours?

2. What is the horsepower for the vacuum cleaner?

3. Find the horsepower of a 4-cylinder engine that has a 3-inch piston diameter.

B Use the formula $k = \frac{tw}{1000}$ to complete this table.

	Appliance	t	w	k
4.	Hot comb	3	400	
5.	Iron	12	1100	
6.	Radio	50	15	
7.	Sewing machine		80	2.24
8.	Toaster		1600	11.20
9.	Refrigerator		250	25.00
10.	Electric range	2.5	12,000	
11.	Hair dryer	20		15.00

12. At $0.023 per kilowatt-hour, how much does it cost to run the hot comb? The radio? The toaster?

13. How long must you use the sewing machine to use 1 kilowatt-hour of electricity?

14. How long must you use the electric range to use 1 kilowatt-hour of electricity? Express your answer as a fraction of an hour.

15. At $0.03 per kilowatt-hour, how much does it cost to run the clock for 1 year (365 days)?

16. At $0.04 per kilowatt-hour, how much can you save by using a 60-watt bulb instead of a 100-watt bulb for 600 hours?

Use the formula $h = \frac{w}{750}$ to complete this table.

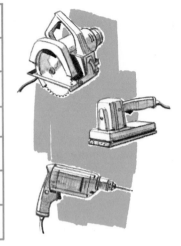

	Appliance	w	h
17.	Power saw	1500	
18.	Trash compactor		$\frac{1}{3}$
19.	Power sander	1000	
20.	Furnace fan	375	
21.	Power drill		$\frac{3}{4}$
22.	Vacuum cleaner		$1\frac{2}{3}$

Use the formula $h = 0.4 \times n \times d^2$ to complete this table.

	Car	n	d	h
23.	A	6	4.00	
24.	B		4.00	51.2
25.	C	8	3.75	
26.	D	4	3.25	
27.	E		4.25	57.8

[C] Stopping distance is the distance the car travels after you notice an obstacle and decide to stop. It depends on your speed. This formula applies to an alert driver whose car has good brakes and is on dry pavement.

stopping
distance   speed
(feet)   (mph)

$$d = 1.1s + 0.05s^2$$

Example: Find the stopping distance at 20 mph.

$$d = 1.1s + 0.05s^2$$

$$= (1.1 \times 20) + (0.05 \times 20^2)$$

$$= (1.1 \times 20) + (0.05 \times 400)$$

$$= \quad 22 \quad + \quad 20$$

$$= 42 \quad \text{The stopping distance is 42 feet.}$$

28. Use the formula to complete this table.

Speed s		10	20	30	40	50	60	70	80
Stopping distance d			42						

29. Is the stopping distance at 40 mph double or more than double the stopping distance at 20 mph?

30. Find the difference between the stopping distances for 10 and 20 mph. For 20 and 30 mph. For 30 and 40 mph.

31. Are these differences the same?

32. Can you find a pattern in these differences?

33. Does the rest of the table follow this pattern?

14.3 ◆ PER CENT

Many per cent problems can be solved using decimals.

Example 1: The 5% sales tax on a bill was $2.85. What was the bill before adding the sales tax?

Let x = amount of bill before sales tax

$0.05x$ = amount of sales tax

$$0.05x = 2.85$$

$$\frac{0.05x}{0.05} = \frac{2.85}{0.05}$$

$$x = 57 \quad \text{The bill was \$57.}$$

Example 2: Art bought a shirt on sale for $3.50. What was the original price of the shirt?

> ALL ITEMS
> 30%
> OFF!

Let x = original price

$0.30x$ = amount of discount

The original price minus the discount is $3.50.

$$x - 0.30x = 3.50$$

$$1x - 0.30x = 3.50$$

$$0.70x = 3.50$$

$$\frac{0.70x}{0.70} = \frac{3.50}{0.70}$$

$$x = 5 \quad \text{The original price was \$5.00.}$$

Exercises

A Give an equation for each problem.

1. 80% of a number is 4.

2. The price was $4.00 after a 20% reduction.

3. 20% of the cost was $12.

4. The broker's 8% fee was $28.16.

5. The amount was $5500 after a 6% commission was deducted.

B Solve each problem.

6. Ruth paid $1200 in income tax. She figured that this was 15% of her gross income. What was her gross income?

7. Shoe salespeople at Thornton's make 3% commission. How much must a salesperson sell to make $150 in commission?

8. The profit on each item Helen sells is 5%. How much must she sell to make a profit of $50?

9. Iris works at Lyle's Restaurant. She receives 15% in tips on each bill. If Iris wants to make $30 in tips in a night, how much should her customers' bills total?

10. At the age of 7, a girl is about 74% of her adult height. If a 7-year-old girl is 48 inches tall, how tall can she expect to be? Give your answer to the nearest inch.

11. At the age of 10, a boy is about 78% of his adult height. If a 10-year-old boy is 56 inches tall, how tall can he expect to be? Give your answer to the nearest inch.

12. The radio was discounted 25%. What was the price of the radio before the discount?

SALE PRICE
$11.25

13. The TV was discounted 15%. What was the price of the TV before the discount?

SALE PRICE
$63.75

14. An actor's agent receives 10% commission. How much must the actor make to have $450 left after the commission is deducted?

15. The Bartons are selling their house. The real-estate agent's commission is 7%. The Bartons want to have $40,000 left after the commission is deducted. What should be the selling price? Give your answer to the nearest thousand dollars.

16. Mark works for Stein's Department Store. He gets a 20% discount on everything he buys at Stein's. He has $16 to spend on a ski sweater. How expensive a sweater can he buy, if he buys the sweater at Stein's?

17. Stan wants to sell his shares of stock without losing any money. To do this, he must receive at least $23 a share after the broker's 8% commission is deducted. At what price should he sell the stock?

C Solve each problem.

Example: Donna pays 3% state income tax on the difference between her gross income and $1000. This year she paid $270. What was her gross income?

$$\text{Let } g = \text{gross income}$$

$$0.03(g - 1000) = 270$$

$$\frac{0.03(g - 1000)}{0.03} = \frac{270}{0.03}$$

$$g - 1000 = 9000$$

$$g - 1000 + 1000 = 9000 + 1000$$

$$g = 10000 \qquad \text{Her gross income was \$10,000.}$$

18. Mr. and Mrs. Ilfeld pay 2% city income tax on the difference between their combined gross income and $2400. They paid $352 this year. What was their combined income?

19. Jerry makes $500 a month plus 2% commission on his sales. How much must he sell to make $750 this month?

20. Irene makes 5% commission on all her sales over $500. How much must she sell to make $300 in commission?

This formula can be used to find the areas of the figures shown.

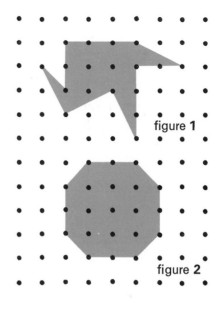

figure **1**

$$A \;=\; \underset{\substack{\text{number}\\\text{of dots}\\\text{on border}}}{0.5b} \;+\; \underset{\substack{\text{number}\\\text{of dots}\\\text{inside}}}{i} \;-\; 1$$

Example 1: Find the area of figure **1**.

$$b = 15 \text{ and } i = 3$$
$$A = 0.5b + i - 1$$
$$= (0.5 \times 15) + 3 - 1$$
$$= 7.5 + 3 - 1$$
$$= 9.5 \qquad \text{9.5 square units}$$

figure **2**

This formula gives the water pressure in the ocean.

$$\underset{\substack{\text{pressure}\\\textit{(tons per}\\\textit{square inch)}}}{p} \;=\; \underset{\substack{\text{depth}\\\textit{(miles)}}}{1.15d}$$

Example 2: To the nearest hundredth, find the depth at which the water pressure is 0.5 ton per square inch.

$$p = 1.15d$$
$$0.5 = 1.15d$$
$$\frac{0.5}{1.15} = \frac{1.15d}{1.15}$$
$$0.43 \approx d \qquad \text{0.43 miles}$$

is approximately equal to

This formula shows how the temperature and the chirps a cricket makes are related.

temperature in degrees Fahrenheit → t

number of chirps per minute → n

$$t = \frac{n}{4} + 40$$

Example 3: How many chirps at 90°F.?

$$t = \frac{n}{4} + 40$$

$$90 = \frac{n}{4} + 40$$

$$90 - 40 = \frac{n}{4} + 40 - 40$$

$$50 = \frac{n}{4}$$

$$4 \times 50 = 4 \times \frac{n}{4}$$

$$200 = n \qquad \text{200 cricket chirps at 90°F.}$$

Exercises

A Find the border dots b and the interior dots i for each figure.

1. 2. 3.

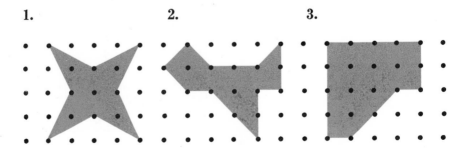

B Use the formula $A = 0.5b + i - 1$ to find the area of each figure.

4. figure in Exercise **1**

5. figure in Exercise **2**

6. figure in Exercise **3**

7. figure **2** on page 413

8. 9. 10.

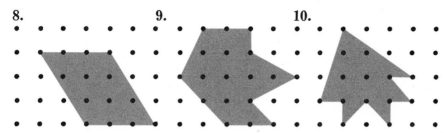

11. How many interior dots must a figure have if $A = 4$ and $b = 6$? Try to draw such a figure.

12. How many border dots must a figure have if $A = 4$ and $i = 1$? Try to draw such a figure.

Use the formula $p = 1.15d$ to answer each question.

13. In 1960, the bathyscaphe *Trieste* descended to 35,800 feet (6.78 miles) below sea level— the deepest spot in the ocean. What is the water pressure at that depth?

14. The average depth of the ocean is 12,447 feet (2.36 miles). What is the water pressure at that depth?

15. In 1967, Evelyn Patterson dove 125 feet (0.024 mile), holding her breath. What is the water pressure at that depth?

16. In 1968, John Gruener and R. Neal Watson dove 437 feet (0.083 mile) wearing scuba gear. What is the water pressure at that depth?

17. A whale can dive 3000 feet (0.57 mile). What is the water pressure at that depth?

18. At what depth is the water pressure 1.5 tons per square inch? 2.5 tons per square inch?

Use the formula $t = \frac{n}{4} + 40$ to complete this table.

19. Cricket Chirps

n		160			220		188	
t	55		65	75		72		100

C This formula is used to find the weight of a cube of ice.

$$w \;=\; 0.033e^3$$

weight (pounds) — length of edge (inches)

Example: Find the weight of a 4-inch cube of ice.

$$w = 0.033e^3$$

$$= 0.033 \times 4^3$$

$$= 0.033 \times (4 \times 4 \times 4)$$

$$= 0.033 \times 64$$

$$= 2.112 \qquad \text{The weight is 2.112 pounds.}$$

20. Find the weight of a cube of ice with a 2-inch edge.

21. A cubic foot of water weighs 62.4 pounds. Find the weight of a cubic foot of ice. Which is heavier—water or ice?

Interest on a savings account can be paid every year, every 6 months, every 3 months, or every day. The amount of interest is based on this formula.

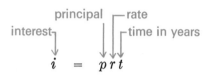

$$i \;=\; p\,r\,t$$

Example 1: Find the interest on $300 at $5\frac{1}{4}\%$ for 6 months.

$$r = 5\tfrac{1}{4}\% \qquad t = \tfrac{1}{2} \text{ or } 0.5, \text{ since}$$
$$= 5.25\% \qquad 6 \text{ months} = \tfrac{1}{2} \text{ year.}$$
$$= 0.0525$$

$$i = prt$$
$$= 300 \times 0.0525 \times 0.5$$
$$= 7.875 \qquad \text{The interest is rounded to \$7.87.}$$

Example 2: Find the amount in the bank.

$$a \;=\; p \;+\; i$$
$$= 300 + 7.87$$
$$= 307.87 \qquad \text{The amount in the bank is \$307.87.}$$

Exercises

A Express each per cent as a decimal.

1. 4% **2.** 5% **3.** 5.5% **4.** $5\frac{1}{2}\%$

5. 3.75% **6.** $4\frac{1}{4}\%$ **7.** $7\frac{1}{2}\%$ **8.** $6\frac{3}{4}\%$

Express in years.

9. 3 months   **10.** 1 month   **11.** 6 months

Complete the following table.

	Principal	Rate	Time	Interest	Amount
12.	$ 1200	5%	1 mo		
13.	400	6%	3 mo		
14.	275	$3\frac{3}{4}\%$	1 yr		
15.	850	4%	6 mo		
16.	10,000	$5\frac{1}{4}\%$	3 mo		
17.	6000	$4\frac{1}{4}\%$	1 mo		
18.	360	$5\frac{1}{2}\%$	6 mo		
19.	85	$3\frac{1}{2}\%$	1 yr		

20. A special savings account sends you a check for the interest earned each month. The rate is 6%. How much should you have in the account to get a check for $10 each month?

21. How much should you have in an account to earn $50 interest in 3 months at 5%?

C Banks usually *compound* interest. The principal for each period is the amount (principal plus interest) for the preceding period.

Example: Find the amount in the bank at the end of 6 months for $1000 at 5% compounded quarterly (every $\frac{1}{4}$ year).

$i = prt$

$= 1000 \times 0.05 \times 0.25$

$i = 12.50$

$a = p + i$

$= 1000 + 12.50$

$= 1012.50$ after 3 months

$i = prt$

$= 1012.50 \times 0.05 \times 0.25$

≈ 12.65

$a = p + i$

$= 1012.50 + 12.65$

$= 1025.15$ after 6 months

22. How much would be in the bank at the end of 1 year?

23. Find the amount in the bank at the end of 1 year for $1000 at 5% compounded semiannually (every 6 months).

One domino can cover two squares on the checkerboard. Can you cover the checkerboard with dominoes? How many dominoes do you need?

Now suppose two opposite corners are cut off. Can you use 31 dominoes to cover the board?

Exercises

A Answer these questions about the puzzle.

1. After the two corners are cut off, how many black squares remain? How many red squares?

2. Can a domino ever cover two squares that are the same color?

3. After 30 dominoes are placed on the board, are the squares that remain the same color or different colors?

4. Is it possible to solve this puzzle?

B Solve the following puzzles.

5. Mr. and Mrs. Kidd have 15 children. The children were born at $1\frac{1}{2}$-year intervals. The oldest child is 8 times as old as the youngest. How old is the oldest child?

(*Hint:* Guess reasonable ages for the oldest and youngest child.)

6. There are 30 students in a class. Show that at least 3 students have birthdays in the same month.

7. 13 matches are arranged to make 6 regions that are the same size and shape. Arrange 12 matches to make 6 regions that are the same size and shape.

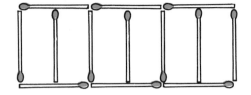

(*Hint:* Think of regions that are neither square nor rectangular.)

8. A woman was traveling with her young son, a carton of cakes, and a wolf. She had to cross a river in a small boat large enough only for herself and one of the three. If she left her son alone with the cakes, he would eat them. If she left the wolf alone with the boy, the wolf would eat him. How could she make the crossing?

(*Hint:* Which two of the three could be left alone on the riverbank?)

9. How many posts placed 1 yard apart are needed to fence the field?

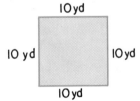

10. Find the product of 1, 2, 3, 4, 5, 6, 7, 8, 9, and 0 as fast as you can.

11. An amoeba reproduces by dividing into 2 amoebas every minute. Assume you start with 1 amoeba. Then after 1 minute you have 2, after 2 minutes you have 4, after 3 minutes you have 8, and so forth. If you start with 1 amoeba, it takes 30 minutes to fill a jar. If you start with 2 amoebas, how long will it take to fill the jar?

12. Mrs. Grant left some cookies in the kitchen with a note instructing each child to take a third of the cookies. Jake walked in and took a third of the cookies. Later Emma walked in, and thinking she was the first, took a third of the cookies she found. Later Dick walked in, and also thinking he was the first, took a third of the cookies he found. Mrs. Grant returned and found 8 cookies in the dish. How many cookies had Mrs. Grant left for the children?

(*Hint:* The 8 cookies were $\frac{2}{3}$ of the cookies Dick found.)

13. Copy the diagram. Then connect the dots with 4 straight lines, without lifting your pencil off the page.

14. A student made a survey and reported these results. For this effort, the student received an F. Can you see why?

total surveyed	100
likes hot dogs	73
likes hamburgers	68
likes both hot dogs and hamburgers	43
likes neither	4

15. 12 matches form 3 squares. Move 3 matches to get 5 squares.

(*Hint:* The squares do not have to be the same size.)

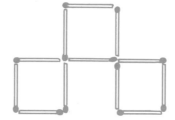

C Try these number puzzles.

Example: Arrange three 9's to make 11. $\frac{99}{9}$

16. Arrange three 9's to make 10.

17. Arrange three 9's to make 19.

(*Hint:* You can use a decimal point.)

18. Arrange eight 8's to make 100.

VOCABULARY

Match each item with a suitable example.

1. formula   **a.** $5\frac{1}{4}\%$

2. cross products for $\frac{6}{8} = \frac{x}{12}$ **b.** $k = \frac{tw}{1000}$

3. per cent   **c.** $\frac{6}{8} = \frac{x}{12}$

4. proportion   **d.** $6 \times 12 = 8x$

CHAPTER REVIEW

14.1   Use a proportion to solve each problem.

1. There are 90 calories in 2 slices of bacon. How many calories are in 5 slices?

2. To make green paint, you mix 3 gallons of yellow for every 2 gallons of blue paint. How much of each should you mix to make 10 gallons of green paint?

14.2   Use the formula $k = \frac{tw}{1000}$ to answer each question.

3. How many kilowatt-hours of electricity are used when you run a 5000-watt clothes dryer for 2 hours?

4. How many hours must you run a 300-watt sunlamp to use 6 kilo-watt-hours of electricity?

5. At $0.03 per kilowatt-hour, how much does it cost to run a 150-watt fan for 180 hours?

Use the formula $h = \frac{w}{750}$ to answer each question.

6. Find the horsepower rating for a 1125-watt vacuum cleaner.

7. Find the number of watts for a $2\frac{1}{4}$-horsepower saw.

8. Use the formula $h = 0.4 \times n \times d^2$ to find the horsepower rating of a 4-cylinder engine that has a 3.5-inch piston diameter.

Solve each problem. 14.3

9. Mr. Walsh put $340 in a profit-sharing fund last year. This was 2% of his gross income. What was his gross income?

10. The book was discounted 20%. What was the price of the book before the discount?

SALE PRICE
$10.80

Use the formula $A = 0.5b + i - 1$ to find the area of each figure. 14.4

11.   **12.**   **13.**

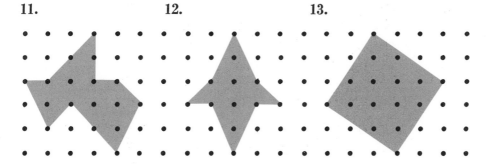

Use the formula $p = 1.15d$ to answer each question.

14. What is the water pressure at a depth of 4 miles?

15. At what depth is water pressure 2.3 tons per square inch?

Use the formula $t = \frac{n}{4} + 40$ to answer each question.

16. At what temperature does a cricket chirp 120 times per minute?

17. How many times does a cricket chirp each minute at 85°F.?

Use the formula $i = prt$ to answer each question. 14.5

18. Find the interest on $2500 at 5% for 3 months.

19. Find the interest on $400 at $4\frac{1}{2}$% for 6 months. Then find the amount in the bank after the interest is added to the principal.

20. How much did Miss Davis have in a savings account, if she received $42 interest for 1 year? The interest rate was $5\frac{1}{4}$%.

CHAPTER TEST

Use a proportion to solve each problem.

1. Walking burns 80 calories in 15 minutes. How long must you walk to burn 240 calories?

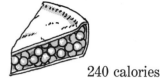

240 calories

2. 1 ounce of cola syrup is added for every 4 ounces of carbonated water. How much syrup is needed to make 60 ounces of cola?

Use a formula to solve each problem.

3. How many kilowatt-hours of electricity are used when you play a 150-watt stereo for 20 hours? ($k = \frac{tw}{1000}$)

4. Find the number of watts for a $\frac{1}{2}$-horsepower fan. ($h = \frac{w}{750}$)

5. Find the horsepower rating of a 6-cylinder engine that has a 3.75-inch piston diameter. ($h = 0.4 \times n \times d^2$)

6. Find the area of this figure. ($A = 0.5b + i - 1$)

7. What is the water pressure at a depth of 2.5 miles? ($p = 1.15d$)

8. How many times does a cricket chirp each minute at 60°F.? ($t = \frac{n}{4} + 40$)

9. Find the interest on $1000 at $5\frac{1}{2}\%$ for 6 months. Then find the amount in the bank after the interest is added to the principal. ($i = prt$; $a = p + i$)

Solve each problem.

10. An author received a check for $150. This was 5% of the sales of his book. What were the sales for the book?

11. Marcia bought a skirt on sale for $12.00. What was the original price of the skirt?

ALL ITEMS
20% OFF!

Activities for Chapter 14

Activity 1

Here is a way to multiply two numbers.

$$13 \times 85$$

Divide by 2.   Multiply by 2.

a. First divide one number by 2. Discard any remainder. Continue until you get to 1.

13	85
6	170
3	340
1	680

b. Then multiply the other number by 2. Continue until you have as many products as quotients.

c. Draw a line through any even quotient(s) and the corresponding product(s). – – – – – – – –

13	85
~~6~~	~~170~~
3	340
1	680
	1105

$$13 \times 85$$

d. Add the remaining numbers in the product column. That sum is the product.

Use this method to find each product.

1. 19×18 **2.** 121×34 **3.** 32×111 **4.** 28×101

Activity 2

A gardener wants to enclose a rectangular plot of 36 square feet. He wants to use the smallest amount of fence possible. What should be the dimensions of the plot?

The table lists rectangles with whole-number dimensions and areas of 36 square feet.

1. Complete the table.

2. What length and width give the smallest perimeter?

3. What shape should the plot be?

l	w	$p = 2l + 2w$
36	1	74
18	2	
12	3	
9	4	
6	6	

Mathematics and Electricity

The number of *watts* is indicated for most appliances. Appliances like hot combs, hair dryers, and toasters operate on 110 to 120 *volts*. Other appliances like clothes dryers, electric hot-water heaters, and some airconditioners require 220 to 240 volts. Fuses prevent overloading a circuit. A 20-*ampere* fuse will blow if more than 20 amperes are flowing through the circuit. Watts P, volts E, and amperes I are related by the formula $P = EI$.

Example: How many amperes does a 480-watt freezer draw on 120 volts?

$$P = EI$$

$$480 = 120I$$

$$\frac{480}{120} = \frac{120I}{120}$$

$$4 = I \qquad \text{4 amperes}$$

1. Complete the table to find the total number of amperes at 120 volts. Give each answer to the nearest tenth.

2. Suppose all the appliances in Exercise **1** are on the same circuit. Could you use all the appliances at the same time with a 30-ampere fuse?

Appliance	Watts P	Amperes I
Blender	240	
Refrigerator	300	
Room heater	1600	
Iron	1000	
Hair dryer	750	
Light fixture	100	
Total		

Match each digit of 765.4321 with the correct place value below.   7.1

1. tens

2. tenths

3. hundreds

4. thousandths

5. hundredths

6. ones

Compute.   ES

7. 70×80

8. 900×500

9. 200×90

10. $80 + 90 + 60$

11. $50 + 90 + 700$

12. $300 + 900 + 60$

13. $600 \div 30$

14. $5000 \div 500$

15. $7000 \div 20$

16. $700 - 500$

17. $900 - 60$

18. $7500 - 800$

Complete.

19. 1 ft = _____ in

20. 3 ft = _____ yd

21. 1 yd = _____ in

22. 1 lb = _____ oz

23. 1 ton = _____ lb

24. 1 pt = _____ c

25. 1 gal = _____ qt

26. 1 qt = _____ pt

27. 1 gal = _____ pt

28. 1 m = _____ cm

29. 1 cm = _____ mm

30. 1 km = _____ m

Answer each question.

31. How many square inches are in 1 square foot?

32. How many square centimeters are in 1 square meter?

33. How many cubic feet are in 1 cubic yard?

Approximation and Measurement _____ 15

Measurement plays a major role in pollution control. Highly sensitive instruments measure the amount of hydrocarbons and other pollutants in automobile exhaust. This is only one of the many uses of measurement in daily life.

In this chapter you will estimate results of computation, review English and metric units of measure, and solve practical problems dealing with measurement.

When speaking of the same sporting event, different people report the attendance in different ways.

A sportscaster _ _ _ _ _ _ 42,400 excited fans are enjoying . . .

An accountant _ _ _ _ _ 42,364 tickets sold . . .

A sports reporter _ _ _ _ 42,000 see X romp Y . . .

For many purposes, an exact number is not needed. Two of the persons reporting have *rounded* the number in attendance.

Example 1:   Round 42,364 to the nearest hundred.

To round here, you check here.

4 2, 3 6 4

If this digit is 5 or greater, increase hundreds digit by 1.

42,364 ≈ 42,400   (to the nearest hundred)

Example 2: Round 42,364 to the nearest thousand.

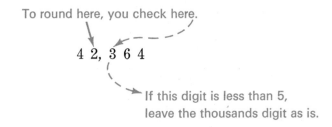

To round here, you check here.

4 2, 3 6 4

If this digit is less than 5,
leave the thousands digit as is.

42,364 ≈ 42,000   (to the nearest thousand)

Example 3: Round as indicated.

number	to the nearest		
	one	tenth	hundredth
43.5762	44	43.6	43.58
1.6218	2	1.6	1.62
0.0421	0	0.0	0.04

Exercises

Ⓐ Tell which digit you would check when rounding to the nearest ten. To the nearest hundred. To the nearest thousand.

1. 5801   **2.** 546   **3.** 38,542   **4.** 645,123

5. 3592.1   **6.** 32,546.78   **7.** 50,613.82   **8.** 1624.578

Tell which digit you would check when rounding to the nearest one. To the nearest tenth. To the nearest hundredth. To the nearest thousandth.

9. 6.0123   **10.** 0.2345   **11.** 0.9152   **12.** 8.0576

13. 0.5724   **14.** 9.13428   **15.** 19.60572   **16.** 742.0536

B Round as indicated.

number	to the nearest			
	one	tenth	hundredth	thousandth
17. 0.4532				
18. 0.6051				
19. 9.0826				
20. 24.0580				
21. 132.5158				

number	to the nearest		
	ten	hundred	thousand
22. 1762			
23. 9835			
24. 14.508			
25. 672.54			
26. 80,521.3			

C Round π as indicated.

The number π can never be expressed exactly as a decimal. However, it can be calculated to as many decimal places as you like. For example,
$$\pi \approx 3.14159265358973 \ldots$$

$$\pi = \frac{c}{d}$$

27. to the nearest hundred thousandth

28. to the nearest millionth

29. to the nearest billionth

30. to the nearest hundred millionth

31. to the nearest ten millionth

15.2 ◆ ESTIMATING

In a situation like that shown above, it is more convenient to make an estimate than to do the computation.

Example 1: Would 1 bag be enough to fertilize the yard?

Round both numbers.
Then multiply.

82 × 97
↓   ↓
80 × 100 = 8000

There are approximately 8000 square feet of yard. Obviously 1 bag of fertilizer is not enough.

Example 2: Could you fertilize a garden plot 43 feet wide by 126 feet long with one bag of fertilizer?

Round both numbers.
Then multiply.

43 × 126
↓   ↓
40 × 130 = 5200

There are approximately 5200 square feet of garden. One bag covers 5500 square feet and should be enough.

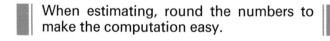

When estimating, round the numbers to make the computation easy.

Exercises

A Tell how you would estimate each answer.

1. 32×32 **2.** 89×11 **3.** $11 + 39 + 87$

4. $896 \div 32$ **5.** $1012 \div 9$ **6.** $989 - 285$

7. 888×75 **8.** $638 - 185$ **9.** $135 + 27 + 212$

Select the *best estimate* for each exercise.

10. 12×12 100,   225,   or 400

11. $2860 \div 46$ 50,   60,   or 70

12. $989 + 1384$ 2200,   2300,   or 2400

13. $503 - 278$ 200,   250,   or 300

14. 888×396 320,000,   360,000,   or 400,000

B Write your estimate for each answer. Then compute and compare your estimated answer with your computed answer.

15. 196×211 **16.** 1223×46

17. 18×52 **18.** $6384 \div 84$

19. $19 + 51 + 48$ **20.** $113 + 308 + 509$

21. $991 - 207$ **22.** 54×56

23. 85×95 **24.** 28×450

Solve each problem. First estimate, then compute each answer.

25. How long will it take to fly 232 miles at a ground speed of 80 miles per hour?

26. A miler can run a mile in 3 minutes 56 seconds. How fast could the miler run a quarter-mile at that same rate?

27. A car averages about 19 miles per gallon. How many gallons would it take to go 412 miles?

28. How many people will the elevator hold safely? Assume that the average person weighs about 170 pounds.

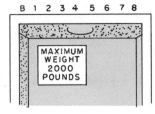

29. A golfer hit 12 drives for a total of 2112 yards. How many yards did he average for each drive?

30. Rose is earning $15,000 a year. If she gets a 12% raise next year, how much will she be earning then?

C Solve each problem. First estimate, then compute each answer.

31. Jane read a 330-page book in 5 hours. Jane reads at a rate of 415 words a minute.

    a. How many pages did Jane read an hour?

    b. How many words are there in the book?

    c. How many words are there on a page?

32. Assume you have a car that averages 15 miles per gallon. You expect to drive the car 15,000 miles in the coming year. Figure out the estimated cost per mile for each expense given below. Then figure the total estimated expense per mile.

estimated cost
per mile

    a. depreciation (per year): $1500   ————

    b. gas cost (per gallon): $0.74   ————

    c. maintenance (every 6000 miles): $60   ————

    d. insurance (per year): $150   + ————

    e. total expense per mile   ————

In everyday life, there are many times when you need to estimate. How long is this room? How wide is my yard? Do I have enough gas to go 50 miles? Is one gallon of paint enough to paint the room?

Suggestions to help you estimate

Measure the length of your step (average is $2\frac{1}{2}$ to 3 feet). To estimate the area of a room, garden, and so on, step off the length and width and multiply.

The average height of each story of a building is 15 feet. To estimate the height of a building, count the number of stories and multiply by 15.

Volumes of rooms, boxes, buildings, and so on, can be estimated by finding the area of the base or floor and then multiplying the area by an estimated height.

Exercises

A Tell which number in ( ) is the *best estimate*.

1. A Volkswagen auto is about (5, 10, 15, 30) feet long.

2. A school bus is about (10, 30, 50, 80) feet long.

3. A telephone pole is about (10, 20, 50, 200) feet high.

4. A 3-story building is about (15, 30, 45, 80) feet high.

5. A 17-foot by 23-foot rectangle has an area of about (200, 400, 600, 800) square feet.

6. A room 20 feet long, 18 feet wide, and 9 feet high has a volume of about (47, 180, 400, 4000) cubic feet.

B Make estimates for the following. Compare your estimates with those of your classmates.

7. the length of the block where your school is located

8. the width of your school building

9. the width of the street in front of your school

10. the area of your gym floor

11. the area of your classroom

12. the volume of your classroom

13. the height of your school

14. the volume of your gym

15. the height of your school flagpole

16. the area of your playground

17. the volume of your school

Estimate the answer to each problem. Then solve the problem and compare the two answers.

18. What is the area of the swimming pool surface?

19. If the average depth of the swimming pool is 6 feet, how many cubic feet of water will the pool hold?

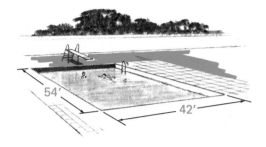

20. Water weighs about 62.4 pounds per cubic foot. How much will the water in the pool weigh?

21. A baseball stadium has 40 sections. Each section has 38 rows of seats with 39 seats in a row. How many people will the stadium seat?

22. A book weighs 2.98 pounds. How much will a carton of 32 such books weigh?

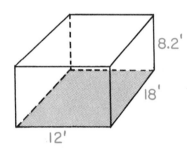

23. What is the floor area of the room shown?

24. What is the volume of the room?

25. A Cessna 172 airplane uses 8.6 gallons of fuel an hour. The tanks hold a total of 38 gallons. How many full hours can the pilot fly without refueling?

C Estimate each answer. (*Note:* Be sure the units are the same.)

26. A football field is 100 yards long and 160 feet wide. What is the area of the field?

27. If sod is laid for $2.15 a square yard, what would be the approximate cost to lay sod on the football field in Exercise 26?

28. Player A gets 3 hits in 10 times up at bat. Player B gets 1 hit in 4 times up. Last year each player batted 537 times. Who had the higher average? How many more hits did that player have?

15.4 ◆ ENGLISH UNITS OF MEASURE

You are probably familiar with the following units of measure and common equivalents.

To measure	you can use	common equivalents
Length	inches (in), feet (ft), yards (yd), miles (mi)	1 ft = 12 in 3 ft = 1 yd 1 mi = 5280 ft
Area	square (sq) in, sq ft, sq yd, sq mi	1 sq ft = 144 sq in 1 sq yd = 9 sq ft
Volume	cubic (cu) in, cu ft, cu yd	1 cu ft = 1728 cu in 1 cu yd = 27 cu ft
Mass	ounces (oz) pounds (lb) tons	16 oz = 1 lb 2000 lb = 1 ton
Capacity	cups (c), pints (pt), quarts (qt), gallons (gal)	1 pt = 2 c 1 qt = 2 pt 1 gal = 4 qt

Exercises

A Tell suitable units for measuring the following.

1. the length of a car

2. the weight of a car

3. the area of a garden

4. the volume of a freezer

5. the length of a worm

6. the weight of a worm

7. the length of a football field

8. your weight

9. your height

10. the amount of milk you buy

Complete.

Examples: $12 \text{ yd} = \underline{} \text{ in}$ $248 \text{ oz} = \underline{} \text{ lb}$

$1 \text{ yd} = 36 \text{ in}$ $1 \text{ oz} = \frac{1}{16} \text{ lb}$

$(12 \times 1) \text{ yd} = (12 \times 36) \text{ in}$ $(248 \times 1) \text{ oz} = (248 \times \frac{1}{16}) \text{ lb}$

$12 \text{ yd} = \underline{\quad 432 \quad} \text{ in}$ $248 \text{ oz} = \underline{\quad 15\frac{1}{2} \quad} \text{ lb}$

11. $15 \text{ ft} = \underline{} \text{ in}$ **12.** $320 \text{ oz} = \underline{} \text{ lb}$

13. $27 \text{ yd} = \underline{} \text{ ft}$ **14.** $3 \text{ sq ft} = \underline{} \text{ sq in}$

15. $6 \text{ mi} = \underline{} \text{ ft}$ **16.** $108 \text{ sq ft} = \underline{} \text{ sq yd}$

17. $30 \text{ yd} = \underline{} \text{ ft}$ **18.** $64 \text{ oz} = \underline{} \text{ lb}$

19. $4 \text{ cu ft} = \underline{} \text{ cu in}$ **20.** $3456 \text{ cu in} = \underline{} \text{ cu ft}$

21. $4.5 \text{ sq yd} = \underline{} \text{ sq ft}$ **22.** $2.5 \text{ cu yd} = \underline{} \text{ cu ft}$

23. $18{,}480 \text{ ft} = \underline{} \text{ mi}$ **24.** $62 \text{ ft} = \underline{} \text{ yd}$

25. $22 \text{ lb} = \underline{} \text{ oz}$ **26.** $576 \text{ sq in} = \underline{} \text{ sq ft}$

27. $108 \text{ cu ft} = \underline{} \text{ cu yd}$ **28.** $9 \text{ c} = \underline{} \text{ pt}$

29. $5000 \text{ lb} = \underline{} \text{ tons}$ **30.** $3.25 \text{ tons} = \underline{} \text{ lb}$

31. $6 \text{ pt} = \underline{} \text{ qt}$ **32.** $4 \text{ gal} = \underline{} \text{ qt}$

33. $12 \text{ qt} = \underline{} \text{ gal}$ **34.** $6 \text{ qt} = \underline{} \text{ pt}$

35. $3 \text{ gal} = \underline{} \text{ pt}$ **36.** $48 \text{ c} = \underline{} \text{ qt}$

37. $10 \text{ pt} = \underline{} \text{ gal}$ **38.** $1.5 \text{ lb} = \underline{} \text{ oz}$

Complete.

$1 \text{ nautical mile} \approx 1.15 \text{ statute mile}$ $1 \text{ stat mi} \approx 0.87 \text{ naut mi}$

39. $7 \text{ naut mi} \approx \underline{} \text{ stat mi}$ **40.** $8 \text{ stat mi} \approx \underline{} \text{ naut mi}$

41. $5 \text{ naut mi} \approx \underline{} \text{ stat mi}$ **42.** $2.5 \text{ stat mi} \approx \underline{} \text{ naut mi}$

43. $3.5 \text{ naut mi} \approx \underline{} \text{ stat mi}$ **44.** $2.25 \text{ stat mi} \approx \underline{} \text{ naut mi}$

15.5 ◆ COMPARING MEASUREMENTS

You can buy some beverages in quarts ($\frac{1}{4}$ of a gallon) as well as in fifths ($\frac{1}{5}$ of a gallon).

Example 1: Which is the better buy?

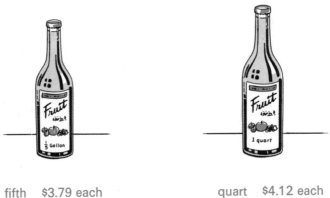

fifth $3.79 each   quart $4.12 each

To compare prices, change both capacities to the same unit.

$3.79 ⟵ cost per bottle ⟶ $ 4.12
×5 ⟵ bottles per gallon ⟶ ×4
$18.95 ⟵ cost per gallon ⟶ $16.48

The quart is the better buy.

Example 2: A beverage costs $3.72 a fifth. What would be an equivalent price for a quart?

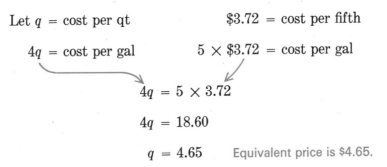

Let q = cost per qt $3.72 = cost per fifth

$4q$ = cost per gal $5 \times \$3.72$ = cost per gal

$$4q = 5 \times 3.72$$

$$4q = 18.60$$

$$q = 4.65$$ Equivalent price is $4.65.

Exercises

A Tell which is greater.

1. 49 in or 4 ft
2. 14 ft or 5 yd
3. 48 oz or 3 lb
4. 6 pt or 3 c
5. 8 pt or 4 qt
6. 10 qt or 3 gal
7. 3 tons or 5000 lb
8. 5 ft or 50 in
9. 2 mi or 10,000 ft
10. 3 qt or 12 pt
11. 8 gal or 35 qt
12. 72 in or 2 yd
13. 4 yd or 12 ft
14. 2 lb or 32 oz
15. 15,000 ft or 2 mi
16. 3000 lb or 2 tons
17. 6 c or 3 pt
18. 4 yd or 140 in

B Which is the better buy?

19. 60¢ per qt
    $2.60 per gal
20. $3.50 per fifth
    $3.85 per qt
21. 21¢ per ft
    2.5¢ per in
22. $1.25 for 100 lb
    $47.50 for 2 tons
23. 18¢ for 9 oz
    35¢ for 1 lb
24. 35¢ per qt
    $2.75 per gal
25. 16¢ for 4 oz
    39¢ for 12 oz
    50¢ for 1 lb
26. $1.35 per pt
    $2.60 per qt
    $2.09 per fifth

Solve each problem.

27. A beverage costs $2.96 a fifth. What would be an equivalent price for a quart?

28. A beverage costs $4.15 a quart. What would be the equivalent price for a fifth?

Solve each problem.

29. Gasoline weighs 6 pounds per gallon. What is the weight of a quart of gasoline? Of a pint? Of a cup?

30. Oil weighs 7.5 pounds per gallon. What is the weight of 6 quarts? Of 10 quarts?

31. An airplane is filled with 36 gallons of gasoline and 10 pints of oil. How much would the gas and oil add to the weight of the plane?

32. The airplane in Exercise **31** left the gas pump with a gross weight of 1945 pounds. The plane uses 8.5 gallons of gasoline per hour. The plane flew exactly two hours and used $\frac{1}{2}$ quart of oil. What would be the gross weight of the plane at that time?

Balance the Cup

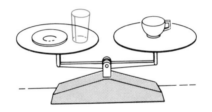

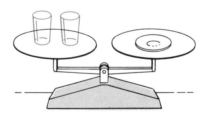

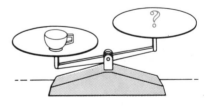

How many glasses will balance the cup?

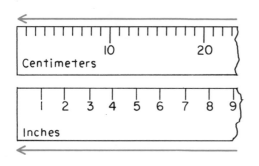

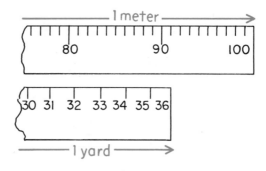

The **meter** is the basic unit of length in the metric system.

Metric prefixes correspond to powers of ten as shown. The most commonly used prefixes are in color. Be sure you know them. They are used for all units of measure in the metric system.

prefix	symbol	meaning	examples
kilo	k	1000	1000 meters (m) = 1 kilometer (km)
hecto	h	100	100 m = 1 hectometer (hm)
deka	da	10	10 m = 1 dekameter (dam)
(none)		1	1 m = 1 m
deci	d	0.1	0.1 m = 1 decimeter (dm)
centi	c	0.01	0.01 m = 1 centimeter (cm)
milli	m	0.001	0.001 m = 1 millimeter (mm)

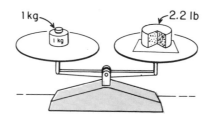

The **kilogram** (1000 grams) is the basic unit of mass in the metric system.

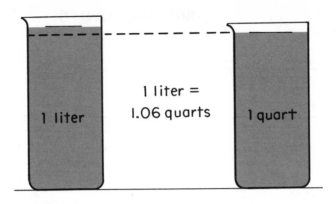

1 liter

1 liter =
1.06 quarts

1 quart

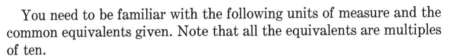

The **liter** is a unit of capacity in the metric system.

You need to be familiar with the following units of measure and the common equivalents given. Note that all the equivalents are multiples of ten.

To measure	you can use	common equivalents	
Length	km, m, cm, mm	1 km = 1000 m 1 m = 100 cm 1 m = 1000 mm	1 m = 0.001 km 1 cm = 0.01 m 1 mm = 0.001 m
Area	km² (square km), m², cm², mm²	1 m² = 1 centare (ca) 1 hectare (ha) = 10,000 m²	
Volume	km³ (cubic km), m³, cm³, mm³	1 dm³ = 1000 cm³ 1 dm³ = 1 liter (l)	
Mass	kg (kilograms), g, cg, mg	1 kg = 1000 g 1 g = 100 cg 1 g = 1000 mg	1 g = 0.001 kg 1 cg = 0.01 kg 1 mg = 0.001 g
Capacity	kl (kiloliters), l, cl, ml	1 kl = 1000 l 1 l = 100 cl 1 l = 1000 ml	1 l = 0.001 kl 1 cl = 0.01 l 1 ml = 0.001 l

Exercises

A Tell suitable units for measuring the following.

1. the length of a car
2. the weight of a car
3. the area of a garden
4. the volume of a freezer
5. the length of a worm
6. the weight of a worm
7. the length of a football field
8. your weight
9. your height
10. the amount of milk you buy

B Complete.

Examples: $1.6 \, \text{km} = \underline{\hspace{1.5cm}} \text{m}$ $42 \, \text{mm} = \underline{\hspace{1.5cm}} \text{m}$

$1 \, \text{km} = 1000 \, \text{m}$ $1 \, \text{mm} = 0.001 \, \text{m}$

$(1.6 \times 1) \, \text{km} = (1.6 \times 1000) \, \text{m}$ $(42 \times 1) \, \text{mm} = (42 \times 0.001) \, \text{m}$

$1.6 \, \text{km} = \underline{\quad 1600 \quad} \text{m}$ $42 \, \text{mm} = \underline{\quad 0.042 \quad} \text{m}$

11. $4.52 \, \text{km} = \underline{\hspace{1cm}} \text{m}$
12. $1.65 \, \text{m} = \underline{\hspace{1cm}} \text{km}$
13. $1.9 \, \text{m} = \underline{\hspace{1cm}} \text{cm}$
14. $16 \, \text{cm} = \underline{\hspace{1cm}} \text{m}$
15. $42 \, \text{m} = \underline{\hspace{1cm}} \text{mm}$
16. $750 \, \text{mm} = \underline{\hspace{1cm}} \text{m}$
17. $6 \, \text{m}^2 = \underline{\hspace{1cm}} \text{ca}$
18. $5 \, \text{ha} = \underline{\hspace{1cm}} \text{m}^2$
19. $9 \, \text{dm}^3 = \underline{\hspace{1cm}} \text{cm}^3$
20. $1.8 \, \text{dl} = \underline{\hspace{1cm}} \text{l}$
21. $8.5 \, \text{kg} = \underline{\hspace{1cm}} \text{g}$
22. $2600 \, \text{g} = \underline{\hspace{1cm}} \text{kg}$
23. $16 \, \text{g} = \underline{\hspace{1cm}} \text{cg}$
24. $127 \, \text{cg} = \underline{\hspace{1cm}} \text{g}$
25. $2.4 \, \text{g} = \underline{\hspace{1cm}} \text{mg}$
26. $402 \, \text{mg} = \underline{\hspace{1cm}} \text{g}$
27. $18 \, \text{kl} = \underline{\hspace{1cm}} \text{l}$
28. $16 \, \text{l} = \underline{\hspace{1cm}} \text{kl}$
29. $14.2 \, \text{l} = \underline{\hspace{1cm}} \text{cl}$
30. $7502 \, \text{cl} = \underline{\hspace{1cm}} \text{l}$
31. $16.2 \, \text{l} = \underline{\hspace{1cm}} \text{ml}$
32. $29.06 \, \text{ml} = \underline{\hspace{1cm}} \text{l}$

Complete.

33. $1 \text{ km}^2 = \underline{\hspace{1.5cm}} \text{ m}^2$ **34.** $1 \text{ m}^2 = \underline{\hspace{1.5cm}} \text{ cm}^2$

35. $1 \text{ m}^2 = \underline{\hspace{1.5cm}} \text{ mm}^2$ **36.** $1 \text{ km}^2 = \underline{\hspace{1.5cm}} \text{ mm}^2$

37. $1 \text{ km}^3 = \underline{\hspace{1.5cm}} \text{ m}^3$ **38.** $1 \text{ m}^3 = \underline{\hspace{1.5cm}} \text{ cm}^3$

39. $1 \text{ m}^3 = \underline{\hspace{1.5cm}} \text{ mm}^3$ **40.** $1 \text{ km}^3 = \underline{\hspace{1.5cm}} \text{ mm}^3$

Which Card Is It ?

1.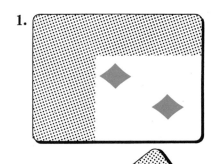

2.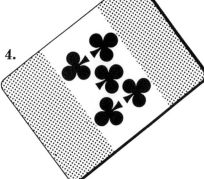

3.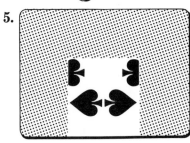

4.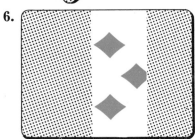

5.

6.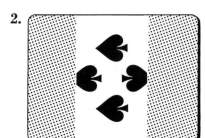

You often find it necessary to compute with measures.

Example 1: What is the combined length of the two banners?

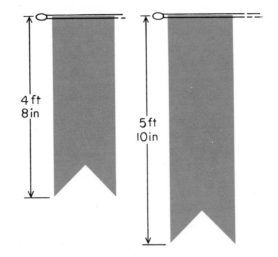

4 ft
8 in

5 ft
10 in

5 ft 10 in
+4 ft 8 in
_____
9 ft 18 in   Rename 18 in
              as 1 ft 6 in.
1 ft 6 in
_____
10 ft 6 in

Example 2: The butcher had 12 lb 4 oz of ground beef. After selling 3 lb 11 oz, how much ground beef was left?

12 lb 4 oz   11 > 4 so rename
− 3 lb 11 oz   as shown.
               Then subtract.

          11   20
12 lb 4 oz
− 3 lb 11 oz
_____
8 lb 9 oz

Computing with metric measures is easier because the units follow the pattern of place values in decimal numerals.

Example 3: Add 8.9 cm, 37 mm, and 0.16 m.

Here are three ways to do this addition. Note how easy it is to make the units the same in each case.

8.9 cm	⟶	8.9 cm	⟶	89 mm	⟶	0.089 m
37 mm	⟶	3.7 cm	⟶	37 mm	⟶	0.037 m
+0.16 m	⟶	+16.0 cm	⟶	+160 mm	⟶	+0.16 m
		28.6 cm		286 mm		0.286 m

Example 4: Subtract 1.455 kg from 4325 g.

Here are two ways to do this subtraction.

$$
\begin{array}{rcl}
4325 \text{ g} & \longrightarrow & 4325 \text{ g} \longrightarrow 4.325 \text{ kg} \\
-1.455 \text{ kg} & \longrightarrow & -1455 \text{ g} \longrightarrow -1.455 \text{ kg} \\
\hline
& & 2870 \text{ g} \longrightarrow 2.870 \text{ kg}
\end{array}
$$

Exercises

Ⓐ Complete.

1.
$$
\begin{array}{r}
8 \text{ ft } 6 \text{ in} \\
+2 \text{ ft } 7 \text{ in} \\
\hline
10 \text{ ft } 13 \text{ in}
\end{array}
$$

   11 ft __ in

2.
$$
\begin{array}{r}
14 \text{ lb } 6 \text{ oz} \\
+9 \text{ lb } 15 \text{ oz} \\
\hline
23 \text{ lb } 21 \text{ oz}
\end{array}
$$

   __ lb 5 oz

3.
$$
\begin{array}{r}
15.6 \text{ cm} \longrightarrow \text{ __ mm} \\
+88 \text{ mm} \longrightarrow +88 \text{ mm}
\end{array}
$$

4.
$$
\begin{array}{r}
15.6 \text{ cm} \longrightarrow 15.6 \text{ cm} \\
+88 \text{ mm} \longrightarrow +\text{__ cm}
\end{array}
$$

Tell how you would rename so you can subtract in each of the following.

5.
$$
\begin{array}{r}
9 \text{ lb } 4 \text{ oz} \\
-6 \text{ lb } 8 \text{ oz} \\
\hline
\end{array}
$$

6.
$$
\begin{array}{r}
6 \text{ ft } 3 \text{ in} \\
-2 \text{ ft } 8 \text{ in} \\
\hline
\end{array}
$$

7.
$$
\begin{array}{r}
14.6 \text{ m} \\
-3.08 \text{ cm} \\
\hline
\end{array}
$$

Ⓑ Compute.

8.
$$
\begin{array}{r}
12 \text{ lb } 4 \text{ oz} \\
+4 \text{ lb } 12 \text{ oz} \\
\hline
\end{array}
$$

9.
$$
\begin{array}{r}
18 \text{ ft } 7 \text{ in} \\
26 \text{ ft } 5 \text{ in} \\
+6 \text{ ft } 9 \text{ in} \\
\hline
\end{array}
$$

10.
$$
\begin{array}{r}
27.54 \text{ m} \\
3895 \text{ cm} \\
+65.9 \text{ m} \\
\hline
\end{array}
$$

11.
$$
\begin{array}{r}
180 \text{ km} \\
-31007 \text{ m} \\
\hline
\end{array}
$$

12.
$$
\begin{array}{r}
12.06 \text{ cm} \\
-88 \text{ mm} \\
\hline
\end{array}
$$

13.
$$
\begin{array}{r}
4 \text{ ft } 8 \text{ in} \\
\times 5 \\
\hline
\end{array}
$$

14.
$$
\begin{array}{r}
8 \text{ lb } 9 \text{ oz} \\
\times 18 \\
\hline
\end{array}
$$

15.
$$
\begin{array}{r}
3 \text{ gal } 2 \text{ qt} \\
\times 8 \\
\hline
\end{array}
$$

16.
$$
\begin{array}{r}
8 \text{ ft } 4 \text{ in} \\
\times 15 \\
\hline
\end{array}
$$

17. $3\overline{)3 \text{ ft } 9 \text{ in}}$

18. $3\overline{)3 \text{ yd } 4 \text{ in}}$

19. $25\overline{)84 \text{ kg}}$

Solve each problem.

20. The tallest giraffe measured was 19 feet 3 inches. The fat-tailed shrew (the smallest mammal) is $1\frac{1}{2}$ inches long. What is the difference between these measurements?

21. The world's largest park is Kafue in Zambia, Africa. It has a land area of 5,363,000 acres or 8650 square miles. How many acres are there in a square mile?

22. Each of 2 baseball games lasted 2 hours 38 minutes. What was the total time for both games? If there was an 18-minute break between the 2 games, how long was it from the time the first game started until the last game ended?

C Solve each problem.

23. A Kris Kristofferson album has the following times on sides 1 and 2. (*Note:* 2:43 means 2 minutes 43 seconds.)

Side 1: 2:43, 4:42, 4:22, 3:03, 2:24, 2:39

Side 2: 3:34, 3:35, 3:17, 3:25, 2:55, 4:32

Which side is longer? By how much?

24. The longest a person has been deprived of sleep is 227 hours. How would you express this in days and hours?

25. The highest speed recorded for a spider is 1.73 feet per second. What is this in miles per hour?

26. The largest spider has a leg span of 10 inches. The largest spider crabs have leg spans of $12\frac{1}{2}$ feet. What is the difference in leg spans?

VOCABULARY

Choose the answer in ( ) that best completes each sentence.

1. 4.185 rounded to the nearest hundredth is (4.2, 4.18, 4.19).

2. The best estimate for a 5-story building is (75, 100, 125) feet.

3. To measure mass, you could use (liters, meters, grams).

4. 1 centimeter means (100 meters, 0.1 meter, 0.01 meter).

CHAPTER REVIEW

15.1   Round as indicated.

number	to the nearest			
	ten	one	tenth	hundredth
1. 54.129				
2. 7.650				
3. 19.3108				
4. 205.063				

15.2   Write your estimate for each answer.

5. 312×57 **6.** 470×912 **7.** $8250 \div 22$

8. $196000 \div 45$ **9.** $345 + 697$ **10.** $28 + 72 + 185$

11. $416 + 273 + 550$ **12.** $526 - 288$ **13.** $69831 - 2650$

15.3   Estimate the answer to each problem.

14. What is the floor area of the room?

15. What is the volume of the room?

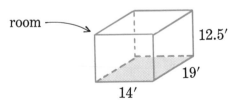

16. A box of screws weighs 3.62 pounds. How much will a carton of 48 of these boxes weigh?

Complete.

17. 84 in = ___ ft

18. 4 lb = ___ oz

19. 14 qt = ___ gal

20. 10 qt = ___ pt

21. 16 yd = ___ ft

22. 5280 ft = ___ mi

23. 5000 lb = ___ tons

24. 6 gal = ___ qt

25. 44 oz = ___ lb

26. 5 pt = ___ c

27. 108 in = ___ yd

28. 31 tons = ___ lb

Which is the better buy ?

29. 48¢ per qt
25¢ per pt

30. $2.64 per fifth
$3.18 per quart

31. 28¢ per ft
2.5¢ per in

32. 20¢ for 12 oz
28¢ for 1 lb

33. $2.38 per pt
$4.75 per qt

34. 32¢ per pt
$2.36 per gal

Complete.

35. 3.5 km = ___ m

36. 62 m = ___ cm

37. 75 cg = ___ mg

38. 0.054 kg = ___ g

39. 16 m = ___ km

40. 4.2 g = ___ mg

41. 425 mm = ___ m

42. 6 l = ___ ml

43. 550 ml = ___ l

44. 1954 g = ___ kg

45. 325 g = ___ mg

46. 25 mm = ___ m

Compute.

47. 16 ft 10 in
+25 ft 10 in

48. 16 lb 12 oz
−8 lb 14 oz

49. 416.04 m
+2509 cm

50. . 6 qt
−4 qt 1 pt

51. 5042 g
−2.075 kg

52. 3.460 mg
×4

53. 6 gal 3 qt
×9

54. 14)5 yd 24 in

55. 12)6.12 m

CHAPTER TEST

Round as indicated.

number	to the nearest		
	hundred	one	tenth
1. 765.21			
2. 425.902			
3. 1954.465			

Write your estimate for each answer.

4. 354×63

5. $96 + 27 + 33$

6. 412×285

7. $626 \div 34$

8. $2750 - 815$

9. $4281 \div 18$

Complete.

10. 6 ft = _____ in

11. 30 in = _____ ft

12. 3 qt = _____ pt

13. 14 pt = _____ qt

14. 9 yd = _____ ft

15. 18 oz = _____ lb

16. 5 c = _____ pt

17. 9 gal = _____ pt

18. 5.5 tons = _____ lb

19. 4.8 km = _____ m

20. 1.6 cm = _____ mm

21. 92 mm = _____ cm

22. 5.8 g = _____ mg

23. 0.12 kg = _____ g

24. 6 l = _____ kl

25. 420 ml = _____ l

26. 454 g = _____ kg

27. 0.12 m = _____ cm

Compute.

28.　　10 lb　8 oz
　　　 +9 lb 15 oz

29.　　73 yd 1 ft
　　　 −9 yd 2 ft

30. 6.542 g
　　　　×4

31. 9 qt 1 pt
　　　 ×17

32. $6)\overline{3.12 \text{ m}}$

33.　　 9.76 m
　　　　395 cm
　　 +14.12 m

Activities for Chapter 15

Activity 1

To estimate the number of dots, count the dots in 1 square unit (1 cm² in this case).

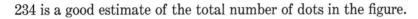

26 dots in 1 cm² – – – – –

Multiply that number by the number of square units there are.

$$26 \times 9 = 234$$

234 is a good estimate of the total number of dots in the figure.

Estimate the number of dots in each figure below.

1. 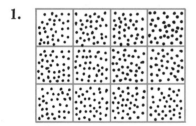 2.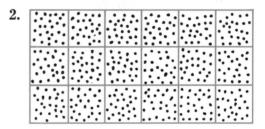

Activity 2

Find out how a blood-count test is performed.

Activity 3

Trace around your foot on a piece of grid paper (1-inch squares). Estimate the surface area of the bottom of your feet. Remember to multiply by the number of feet you have.

Compute the pressure (pounds per square inch) you exert on whatever surface you are standing. To do this, divide your weight by the surface area of your feet.

Repeat the activity using shoes, boots, crutches, and so on.

Mathematics and Conservation

Airplanes, autos, canoes, ears, and eyes are but a few of the tools used by Department of Conservation agents in watching the ups and downs of various game species.

Agents drive predetermined routes, stop at one–mile intervals for two minutes, and listen for male pheasants to crow. The agent's count is an annual index to the number of breeding males, which indicates an increase, decrease, or stability in the pheasant population.

Agents drive predetermined routes and count the number of rabbits seen in one hour. The agent's count is compared with last year's count to indicate an increase, decrease, or stability in the rabbit population.

1. Tell how you might estimate the population of some wildlife species in your area.

2. Why is it important to have accurate estimates of an increase, decrease, or stability in wildlife populations?

Find the value.

1. 5^2 **2.** 11^2 **3.** 21^2 4.4

4. $\frac{1}{3} \times \frac{1}{3}$ **5.** $\frac{3}{4} \times \frac{3}{4}$ **6.** $\frac{3}{10} \times \frac{3}{10}$ 6.2

7. 1.5×1.5 **8.** 0.3×0.3 **9.** 0.17×0.17 7.3

Express each number as the square of a number.   4.4

10. 4   **11.** 25   **12.** 64

13. 36   **14.** 9   **15.** 49

16. 16   **17.** 81   **18.** 100

Find each quotient to the hundredths place.   7.5

19. $1.6 \overline{)3.00}$ **20.** $2.2 \overline{)5.00}$

21. $2.4 \overline{)6.00}$ **22.** $2.9 \overline{)8.00}$

23. $3.5 \overline{)12.00}$ **24.** $4.5 \overline{)20.00}$

Solve.   1.5

25. $n = 36 + 64$ **26.** $n = 144 + 25$

27. $25 = n + 9$ **28.** $169 = n + 144$

29. $289 = 225 + n$ **30.** $841 = 441 + n$

Square Root _____ 16

Using pictures from weather satellites or radar, weather forecasters can use the following formula to estimate how long a storm will last.

$$t = \sqrt{\frac{d^3}{216}}$$

time (hr)   diameter (mi)

To solve for t, you must find a *square root*. In this chapter you will learn how to find square roots and to solve practical problems by using the Pythagorean Property.

456

To cut the square opening in the steel plate, you need to know the length of a side. The area can be named by s^2. You could solve $s^2 = 64$ to answer the problem.

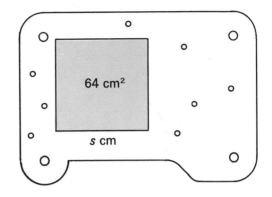

64 cm²

s cm

$s^2 = 64$ means $s \times s = 64$.

You know: $\begin{cases} 8 \times 8 = 64. \\ {}^{-}8 \times {}^{-}8 = 64. \end{cases}$

We say: 8 and ${}^{-}8$ are **square roots** of 64.

We write: $\sqrt{64} = 8$ and $-\sqrt{64} = {}^{-}8.$

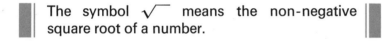

The positive square root of 64 is 8.   The negative square root of 64 is ${}^{-}8$.

Every positive number has two square roots—one positive, the other negative. Zero has only one square root: $\sqrt{0} = 0$.

> The symbol $\sqrt{}$ means the non-negative square root of a number.

Now you can answer the problem about the steel plate. Since you are interested only in the length, and not the direction, of each side, the negative square root does not apply. Each side of the square should be 8 cm long.

Example 1: Solve $a^2 = 16$.

$$a^2 = 16 \text{ means } a \times a = 16.$$

$$\text{Since } 4 \times 4 = 16$$

$$\text{and } {}^{-}4 \times {}^{-}4 = 16,$$

$$\text{the solutions are 4 and } {}^{-}4.$$

Example 2: Find $\sqrt{400}$.

$\sqrt{400}$ is a positive number k such that $k^2 = 400$.

Since $20^2 = 400$, you know that $\sqrt{400} = 20$.

Exercises

A How would you solve each equation?

1. $x^2 = 1$ **2.** $y^2 = 9$ **3.** $z^2 = 25$

4. $z^2 = 36$ **5.** $w^2 = 4$ **6.** $a^2 = 0$

B Solve each equation.

7. $b^2 = 16$ **8.** $c^2 = 49$ **9.** $m^2 = 64$

10. $k^2 = 100$ **11.** $n^2 = 81$ **12.** $p^2 = 36$

Find each square root.

13. $\sqrt{9}$ **14.** $\sqrt{36}$ **15.** $\sqrt{49}$

16. $\sqrt{64}$ **17.** $\sqrt{81}$ **18.** $\sqrt{25}$

19. $\sqrt{4}$ **20.** $\sqrt{100}$ **21.** $\sqrt{144}$

22. $\sqrt{196}$ **23.** $\sqrt{225}$ **24.** $\sqrt{256}$

C Find each square root.

25. $-\sqrt{4}$ **26.** $-\sqrt{49}$ **27.** $-\sqrt{81}$

28. $-\sqrt{100}$ **29.** $-\sqrt{121}$ **30.** $-\sqrt{144}$

31. $-\sqrt{196}$ **32.** $-\sqrt{289}$ **33.** $-\sqrt{324}$

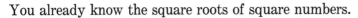

You already know the square roots of square numbers.

$$1^2 = 1, \quad \text{so} \quad \sqrt{1} = 1.$$
$$2^2 = 4, \quad \text{so} \quad \sqrt{4} = 2.$$
$$3^2 = 9, \quad \text{so} \quad \sqrt{9} = 3.$$

square numbers

That makes it easy to estimate the square roots of other whole numbers.

x	1	2	3	4	5	6	7	8	9	10	$\cdots$
$\sqrt{x}$	1	$\sqrt{2}$	$\sqrt{3}$	2	$\sqrt{5}$	$\sqrt{6}$	$\sqrt{7}$	$\sqrt{8}$	3	$\sqrt{10}$	$\cdots$

Example 1: Estimate $\sqrt{3}$ between two whole numbers.

3 is between 1 and 4. —— in the x row

So, $\sqrt{3}$ is between $\sqrt{1}$ and $\sqrt{4}$,

or $\sqrt{3}$ is between 1 and 2.

in the $\sqrt{x}$ row

Example 2: Estimate $\sqrt{3}$ to the tenths place.

In the $\sqrt{x}$ row, $\sqrt{3}$ appears nearer to 2 than to 1. An estimate for $\sqrt{3}$ is

1.6 or 1.7.

Example 3: Estimate $\sqrt{3}$ to the hundredths place.

Suppose your estimate in Example 2 was 1.6.

$$1.6 \overline{)3.0000} \quad \begin{array}{c} 1.87 \end{array}$$

Divide 3 by the estimate 1.6.

$$\frac{1.6 + 1.87}{2} \approx 1.73$$

Find the average of the divisor and the quotient. Compute to the hundredths place.

$$\sqrt{3} \approx 1.73$$

Exercises

A Estimate each square root between two whole numbers.

1. $\sqrt{2}$ 2. $\sqrt{5}$ 3. $\sqrt{6}$

4. $\sqrt{7}$ 5. $\sqrt{8}$ 6. $\sqrt{10}$

7. $\sqrt{13}$ 8. $\sqrt{18}$ 9. $\sqrt{29}$

B Estimate each square root to the tenths place.

10. $\sqrt{5}$ 11. $\sqrt{8}$ 12. $\sqrt{10}$

13. $\sqrt{14}$ 14. $\sqrt{20}$ 15. $\sqrt{30}$

Estimate each square root to the hundredths place.

16. $\sqrt{5}$ 17. $\sqrt{8}$ 18. $\sqrt{10}$

19. $\sqrt{12}$ 20. $\sqrt{18}$ 21. $\sqrt{24}$

22. $\sqrt{35}$ 23. $\sqrt{42}$ 24. $\sqrt{54}$

C Estimate each square root to the hundredths place.

25. $-\sqrt{2}$ 26. $-\sqrt{3}$ 27. $-\sqrt{6}$

28. $-\sqrt{12}$ 29. $-\sqrt{15}$ 30. $-\sqrt{21}$

You have just learned how to find approximations of square roots. Such approximations are listed in the table of square roots on page 487. The table also lists the squares of the whole numbers 1–150.

Example 1: Use the table of square roots to find an approximation for $\sqrt{29}$.

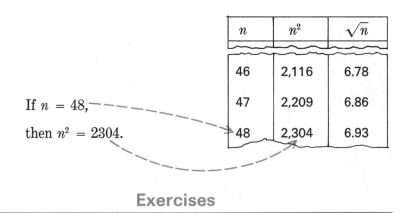

n	n^2	$\sqrt{n}$
26	676	5.10
27	729	5.20
28	784	5.29
29	841	5.39

If $n = 29$,

then $\sqrt{n} \approx 5.39$.

Example 2: Use the table of squares to find 48^2.

n	n^2	$\sqrt{n}$
46	2,116	6.78
47	2,209	6.86
48	2,304	6.93

If $n = 48$,

then $n^2 = 2304$.

Exercises

Ⓐ Tell how to use the table to find the following.

1. $\sqrt{7}$ **2.** $\sqrt{79}$ **3.** $\sqrt{142}$

4. 15^2 **5.** 87^2 **6.** 119^2

Use the table to find the following.

   7. $\sqrt{18}$ **8.** $\sqrt{42}$ **9.** $\sqrt{94}$

   10. $\sqrt{110}$ **11.** $\sqrt{128}$ **12.** $\sqrt{149}$

   13. 14^2 **14.** 37^2 **15.** 69^2

   16. 86^2 **17.** 108^2 **18.** 134^2

   19. $\sqrt{29}$ **20.** 71^2 **21.** $\sqrt{63}$

   22. 92^2 **23.** $\sqrt{122}$ **24.** 146^2

C Find an approximation for each of the following.

   25. $-\sqrt{5}$ **26.** $-\sqrt{2}$ **27.** $-\sqrt{8}$

   28. $-\sqrt{15}$ **29.** $-\sqrt{32}$ **30.** $-\sqrt{48}$

   31. $-\sqrt{41}$ **32.** $-\sqrt{56}$ **33.** $-\sqrt{75}$

On Target

To qualify for the archery team, you must score at least 400 points in 5 shots. In how many ways is it possible to score exactly 400 points?

To solve a problem, Jean had to find $\sqrt{400}$. The n-column in the square-root table lists whole numbers only to 150.

She experimented and discovered two ways to find $\sqrt{400}$.

Example 1: Find $\sqrt{400}$.

400 is given in the n^2-column of the table.

$$400 = 20^2$$

$$\sqrt{400} = 20$$

n	n^2	$\sqrt{n}$
19	361	4.36
20	400	4.47
21	441	4.58

Example 2: Find $\sqrt{400}$.

$\sqrt{400} = \sqrt{4 \times 100}$ Both factors are square numbers.

$= \sqrt{4} \times \sqrt{100}$

$= 2 \times 10$

$= 20$

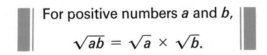

For positive numbers a and b,

$$\sqrt{ab} = \sqrt{a} \times \sqrt{b}.$$

Example 3: Find $\sqrt{280}$.

280 > 150, so 280 is not in the n-column of the table.

280 is not in the n^2-column either. Since 280 is between 256 and 289, you can estimate $\sqrt{280}$ between 16 and 17.

n	n^2	$\sqrt{n}$
16	256	4.00
17	289	4.12

$$\sqrt{280} = \sqrt{4 \times 70}$$ — Look for a square-number factor.

$$= \sqrt{4} \times \sqrt{70}$$ Both numbers are in the *n*-column.

$$\approx 2 \times 8.37$$ Find $\sqrt{70}$ in the table.

$$\approx 16.74$$

Exercises

A Find each square root in the table.

1. $\sqrt{169}$ 2. $\sqrt{196}$ 3. $\sqrt{576}$ 4. $\sqrt{484}$

5. $\sqrt{841}$ 6. $\sqrt{1296}$ 7. $\sqrt{2601}$ 8. $\sqrt{3969}$

To find the square root, how would you name each number as a product?

Example: To find $\sqrt{1300}$, name 1300 as 100×13.

9. $\sqrt{300}$ 10. $\sqrt{2100}$ 11. $\sqrt{999}$ 12. $\sqrt{810}$

13. $\sqrt{250}$ 14. $\sqrt{360}$ 15. $\sqrt{320}$ 16. $\sqrt{1440}$

B Find each square root to the nearest hundredth.

17. $\sqrt{640}$ 18. $\sqrt{280}$ 19. $\sqrt{1000}$ 20. $\sqrt{750}$

21. $\sqrt{1500}$ 22. $\sqrt{500}$ 23. $\sqrt{189}$ 24. $\sqrt{204}$

25. $\sqrt{720}$ 26. $\sqrt{540}$ 27. $\sqrt{168}$ 28. $\sqrt{175}$

29. $\sqrt{490}$ 30. $\sqrt{396}$ 31. $\sqrt{324}$ 32. $\sqrt{244}$

C Compute.

Example: $\sqrt{144 + 25} = \sqrt{169}$ $\sqrt{144} + \sqrt{25} = 12 + 5$

$$= 13 \qquad\qquad\qquad\qquad = 17$$

33. $\sqrt{16 + 9}$ **34.** $\sqrt{16} + \sqrt{9}$ **35.** $\sqrt{64 + 36}$ **36.** $\sqrt{64} + \sqrt{36}$

Compare answers for Exercises 33 and 34 and for Exercises 35 and 36.

37. Is $\sqrt{a + b}$ equal to $\sqrt{a} + \sqrt{b}$?

Compute.

38. $\sqrt{25 - 9}$ **39.** $\sqrt{25} - \sqrt{9}$ **40.** $\sqrt{100 - 36}$ **41.** $\sqrt{100} - \sqrt{36}$

42. Is $\sqrt{a - b}$ equal to $\sqrt{a} - \sqrt{b}$?

Pigs for Poke!

Mr. Porker has 250 pigs to sell. How can he arrange the pigs in 8 pens so he can instantly deliver any number of pigs from 1 to 250 by simply opening the right gate or gates and herding the pigs out?

16.5 ⬤ SQUARE ROOTS OF RATIONAL NUMBERS

You have several ways to find the square root of a whole number. Sometimes you need to find the square root of a rational number.

Example 1: Find $\sqrt{\dfrac{4}{9}}$.

Here are two ways to do it.

$$\sqrt{\frac{4}{9}} = \sqrt{\frac{2}{3} \times \frac{2}{3}} \qquad\qquad \sqrt{\frac{4}{9}} = \frac{\sqrt{4}}{\sqrt{9}}$$

$$= \frac{2}{3} \qquad\qquad\qquad = \frac{2}{3}$$

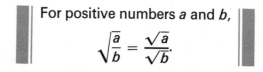

For positive numbers a and b,

$$\sqrt{\frac{a}{b}} = \frac{\sqrt{a}}{\sqrt{b}}.$$

Example 2: Find $\sqrt{0.64}$.

Here are two ways to do it.

$$\sqrt{0.64} = \sqrt{0.8 \times 0.8} \qquad\qquad \sqrt{0.64} = \sqrt{\frac{64}{100}}$$

$$= 0.8 \qquad\qquad\qquad\qquad = \frac{\sqrt{64}}{\sqrt{100}}$$

$$= \frac{8}{10} \text{ or } \frac{4}{5}$$

Exercises

A Name as a product of two equal factors.

1. $\frac{16}{100}$ 2. $\frac{9}{36}$ 3. $\frac{1}{4}$ 4. $\frac{16}{25}$

5. $\frac{64}{81}$ 6. $\frac{25}{100}$ 7. $\frac{49}{64}$ 8. $\frac{9}{16}$

Name as a fraction.

9. 0.09   **10.** 0.81   **11.** 0.16   **12.** 0.04

13. 0.25   **14.** 0.36   **15.** 0.01   **16.** 0.0025

B Find each square root.

17. $\sqrt{\frac{9}{25}}$ **18.** $\sqrt{\frac{16}{49}}$ **19.** $\sqrt{\frac{25}{64}}$ **20.** $\sqrt{\frac{64}{81}}$

21. $\sqrt{\frac{1}{4}}$ **22.** $\sqrt{\frac{49}{100}}$ **23.** $\sqrt{\frac{9}{16}}$ **24.** $\sqrt{\frac{81}{100}}$

25. $\sqrt{0.09}$ **26.** $\sqrt{0.81}$ **27.** $\sqrt{0.04}$ **28.** $\sqrt{0.25}$

29. $\sqrt{0.36}$ **30.** $\sqrt{0.01}$ **31.** $\sqrt{0.0036}$ **32.** $\sqrt{1.44}$

C Find each square root.

Example:

$$\sqrt{\frac{3}{8}} = \frac{\sqrt{3}}{\sqrt{8}}$$

You can avoid division by decimals by doing this:

Choose 2 so the new denominator is a square number.

$$\approx \frac{1.73}{2.83}$$

$$\sqrt{\frac{3}{8}} = \sqrt{\frac{3 \times 2}{8 \times 2}}$$

$$= \sqrt{\frac{6}{16}}$$

$$= \frac{\sqrt{6}}{\sqrt{16}}$$

$$\approx \frac{2.45}{4} \text{ or } 0.61$$

33. $\sqrt{\frac{4}{5}}$ **34.** $\sqrt{\frac{1}{2}}$ **35.** $\sqrt{\frac{2}{3}}$ **36.** $\sqrt{\frac{7}{8}}$

37. $\sqrt{\frac{5}{32}}$ **38.** $\sqrt{\frac{4}{7}}$ **39.** $\sqrt{\frac{7}{18}}$ **40.** $\sqrt{\frac{12}{25}}$

16.6 ● SQUARE ROOT AND EQUATIONS

Many practical problems require you to solve equations like $x^2 = 36$. You already know that this equation has two solutions—one positive and the other negative.

$$x^2 = 36$$

positive solution	negative solution
$x = \sqrt{36}$	$x = -\sqrt{36}$
$= 6$	$= -6$

In practical applications you are usually interested only in a distance or an amount, and not direction, so the negative solution does not apply.

Example 1: Find the positive solution of $x^2 = 16$.

$$x^2 = 16$$
$$x = \sqrt{16} \qquad \text{positive solution}$$
$$x = 4$$

Example 2: Find the positive solution of $x^2 = 21$.

$$x^2 = 21$$
$$x = \sqrt{21} \qquad \text{positive solution}$$
$$x \approx 4.58 \qquad \text{from the table}$$

Example 3: Find the positive solution of $x^2 + 5 = 81$.

$$x^2 + 5 = 81$$
$$x^2 + 5 - 5 = 81 - 5 \qquad \text{Subtract 5 from each side.}$$
$$x^2 = 76$$
$$x = \sqrt{76} \qquad \text{positive solution}$$
$$x \approx 8.72 \qquad \text{from the table}$$

Exercises

A How would you find the positive solution of each equation?

1. $x^2 = 25$ **2.** $x^2 = 30$ **3.** $x^2 + 9 = 90$

4. $x^2 - 5 = 59$ **5.** $3x^2 = 60$ **6.** $\frac{x^2}{2} = 24$

B Find the positive solution of each equation.

7. $x^2 = 9$ **8.** $x^2 = 27$ **9.** $x^2 = 42$

10. $x^2 + 5 = 30$ **11.** $x^2 + 9 = 42$ **12.** $x^2 + 16 = 25$

13. $x^2 - 4 = 60$ **14.** $x^2 - 9 = 81$ **15.** $x^2 - 25 = 144$

16. $3x^2 = 39$ **17.** $2x^2 = 128$ **18.** $5x^2 = 375$

19. $\frac{x^2}{2} = 8$ **20.** $\frac{x^2}{3} = 15$ **21.** $\frac{x^2}{5} = 17$

If a plane is h miles above the earth, it is approximately d miles to the horizon. The relationship between h and d can be expressed by the following formula.

$$d = \sqrt{8000h}$$

Use the formula to complete the following table.

Example: If a plane is 5 miles high, what is the distance to the horizon?

$$d = \sqrt{8000h}$$
$$= \sqrt{8000 \times 5}$$
$$= \sqrt{40000}$$
$$= 200 \quad \text{It is 200 miles to the horizon.}$$

	Altitude	Distance to horizon			Altitude	Distance to horizon
22.	1 mile	_____		**23.**	$1\frac{1}{4}$ miles	_____
24.	2 miles	_____		**25.**	$2\frac{1}{2}$ miles	_____
26.	3 miles	_____		**27.**	3.2 miles	_____

You can also use the formula to find the altitude if the distance to the horizon is known.

Example: How high is a plane which is 20 miles from the horizon?

$$d = \sqrt{8000h}$$

$$20 = \sqrt{8000h}$$

$$400 = 8000h \qquad \text{Square each side.}$$

$$\frac{400}{8000} = \frac{8000h}{8000}$$

$$\frac{1}{20} = h \qquad \text{The plane is } \tfrac{1}{20} \text{ of a mile high.}$$

Complete the following table.

	Altitude	Distance to horizon			Altitude	Distance to horizon
28.	_____	30 miles		**29.**	_____	100 miles
30.	_____	50 miles		**31.**	_____	150 miles
32.	_____	80 miles		**33.**	_____	200 miles

C Solve each equation.

Example: $\sqrt{x} = 5.1$

$$(\sqrt{x})^2 = (5.1)^2 \qquad \text{Square each side.}$$

$$x = 26.01$$

34. $\sqrt{x} = 6$ **35.** $\sqrt{y} = 6.2$ **36.** $\sqrt{r} = \frac{4}{7}$

37. $\sqrt{k} = 49$ **38.** $\sqrt{r} = 25$ **39.** $\sqrt{t} = 128$

Example: $\sqrt{x + 3} = 5$

$\qquad (\sqrt{x + 3})^2 = 5^2$ Square each side.

$\qquad\qquad x + 3 = 25$

$\qquad x + 3 - 3 = 25 - 3$

$\qquad\qquad\qquad x = 22$

40. $\sqrt{x + 7} = 4$ **41.** $\sqrt{x + 5} = 9$ **42.** $\sqrt{x + 11} = 15$

43. $\sqrt{x - 7} = 7$ **44.** $\sqrt{x - 4} = 6$ **45.** $\sqrt{x - 9} = 14$

Pennies

Suppose a person took a job that paid 1¢ the first day, 2¢ the second day, 4¢ the third day, and so on. At the end of 10 days he would have earned more than $10.

How long would it take a person to earn more than $10 if he were paid 2¢ the first day rather than 1¢?

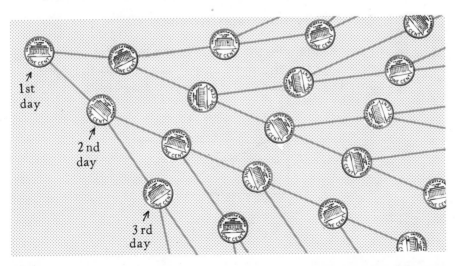

16.7 ◑ THE PYTHAGOREAN PROPERTY

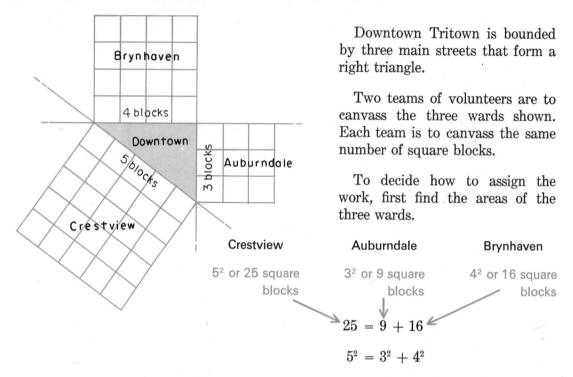

Downtown Tritown is bounded by three main streets that form a right triangle.

Two teams of volunteers are to canvass the three wards shown. Each team is to canvass the same number of square blocks.

To decide how to assign the work, first find the areas of the three wards.

Crestview	Auburndale	Brynhaven
5^2 or 25 square blocks	3^2 or 9 square blocks	4^2 or 16 square blocks

$$25 = 9 + 16$$

$$5^2 = 3^2 + 4^2$$

Hence, one team could canvass Crestview and the other team canvass Auburndale and Brynhaven.

The problem illustrates an important property of right triangles.

Pythagorean Property

In a right triangle, the square of the hypotenuse (side opposite the right angle) is equal to the sum of the squares of the other two sides.

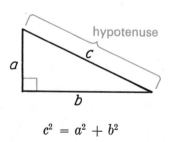

$$c^2 = a^2 + b^2$$

Example 1: Find the measure of side JK.

$$c^2 = a^2 + b^2$$
$$c^2 = 7^2 + 24^2$$
$$c^2 = 49 + 576$$
$$c^2 = 625$$
$$c = \sqrt{625}$$
$$c = 25$$

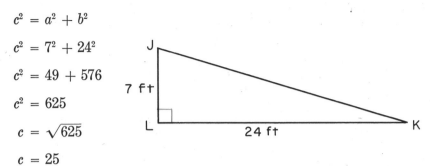

Hence, side JK is 25 feet long.

Example 2: Find the measure of side PQ.

$$c^2 = a^2 + b^2$$
$$17^2 = a^2 + 15^2$$
$$289 = a^2 + 225$$
$$289 - 225 = a^2 + 225 - 225$$
$$64 = a^2$$
$$\sqrt{64} = a$$
$$8 = a$$

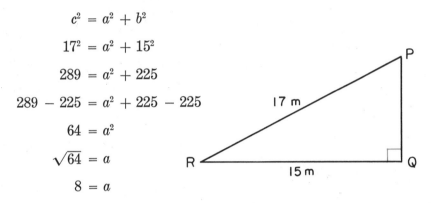

Hence, side PQ is 8 meters long.

Exercises

A   How can you find x in each right triangle?

1.

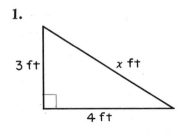

2.

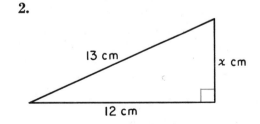

How would you solve each equation ?

3. $25 = 9 + b^2$ **4.** $100 = a^2 + 64$ **5.** $c^2 = 144 + 25$

6. $5^2 = 3^2 + b^2$ **7.** $10^2 = a^2 + 8^2$ **8.** $c^2 = 12^2 + 5^2$

B Use the right triangle below to help you complete the table.

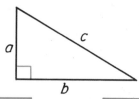

	a	b	c
9.	3	4	___
11.	15	8	___
13.	___	24	25
15.	___	40	41
17.	63	___	65
19.	21	___	29

	a	b	c
10.	5	12	___
12.	24	7	___
14.	___	20	29
16.	___	60	61
18.	45	___	53
20.	8	___	17

C Determine if each triangle is a right triangle.

Examples:

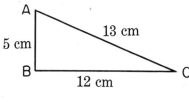

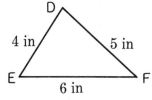

$13^2 \; ⬤ \; 5^2 + 12^2$ $6^2 \; ⬤ \; 5^2 + 4^2$

$169 \; ⬤ \; 25 + 144$ $36 \; ⬤ \; 25 + 16$

$169 = 169$ $36 \neq 41$

△ ABC is a
right triangle.

△ DEF is not
a right triangle.

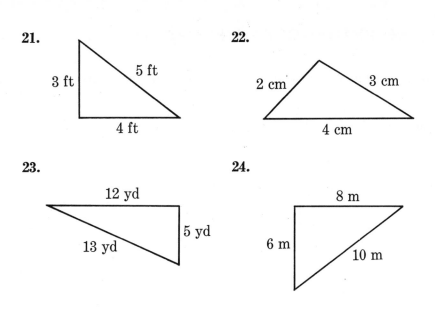

21.

3 ft   5 ft   4 ft

22.

2 cm   3 cm   4 cm

23.

12 yd   5 yd   13 yd

24.

8 m   6 m   10 m

Early Bird

The crow atop the steeple and the songbird in the tree spot a grain of corn at point A at the same time. If the songbird flies twice as fast as the crow, which will get to the corn first?

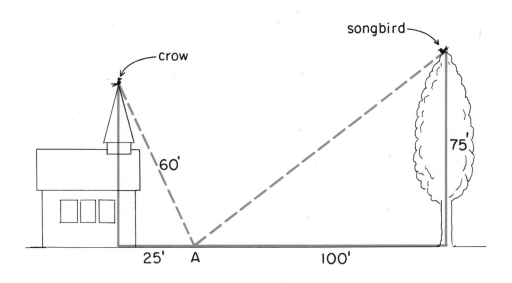

16.8 ⬤ USING THE PYTHAGOREAN PROPERTY

The Pythagorean Property can be used in solving many practical problems.

Example 1: How far is it from point D to point E?

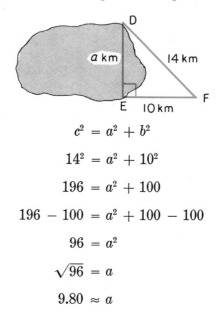

$$c^2 = a^2 + b^2$$

$$14^2 = a^2 + 10^2$$

$$196 = a^2 + 100$$

$$196 - 100 = a^2 + 100 - 100$$

$$96 = a^2$$

$$\sqrt{96} = a$$

$$9.80 \approx a$$

It is approximately 9.8 kilometers from D to E.

Example 2: A telephone pole is to be braced by a guy wire as shown. How high up on the pole should the wire be fastened?

$$c^2 = a^2 + b^2$$

$$39^2 = 15^2 + b^2$$

$$1521 = 225 + b^2$$

$$1521 - 225 = 225 + b^2 - 225$$

$$1296 = b^2$$

$$\sqrt{1296} = b$$

$$36 = b$$

The wire should be fastened 36 feet above the ground.

Exercises

A State an equation like $13^2 = x^2 + 5^2$ for each right triangle.

1.

28 m, x m, 45 m

2.

11 ft, x ft, 61 ft

3.

85 in, x in, 77 in

4.

90 ft, 90 ft, x ft

B Solve each problem.

5. When Joe had let out 100 yards of kite string, his girl friend, Rita, was directly beneath the kite. If Joe is 80 yards from Rita, how high is the kite?

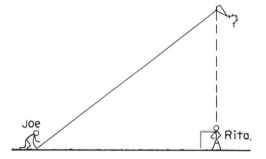

Joe, Rita

6. On a baseball diamond it is 90 feet between bases. How far is it from home plate to second base?

7. On a softball diamond it is 60 feet between bases. How far is it from home plate to second base?

8. What is the height of the TV screen shown at the right?

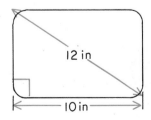

12 in, 10 in

9. The bottom of a 16-foot ladder is placed 5 feet from a building. How high up on the building will the ladder reach?

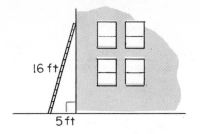

16 ft

5 ft

10. A ship left port and sailed 5 miles west and then 8 miles south. How far was the ship from the port?

11. An inclined ramp rises 4 feet over a horizontal distance of 10 feet. What is the length of the ramp?

4 ft

10 ft

12. The roof of a house is to be built as shown. How long should each rafter be?

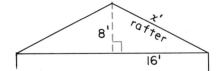

8' rafter x'

16'

C Solve each problem.

Example : The lighthouse at Bernice Point is 16 miles from the lighthouse at Leigh Sound. The point at which the radio beams from these lighthouses make right angles is the same distance from each. What is that distance?

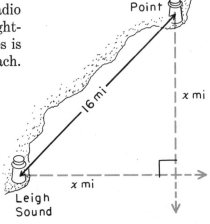

Bernice Point

16 mi

x mi

Leigh Sound

x mi

$$x^2 + x^2 = 16^2$$

$$2x^2 = 256$$

$$\frac{2x^2}{2} = \frac{256}{2}$$

$$x^2 = 128$$

$$x = \sqrt{128}$$

$$x \approx 11.31$$ The point is about 11.31 miles from each lighthouse.

13. How far is point A from each corner of the window?

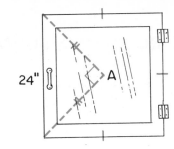

24"

14. If the diagonal of a square is 18 inches long, what is the length of each side?

15. It is 100 meters from one corner of a square parking lot to the opposite corner. What are the dimensions of the parking lot?

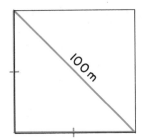

100 m

16. The brace for the gate shown is 44 inches long. What are the dimensions of the gate?

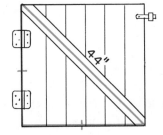

44"

Stuck in the Trunk

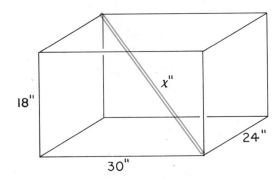

18" x'' 24"   30"

What is the longest stick, to the nearest inch, that can be placed inside the trunk?

16.9 SQUARE ROOT AND FORMULAS

To solve some useful formulas, you have to find square roots. The formula for the duration of a storm is such a formula.

$$t = \sqrt{\frac{d^3}{216}}$$

time in hours ↗   diameter of storm in miles

To make the computation easier, you can change the formula to a more convenient form.

$$t = \sqrt{\frac{d^3}{216}}$$

$$= \frac{\sqrt{d^2 \times d}}{\sqrt{36 \times 6}}$$

$$= \frac{d\sqrt{d} \times \sqrt{6}}{6\sqrt{6} \times \sqrt{6}}$$

$$= \frac{d\sqrt{6d}}{36}$$

Example: Estimate how long a storm will last if its diameter is 12 miles.

$$t = \frac{d\sqrt{6d}}{36}$$

$$= \frac{12\sqrt{6 \times 12}}{36}$$

$$= \frac{\sqrt{6 \times 6 \times 2}}{3}$$

$$= \frac{6\sqrt{2}}{3}$$

$$\approx 2\sqrt{2} \text{ or } 2.82$$

The storm will last about 2.82 hours.

Exercises

A Tell what is done in each step.

1. $A = \pi r^2$

$$\frac{A}{\pi} = \frac{\pi r^2}{\pi}$$

$$\sqrt{\frac{A}{\pi}} = r$$

2. $s = 16t^2$

$$\frac{s}{16} = \frac{16t^2}{16}$$

$$\sqrt{\frac{s}{16}} = t$$

$$\frac{\sqrt{s}}{4} = t$$

B Solve each problem. Use 3.14 for π.

3. How long will a storm last if its diameter is 18 miles?

4. The radius of a circle is 2 meters long. Find the area.

5. The area of a circle is 28.26 square centimeters. Find the radius. Use $r = \sqrt{\frac{A}{\pi}}$.

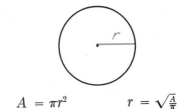

$$A = \pi r^2 \qquad r = \sqrt{\frac{A}{\pi}}$$

6. A helicopter dropped a survival kit. It hit the water 5 seconds later. What was the altitude of the helicopter? Use $s = 16t^2$.

7. Later the helicopter dropped a canister of marking dye from an altitude of 1024 feet. How long did it take to hit the water? Use $t = \frac{\sqrt{s}}{4}$.

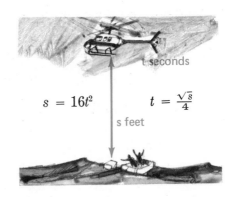

t seconds

$$s = 16t^2 \qquad t = \frac{\sqrt{s}}{4}$$

s feet

8. A basketball has a radius of 4.7 inches. Find the surface area. Use $A = 4\pi r^2$.

C **9.** A spherical storage tank has a surface area of 452.16 square feet. Find the radius. Use $r = \sqrt{\frac{A}{4\pi}}$.

$$A = 4\pi r^2 \qquad r = \sqrt{\frac{A}{4\pi}}$$

▷ VOCABULARY

Use the terms or symbols to correctly complete the sentences.

square root   Pythagorean Property $\sqrt{\quad}$

hypotenuse $-\sqrt{\quad}$

1. Every positive number has a positive and a negative _____.

2. The symbol _____ denotes the non-negative square root of a number.

3. In a right triangle, the _____ is the side opposite the right angle.

4. The symbol _____ denotes the negative square root of a number.

5. The _____ can be symbolized as $c^2 = a^2 + b^2$.

▷ CHAPTER REVIEW

16.1   Find two solutions for each equation.

     1. $a^2 = 9$ **2.** $b^2 = 25$ **3.** $c^2 = 16$

     4. $x^2 = 36$ **5.** $y^2 = 49$ **6.** $z^2 = 81$

16.2   Estimate each square root to the hundredths place.

     7. $\sqrt{2}$ **8.** $\sqrt{3}$ **9.** $\sqrt{7}$

16.3   Use the table on page 487 to find the following.

     10. $\sqrt{21}$ **11.** $\sqrt{45}$ **12.** $\sqrt{96}$

     13. 27^2 **14.** 52^2 **15.** 119^2

16.4   Find each square root to the nearest hundredth.

     16. $\sqrt{250}$ **17.** $\sqrt{490}$ **18.** $\sqrt{604}$

     19. $\sqrt{180}$ **20.** $\sqrt{360}$ **21.** $\sqrt{2700}$

Find each square root. 16.5

22. $\sqrt{\frac{1}{4}}$ **23.** $\sqrt{\frac{4}{9}}$ **24.** $\sqrt{\frac{49}{100}}$

25. $\sqrt{0.49}$ **26.** $\sqrt{0.36}$ **27.** $\sqrt{1.21}$

Find the positive solution of each equation. 16.6

28. $x^2 + 5 = 54$ **29.** $x^2 - 4 = 21$ **30.** $5x^2 = 80$

31. $\dfrac{x^2}{3} = 12$ **32.** $x^2 + 6 = 40$ **33.** $x^2 - 12 = 28$

Use the right triangle below to help you complete the following. 16.7

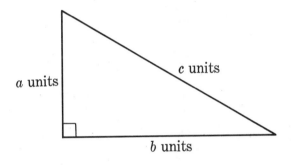

34. $a = 8$, $b = 15$, $c = $ _____ **35.** $a = 3$, $c = 5$, $b = $ _____

36. $b = 24$, $c = 25$, $a = $ _____ **37.** $c = 53$, $b = 28$, $a = $ _____

Solve each problem. 16.8

38. What is the length of the pond shown at the right?

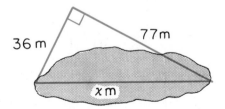

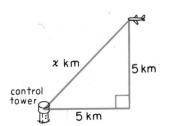

39. What is the distance from the control tower to the airplane?

CHAPTER TEST

Find the number named by each of the following.

1. $\sqrt{36}$ 2. $\sqrt{81}$ 3. $\sqrt{\frac{4}{9}}$

4. $\sqrt{\frac{16}{25}}$ 5. $\sqrt{0.64}$ 6. $\sqrt{0.81}$

Find each square root to the nearest hundredth.

7. $\sqrt{5}$ 8. $\sqrt{8}$ 9. $\sqrt{12}$

10. $\sqrt{288}$ 11. $\sqrt{250}$ 12. $\sqrt{720}$

Find the positive solution of each equation.

13. $x^2 = 25$ 14. $x^2 = 37$ 15. $x^2 + 5 = 41$

16. $x^2 - 9 = 40$ 17. $3x^2 = 48$ 18. $\dfrac{x^2}{2} = 32$

19. $x^2 - 7 = 16$ 20. $x^2 + 9 = 41$ 21. $4x^2 = 80$

Use the Pythagorean Property to solve the following.

22. A weather balloon is 4000 meters high and directly over a point 900 meters from the weather station. How far is the balloon from the station?

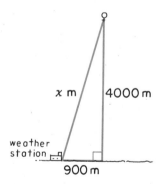

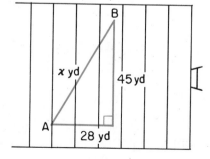

23. How far would a quarterback standing at point A have to throw the ball to complete a pass to a receiver at point B?

Activities for Chapter 16

Activity 1

Builders and surveyors often use the following procedure to check that corners are square (form right angles).

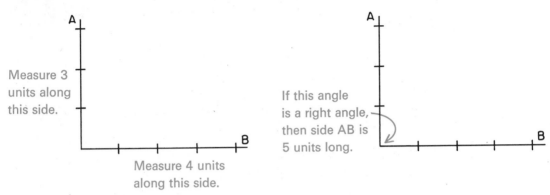

Measure 3 units along this side.

Measure 4 units along this side.

If this angle is a right angle, then side AB is 5 units long.

For greater accuracy, multiples of 3, 4, and 5 (such as 6, 8, 10; 12, 16, 20; and so on) are used. Use the above procedure to check the corners of your classroom, a fence, or a tabletop.

Activity 2

You can use the Pythagorean Property to derive a formula for the diagonal of a square.

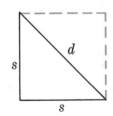

$$d^2 = s^2 + s^2$$
$$d^2 = 2s^2$$
$$d = \sqrt{2s^2}$$
$$d = s\sqrt{2}$$

Example: What is the length of the diagonal below?

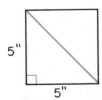

$$d = s\sqrt{2}$$
$$= 5\sqrt{2}$$
$$\approx 5 \times 1.41 \text{ or } 7.05$$

The diagonal is about 7.05 inches long.

Use the above formula to find the diagonal of several squares.

Mathematics and Police Work

You can determine the speed that a car was traveling by measuring the skid marks.

If all four tires skid and the car comes to a stop without hitting another object, you can use these formulas.

Dry, concrete road	*Wet, concrete road*
$s = \sqrt{24d}$	$s = \sqrt{12d}$
speed (mph) distance (ft) car skidded	speed (mph) distance (ft) car skidded

Example: A car skidded to a stop on a dry, concrete road. The skid marks were 48 feet long. How fast was the car traveling?

$$s = \sqrt{24d}$$
$$= \sqrt{24 \times 48}$$
$$= \sqrt{24 \times 24 \times 2}$$
$$= 24\sqrt{2}$$
$$= 33.84 \text{ or } 34 \qquad 34 \text{ mph}$$

Solve these problems.

1. A car skidded to a stop on a dry, concrete road. The skid marks were 120 feet long. How fast was the car traveling?

2. A car skidded to a stop on a wet, concrete road. It left skid marks for 96 feet. How fast was the car traveling?

Table of Squares and Square Roots

n	n^2	$\sqrt{n}$	n	n^2	$\sqrt{n}$	n	n^2	$\sqrt{n}$
1	1	1.00	51	2,601	7.14	101	10,201	10.05
2	4	1.41	52	2,704	7.21	102	10,404	10.10
3	9	1.73	53	2,809	7.28	103	10,609	10.15
4	16	2.00	54	2,916	7.35	104	10,816	10.20
5	25	2.24	55	3,025	7.42	105	11,025	10.25
6	36	2.45	56	3,136	7.48	106	11,236	10.30
7	49	2.65	57	3,249	7.55	107	11,449	10.34
8	64	2.83	58	3,364	7.62	108	11,664	10.39
9	81	3.00	59	3,481	7.68	109	11,881	10.44
10	100	3.16	60	3,600	7.75	110	12,100	10.49
11	121	3.32	61	3,721	7.81	111	12,321	10.54
12	144	3.46	62	3,844	7.87	112	12,544	10.58
13	169	3.61	63	3,969	7.94	113	12,769	10.63
14	196	3.74	64	4,096	8.00	114	12,996	10.68
15	225	3.87	65	4,225	8.06	115	13,225	10.72
16	256	4.00	66	4,356	8.12	116	13,456	10.77
17	289	4.12	67	4,489	8.19	117	13,689	10.82
18	324	4.24	68	4,624	8.25	118	13,924	10.86
19	361	4.36	69	4,761	8.31	119	14,161	10.91
20	400	4.47	70	4,900	8.37	120	14,400	10.95
21	441	4.58	71	5,041	8.43	121	14,641	11.00
22	484	4.69	72	5,184	8.49	122	14,884	11.05
23	529	4.80	73	5,329	8.54	123	15,129	11.09
24	576	4.90	74	5,476	8.60	124	15,376	11.14
25	625	5.00	75	5,625	8.66	125	15,625	11.18
26	676	5.10	76	5,776	8.72	126	15,876	11.22
27	729	5.20	77	5,929	8.77	127	16,129	11.27
28	784	5.29	78	6,084	8.83	128	16,384	11.31
29	841	5.39	79	6,241	8.89	129	16,641	11.36
30	900	5.48	80	6,400	8.94	130	16,900	11.40
31	961	5.57	81	6,561	9.00	131	17,161	11.45
32	1,024	5.66	82	6,724	9.06	132	17,424	11.49
33	1,089	5.74	83	6,889	9.11	133	17,689	11.53
34	1,156	5.83	84	7,056	9.17	134	17,956	11.58
35	1,225	5.92	85	7,225	9.22	135	18,225	11.62
36	1,296	6.00	86	7,396	9.27	136	18,496	11.66
37	1,369	6.08	87	7,569	9.33	137	18,769	11.70
38	1,444	6.16	88	7,744	9.38	138	19,044	11.75
39	1,521	6.24	89	7,921	9.43	139	19,321	11.79
40	1,600	6.32	90	8,100	9.49	140	19,600	11.83
41	1,681	6.40	91	8,281	9.54	141	19,881	11.87
42	1,764	6.48	92	8,464	9.59	142	20,164	11.92
43	1,849	6.56	93	8,649	9.64	143	20,449	11.96
44	1,936	6.63	94	8,836	9.70	144	20,736	12.00
45	2,025	6.71	95	9,025	9.75	145	21,025	12.04
46	2,116	6.78	96	9,216	9.80	146	21,316	12.08
47	2,209	6.86	97	9,409	9.85	147	21,609	12.12
48	2,304	6.93	98	9,604	9.90	148	21,904	12.17
49	2,401	7.00	99	9,801	9.95	149	22,201	12.21
50	2,500	7.07	100	10,000	10.00	150	22,500	12.25

Photograph Credits

PAGE

1   Feminist Resources for Equal Education

31   Courtesy Piper Aircraft Corporation

33   Stephen J. Potter

49   Courtesy Piper Aircraft Corporation

51   Courtesy Grumman American Aviation Corporation

67   Courtesy Eastman Kodak Company

68   Mark Chester

69   Aero Service Corporation

88   Left: Herb Taylor, Jr.
Right: Feminist Resources for Equal Education

102   Wide World Photos

127   Photo Research Int.

129   Rocky Weldon

152   USDA Photo by Murray Lemmon

154   Photo Research Int.

158   A. Devaney, Inc.

176   Courtesy General Motors Corporation

188   Daniel S. Brody

197   H. Armstrong Roberts

199   Jeff Albertson

215   Courtesy The L. S. Starrett Co.

216   A. Devaney, Inc.

218   David W. Corson

PAGE

243   Courtesy North American Rockwell Corporation

276   Rohn Engh

291   Photo Research Int.

293   Courtesy United Airlines

301   Caraballo

303   De Wys, Inc.

315   Larry P. Trone

318   Authenticated News Int.

333   Hays

335   Photo Research Int.

352   Photo Research Int.

358   Courtesy American Motors

368   Thomas J. Richards

372   Barbara Van Cleve

375   Courtesy NYSE

386   Photo Research Int.

387   Martin Vanderwall

389   A. Devaney, Inc.

392   Authenticated News Int.

401   Courtesy Bethlehem Steel Corporation

413   Authenticated News Int.

415   A. Devaney, Inc.

426   Jack E. Whitaker

428   Courtesy Ford Motor Co.

429   Authenticated News Int.

454   Top: H. Armstrong Roberts
Bottom: Grant Heilman

456   A. Devaney, Inc.

Index

A

Absolute value, 223
Addition
  with decimals, 194, 372
  with fractions, 156–157, 172–
    173, 176–177, 179–180,
    188, 375
  identity number of, 143–144
  of integers, 221, 223–224,
    240, 273
  inverse operation of, 133
  on a number line, 221, 240
  of rational numbers, 372,
    375
Area, 59, 159–160, 183, 457
  of a circle, 168, 204
Associative property, 140–141,
  151
Axes, 235

B

Base of a power, 111

C

Checking solutions, 16, 19, 34,
  37, 40, 43
Circle
  area of, 168, 204
  circumference of, 389
Circumference, 389
Closure property, 130

Commutative property, 136–
  137, 151
Comparison
  of decimals, 193
  of fractions, 178, 187, 193,
    370
  of rational numbers, 370
Composite numbers, 108
Coordinates, 73, 234–235
Corresponding
  angles, 341
  sides, 342
Cross products, 175, 312–313

D

Decimals
  addition with, 194, 372
  comparison of, 193
  division with, 199, 201, 215,
    381
  as fractions, 191–192
  multiplication with, 197,
    215–216, 381
  to name ratios, 320
  problem solving with,
    204–205
  subtraction with, 194–195,
    373
Denominator
  of a fraction, 155
  least common, 176–177
Distributive property, 145–146
Divisibility, 104, 106
  rules for, 106, 109

Division

with decimals, 199, 201, 215,
381

with fractions, 169–170,
384

of integers, 232–233

inverse operation of, 133

with rational numbers, 381,
384

by zero, not defined, 144

E

Empty set, 12, 25

as a solution set, 12

Equations

graphing, 23, 46, 257

solving, 15, 34, 37, 49, 244,
246, 249, 252–254, 378–380,
387, 390, 468

two-step, 53–54, 268–269,
392–393

Equivalence

of fractions, 156, 187

of ratios, 309, 312–313

Estimating, 432, 435, 453

Evaluating expressions, 3, 5

Exponents, 111, 208–209

F

Factorization

prime, 109, 118–120

Factors, 103, 108–109

greatest common, 118–119,
161

prime, 108–109, 118–120

Finite sets, 131

Formulas, 31, 33, 57–60, 67,
68, 76, 84–87, 100, 114–
115, 241, 274, 301, 399,

405–409, 413–416, 426,
470, 480–481, 485–486

Fractions

addition with, 156–157, 172–
173, 176–177, 179–180,
188, 375

comparison of, 178, 187, 193,
370

as decimals, 191–192

division with, 169–170,
384

equivalent, 156, 187

lowest terms, 161–162, 164,
187

multiplication with, 159, 164,
166–167, 384

to name ratios, 304–305,
320

on a number line, 369

problem solving with, 181

renaming, 179

subtraction with, 172–173,
175, 177, 179, 376

Function, 76–77, 84

graph of, 76–77, 80–81

vertical line test for,
76–77

G

Graphing, 80–81

equations, 23, 46, 257

functions, 76–77, 80–81

inequalities, 24–25, 46–47,
257–259, 266–267

integers, 219, 221, 234–235

ordered pairs, 73, 88–89, 92–
93, 234–235

solution sets, 23–24, 257–
259, 266–267

Greatest common factor,
118–119, 161

Grouping symbols, 3–4

Identity number, 143–144
Indirect measurement, 348
Inequalities
  comparing numbers using, 370
  graphing, 24–25, 46–47, 257–259, 266
  solving, 19–20, 40, 43, 51, 255, 259–261, 263, 264, 266, 391, 394
  symbols for, 8, 19–20, 259
  two-step, 61–62
Infinite sets, 131
Integers
  addition of, 221, 223–224, 240, 273
  division of, 232–233
  graphing, 219, 221, 234–235
  multiplication of, 228, 230
  negative, 219
  positive, 219
  subtraction of, 226
Interest, 417–418
Inverse operations, 132–133

Measure(s)
  computing with, 447–448
  English units, 438
  estimating, 432, 435, 453
  metric units, 443–444
Measurement
  comparison of, 440
  indirect, 348
Meter, 443
Metric units of measure, 443–444
Micrometer, 191, 215
Mixed numerals, 163
Multiplication
  with decimals, 197, 215–216, 381
  with fractions, 159, 164, 166–167, 384
  identity number of, 143–144
  of integers, 228, 230
  inverse operation of, 133
  on a number line, 228
  of rational numbers, 381, 384
  symbols for, 5

K

Kilogram, 443

L

Latitude, 99
Least common denominator, 176–177
Least common multiple, 120–121, 176–177
Liter, 444
Longitude, 99
Lowest terms, 161–162, 164, 187, 309–311

N

Number line
  addition with, 221, 240
  for integers, 219, 221, 240
  multiplication with, 228
  order on, 219
  for rational numbers, 369
  for whole numbers, 23–25, 46–47
Numbers
  composite, 108
  even, 117
  integers, 219

odd, 114
perfect, 105
prime, 108, 126
rational, 369
square, 111, 114, 487
triangular, 115
Numerator, 155

O

Open sentences, 8, 15, 34,
46
Operations
inverse, 132–133
order of, 2–3
Order
on a number line, 219
of operations, 2–3
Ordered pairs, 70, 76, 88–89,
92–93, 99
graphing, 73, 88–89, 92–93,
234–235

P

Per cent, 315–316, 318
interest, 417–418
to name ratios, 315–320
problem solving with, 323,
326, 410, 412
Perimeter, 3, 59, 162, 196
Point, coordinates of
on a plane, 73, 234–235
Power(s), 111, 127, 192,
208–209
Prime factors, 108–109,
118–120
Prime numbers, 108, 126
Problem solving, 284–296,
419–421
with decimals, 204–205
with equations, 31, 57–60,
67, 284–292

with formulas, 31, 57–60, 67,
84–87, 405–409, 413–416
with fractions, 181
with per cent, 323, 326, 410,
412
with proportions, 312–314,
333, 402
with Pythagorean property,
476
with similar triangles, 348–
350, 352, 365–366
with tables, 80–81, 293–296
Proportion, 312–313, 333, 402,
404
Pythagorean property, 472

R

Radical sign, 457
Rate, 311
Ratio(s) 304–305, 309–312,
315–316, 318, 320, 332
named by a decimal, 320
named by a fraction, 304–
305, 320
named by a per cent, 315–
316, 318, 320
scale drawings, 356–357
in similar triangles, 345,
365–366
Rational numbers
addition of, 372, 375
comparison of, 370
division of, 381, 384
multiplication of, 381, 384
named by decimals, 369
named by fractions, 369
on a number line, 369
square root of, 466
subtraction of, 373, 376
Replacement set, 11, 24
Rounding numbers, 429–430,
432

S

Scale drawings, 356–357
Scientific notation, 208–209
Sentences
  false, 8, 11
  open, 8
  translating, 281
  true, 8, 11
Set(s)
  empty, 12, 25
  finite and infinite, 131
  replacement, 11, 25
  solution, 11, 16, 23–25, 34,
    37, 46–47
Similar
  figures, 336
  triangles, 337, 341–342,
    345–346, 365–366
Solution set, 11, 16, 34, 37,
  46–47
  graph of, 23–25, 46–47,
    257–259
Square of a number, 111, 114
  table of, 487
Square root(s), 456–457
  estimating, 459, 463
  of rational numbers, 466
  table of, 487
  using table of, 461
  of zero, 457

Subtraction
  with decimals, 194–195, 373
  with fractions, 172–173, 175,
    177, 179, 376
  of integers, 226
  inverse operation of, 133
  of rational numbers, 373,
    376

T

Triangles
  right, 472
  similar, 337, 341–342,
    345–346
Triangular numbers, 115

V

Variable(s), 5, 11

Z

Zero
  division by, not defined,
    144
  as identity number, 143–
    144
  square root of, 457